K

Progress in
Psychobiology and
Physiological Psychology

Volume 11

Contributors to This Volume

Kent C. Berridge

Harvey J. Grill

Mark F. Jacquin

Paul R. McHugh

Maria G. Miller

Timothy H. Moran

S. Murray Sherman

H. Philip Zeigler

Progress in
PSYCHOBIOLOGY AND
PHYSIOLOGICAL PSYCHOLOGY

Edited by JAMES M. SPRAGUE

Department of Anatomy
The School of Medicine
University of Pennsylvania
Philadelphia, Pennsylvania

ALAN N. EPSTEIN

Leidy Laboratory
Department of Biology
University of Pennsylvania
Philadelphia, Pennsylvania

Volume 11

1985

ACADEMIC PRESS, INC.

(Harcourt Brace Jovanovich, Publishers)

Orlando ● San Diego ● New York ● London
Toronto ● Montreal ● Sydney ● Tokyo

ACADEMIC PRESS, INC.
Orlando, Florida 32887

United Kingdom Edition published by
ACADEMIC PRESS INC. (LONDON) LTD.
24–28 Oval Road, London NW1 7DX

LIBRARY OF CONGRESS CATALOG CARD NUMBER: 66-29640

ISBN: 0-12-542111-7

PRINTED IN THE UNITED STATES OF AMERICA

85 86 87 88   9 8 7 6 5 4 3 2 1

Contents

Taste Reactivity as a Measure of the Neural Control of Palatability

Harvey J. Grill and Kent C. Berridge

Trigeminal Orosensation and Ingestive Behavior in the Rat

H. Philip Zeigler, Mark F. Jacquin, and Maria G. Miller

The Stomach: A Conception of Its Dynamic Role in Satiety

Paul R. McHugh and Timothy H. Moran

Functional Organization of the W-, X-, and Y-Cell Pathways in the Cat: A Review and Hypothesis

S. Murray Sherman

Contributors

Numbers in parentheses indicate the pages on which the authors' contributions begin.

Kent C. Berridge,* Department of Psychology and Institute of Neurological Sciences, University of Pennsylvania, Philadelphia, Pennsylvania 19104 (1)

Harvey J. Grill, Department of Psychology and Institute of Neurological Sciences, University of Pennsylvania, Philadelphia, Pennsylvania 19104 (1)

Mark F. Jacquin, Department of Anatomy, UMDNJ—Rutgers Medical School, Piscataway, New Jersey 08854 (63)

Paul R. McHugh, Department of Psychiatry and Behavioral Sciences, The Johns Hopkins University School of Medicine, Baltimore, Maryland 21205 (197)

Maria G. Miller, Division of Nutrition, Food and Drug Administration, Washington, D.C. 20204 (63)

Timothy H. Moran, Department of Psychiatry and Behavioral Sciences, The Johns Hopkins University School of Medicine, Baltimore, Maryland 21205 (197)

S. Murray Sherman, Department of Neurobiology and Behavior, State University of New York at Stony Brook, Stony Brook, New York 11794 (233)

H. Philip Zeigler, Biopsychology Program, Hunter College, City University of New York, New York, New York 10021 (63)

* Present address: Department of Psychology, Dalhousie University, Halifax, Nova Scotia, Canada.

This volume continues the tradition set by its predecessors in this series. It presents a small number of essays that summarize interesting issues of behavioral neuroscience from an expert's point of view. Each is monographic, that is, each is a comprehensive review of the research issue but is also a personal statement about the author's role in it and about the controversies that have been raised by its pursuit. The editors believe that these articles meet the high standards set by Eliot Stellar and James Sprague when they began this series in 1966, namely that each contribution be a treatment by a master of one aspect of how brains govern behavior and that, when taken together, the volumes should constitute a continuing handbook of behavioral neuroscience.

There are four essays in this volume. Three deal with control of ingestive behavior and are therefore closely related. In the first, Grill and Berridge review their analysis of the neural substrates of palatability by use of the fixed action patterns of orofacial movements in the rat. They show how it is possible to deal with issues of preference and aversion by direct study of the animal's acceptance and rejection behaviors, and demonstrate how this approach enriches our understanding of how animals select substances for ingestion. Zeigler, Jacquin, and Miller then summarize research demonstrating the surprisingly heavy dependence of the rat on the somatosensory (trigeminal) innervation of the orofacial area for both the appetitive and consumatory phases of ingestion, and they use their results to remind us all of the importance of peripheral sensation for the motivational as well as the reflexive aspects of ingestive behavior. In the third essay, McHugh and Moran trace the history of their discovery of a gastric and upper intestinal system that permits the monkey to adjust its food intake to its caloric needs with almost physical precision, and they relate this to the control of gastric emptying by cholecystokinin.

In his article, Sherman has given us an extensive synthesis and critical review of the functional organization of the different visual pathways from retina to cortex. These are known by the terminology applied to the types of retinal ganglion cells (Y, X, W,), which have been distinguished physiologically. The Y-cell pathway is assigned the most prominent role in form vision; this path, with its cortical representation, appears to be sufficient for good spatial vision. The X-cell pathway is assigned a role in spatial acuity and position sensitivity, thereby providing greater detail in the analysis of the visual scene. This hypothesis is substantially different from previous ideas about these pathways, and it offers an attractively simple explanation for some of the different deficits caused by cortical lesions.

With this volume James Sprague, who is now Emeritus Professor of Anatomy at the University of Pennsylvania, ends his editorial responsibilities. Jim Sprague was a founding editor of what was then called "Progress in Physiological Psychology" and has played a major role in the editing of all eleven volumes in the series. He has left an enduring mark on the series. He has been astute in his choice of authors and has helped each of them to give our readers the whole story of his work. His editorial touch has been light but firm, insisting on clarity without sacrifice of personal style, and he has encouraged our authors to express their zest for the research enterprise in their essays. Fortunately he remains active in research and is a close colleague. Should they be needed, his judgment and editorial skills will still be available to the series. He will be replaced as coeditor by Adrian R. Morrison, Professor of Anatomy in the School of Veterinary Medicine at the University of Pennsylvania, who with Epstein is already at work on preparations for Volume 12. Morrison was a student of Sprague's and follows him as an editor of the series just as Epstein followed his teacher Eliot Stellar, some years ago. The series therefore has new editors, but it will continue to have the same high standards and aspirations.

James M. Sprague
Alan N. Epstein

Contents of Previous Volumes

PROGRESS IN PSYCHOBIOLOGY AND PHYSIOLOGICAL PSYCHOLOGY, VOL. 11

Taste Reactivity as a Measure of the Neural Control of Palatability

Harvey J. Grill and Kent C. Berridge*

*Department of Psychology and
Institute of Neurological Sciences
University of Pennsylvania
Philadelphia, Pennsylvania*

* Present address: Department of Psychology, Dalhousie University, Halifax, Nova Scotia, Canada.

I. Introducing the Problem

A. PALATABILITY AS A RESPONSE MEASURE

Whether an animal will eat when the opportunity arises depends on a complex interaction of environmental, physiological, and associative factors. Three types of information are widely accepted as principal determinants of this decision to feed: taste signals initiated by contact with a food, internal-state signals produced by food intake or starvation, and cues arising from previous associations with the taste of a food. Whether an animal will ingest or reject a food results from a CNS integration of these three factors, which we define as the palatability decision.

Palatability so defined is a response measure. The more common use of palatability is as a stimulus measure. It is generally used as a descriptor of the taste factor, as in "sucrose is a palatable taste." The problem with using palatability as a stimulus measure is that this usage generates an implicit prediction about the type of responses that palatable and unpalatable tastes will evoke. The implication of defining sucrose as a palatable taste and concentrated salt as an unpalatable one is the prediction that animals will ingest the former and reject the latter. We know, however, that this is not the case. Any given taste stimulus does *not* always elicit the same behavioral response. The very same taste may elicit ingestion or rejection or be rated as pleasant or unpleasant depending on the physiological state of the animal when it encounters that taste (Richter, 1956; Cabanac, 1971; Davis and Levine, 1977) and the existence of conditioned associations to the taste's postingestive consequences such as a previous illness or caloric repletion or a visceral illness (Booth, 1972, 1980; Garcia and Koelling, 1966; Rozin and Fallon, 1980).

The choice of a stimulus or a response measure of palatability has an impact on the study of the neural mechanisms of taste. A stimulus view of palatability fosters the hypothesis that the neural signals generated at the taste receptor and the initial processing of these signals within the caudal brain stem are unaltered by internal state and associative input. In contrast, the response view of palatability promotes investigation of whether the taste signal is integrated with internal-state and associative signals early in its central processing. A response measure of palatability even provides for the possibility of centrifugal influences on the taste receptors themselves. The available evidence supporting a caudal brain stem integration of taste and internal-state afferent signals is presently suggestive, as Norgren (1983) notes, but perhaps only because the stimulus view of palatability has dominated and this issue has seldom been addressed.

B. PALATABILITY AS AN INTERVENING VARIABLE

Physiological psychology has long recognized that diverse causal factors can act through a common mechanism (Miller, 1959). Some experimental manipulations may produce a constellation of effects on a variety of appetitive and consummatory behavior related to feeding that closely resembles the constellation of effects produced by other manipulations. For example, the postingestive cues arising from a meal, the addition of quinine to a food, and the previous association of a taste with visceral illness may all affect behavior in similar ways. All of these experimental manipulations reduce consumption of foods with the same taste in a preference test, reduce instrumental responding for that taste, produce a shift in taste-elicited fixed action patterns (FAPs) (in rats), and a shift in hedonic ratings of the food (in humans). All of these behavioral changes reflect the central nervous integration that we are calling palatability.

This association of physiological, environmental, and associative causes into groups defined by their similar behavioral effects has given rise to the psychological concept of central intervening variables. Palatability, hunger, and satiety are examples of central intervening variables. This concept suggests that all of the causal factors within such groups affect a single functional system whose output produces a similar constellation of effects on a set of behaviors. It also implies that the behavioral effect of activating this system does not depend on which particular causal factor activated it. That is, the same behavior is elicited by quinine-adulterated food, by sucrose that had been paired with visceral illness, and by concentrated NaCl when animals had received extra salt in their diet.

Palatability, hunger, and other central intervening variables can be of considerable use in understanding the relations that environmental events have to central neural events, and that central neural events have to behavioral events. These variables must be defined very carefully, however, in order to be useful. Confusion concerning the meaning of concepts like hunger and palatability has led to misunderstandings in the past and even to more recent suggestions that these concepts be dropped entirely from physiological analyses of behavior (Dethier, 1976, 1982; Zeigler, 1983). A number of points can be raised against these suggestions. From a merely descriptive point of view, central intervening variables such as palatability can order factors that would otherwise appear unrelated, such as gustatory stimulation, postingestive consequences, and Pavlovian associations, into comprehensible groups that share common relationships. These common relationships can then be used in two ways. First, they allow one to predict behavior more efficiently than can be done on the basis of physiological knowledge alone. Second, and most important to physiological psychology, these relationships aid in the study of the central nervous system by helping to identify and locate those neural mechanisms that have important roles in the control of a particular behavior (Fentress, 1980; Gallistel, 1980a). The physiological mechanisms of behavior can be identified only by the correlations that exist between physiological and behavioral events. When manipulations of one are followed by a change in the other, we infer a causal connection.

If a central nervous manipulation, like stimulation or lesion, produces a change in a constellation of different behaviors that are also similarly affected by a group of independent variables, like alterations in taste quality or physiological state, then we may be justified in believing that we have found a single functional system that exerts control over a variety of behavioral outcomes. This argument derives from von Holst and von St. Paul's demonstration of the need for "level-adequate terminology," that is, for terms that adequately express the psychological complexity of the behavioral phenomena they represent. For example, if electrical stimulation of a particular brain site elicits neither a stereotyped motor response (e.g., walk forward) nor a behavior that could convincingly be described as a response to a particular sensation (pain, touch, etc.), then the activation of simple sensory or motor systems can be ruled out. If instead the stimulation evokes a set of functionally coordinated actions that bring the animal to a certain goal and are appropriately modified to attain that goal when the situation changes, then one can conclude that the stimulation has affected a motivational system that intercedes between sensory and motor systems (von Holst and von St. Paul, 1963). Likewise, if an experimental manipulation changes the consumption of a particular taste, its value as an instrumental reinforcer, its ability to elicit ingestive neuroendocrine responses, and the type of ingestive fixed action patterns (Tinbergen, 1952) it can evoke, then we can conclude that the taste's central nervous evaluation has been altered.

It is the grouping of causal inputs and behavioral outputs that allows us to identify such functional control systems and helps us to identify the neural networks that embody them. Further, since behavioral studies that identify intervening variables by correlating inputs and outputs provide quantitative information about how different factors affect behavior, these behavioral data can specify the quantitative characteristics that must be shared by the neural mechanism responsible for the behavior. Behavioral data of this kind may include the range of effective stimuli, the quantitative input–output gain, the effective timing of inputs and patterning of outputs, and the values at which asymptotes begin. Such characteristics tell us what we need to know to identify the neural substrate for the behavioral system of interest. This view of physiological psychology has much in common with Hebb's assertion (1949) that to proceed we "must find an anatomical and physiological understanding of what is known psychologically as a concept." This approach has been fruitfully applied to a variety of phenomena, from the resolution of visual Mach bands (the perceived gradations of brightness within an actually uniform band juxtaposed next to bands of differing brightness) into the physiological mechanisms of lateral inhibition in the retina (Schiffman, 1976), to the correlation of the temporal properties of elemental classical conditioning with sensory synaptic changes in *Aplysia* (Hawkins *et al.*, 1983), to the identification of the quantitative properties of reinforcing electrical brain stimulation with the particular neural pathways that share those properties (Gallistel *et al.*, 1981). Such successes illustrate the importance of complex behavioral concepts in the study of the nervous system.

C. FUNCTIONAL AND MECHANISTIC ANALYSES OF BEHAVIOR

In order for central intervening variables like palatability to be useful in studying neural mechanisms of behavior, however, the relationship that such variables bear to the neural mechanisms that mediate the behavioral outcomes must be clearly understood. Palatability evaluations or decisions are purely functional entities. A functional entity is not itself a neural mechanism, nor does it refer to a particular neural mechanism (Powley, 1977). A functional entity refers to a particular relationship between a set of experimental manipulations and a set of behaviors. A functional analysis of behavior therefore cannot replace a physiological or mechanistic analysis. It is equally important, however, to realize that a physiological mechanism cannot replace a functional intervening variable. Each refers to different things and neither is more "real" or "basic" than the other.

It has been argued that a complete physiological analysis of a behavioral system will show a functional one to be empty, misleading, or, at best, redundant (Dethier, 1982). This argument assumes that both kinds of analyses attempt to describe the same kind of thing and that one or the other must be true or best. But each approach is good for separate purposes. Functional analyses (meaning analyses of the functional controls of behavior, not analyses of an evolutionary function of behavior) will always provide the most efficient means of predicting the behavior of a complex system (Dawkins, 1976). And as the complexity of an animal, a neural preparation, or an array of competing stimuli increases, the relative predictive efficiency of a functional analysis will increase proportionally. Further, the argument against functional constructs neglects the fact that, to the degree that a mechanistic explanation can be complete, it must explain the very relations that the functional analysis points out (Fentress, 1980; Gallistel, 1980b). Recognition of those functional relations is often what guides the successful experimenter in elucidating the neural mechanisms of a behavior whether he or she is explicitly aware of it or not.

The central neural integration whose outcome determines palatability is just such a functional entity. It highlights a particular relationship that exists between a set of behaviors that animals direct toward tastes and the set of causal factors that change those behaviors as a group, such as internal-state cues and classically conditioned associations, as well as taste properties themselves. This relationship immediately tells us a number of important things about palatability decisions. First, palatability does not reside in a taste stimulus itself nor in the gustatory receptors that are activated by that taste. The very same taste may be ingested or rejected, may activate positive or negative FAPs, and may be reported as pleasant or unpleasant depending on the present physiological state and classical associations that may exist between that taste and its postingestive effects. For example, while an infusion of sucrose into the mouth elicits a stereotyped set of ingestive FAPs in a naive rat, that ingestive pattern of responses is reduced as the animal becomes sated (Grill and Norgren, 1978d). This sequence of ingestive FAPs can even be switched to an equally clear sequence of distinct, aversive FAPs by previous pairings of that sugar stimulus with LiCl in a classical-conditioning paradigm (Grill, 1975; Berridge et al., 1981). The sucrose taste stimulus is unchanged; yet the central evaluation of the taste that results in a particular consummatory behavior has entirely changed. Likewise, the taste of concentrated NaCl, which elicits aversive FAPs in normal rats, can be made to elicit only ingestive FAPs by sodium-depleting natrorexigenic treatment (Berridge et al., 1984). This switch from aversive to ingestive evaluation can also be elicited from oral morphine addicts when the classical association between the bitter taste of morphine and its postingestive consequences changes the behavior that morphine evokes (Zellner et al., 1984) from aversive to ingestive. The palatability evaluation elicited by taste stimulation is clearly not a constant, although the palatability evaluation of some tastes is more stable, under a broad variety of conditions, than that of others. [For example, taste aversion learning proceeds more rapidly and is less susceptible to latent inhibition when the conditioning stimulus (CS) is a familiar salt or acid taste than when it is a familiar sugar taste (Berridge et al., 1981).] Palatability is a decision that arises within the central nervous system, not an inherent property of a taste itself.

We are not the first to suggest that palatability be defined in this integrative way. Aristotle (in Ross, 1906) remarked that food smells are pleasant when one is hungry and unpleasant when sated. Young (1967) noted that while palatability is commonly attributed to the foodstuff itself, it actually depends on the integration of taste, intraorganic conditions (internal state), and dietary history (taste associations). Davis and Levine (1977) defined palatability as the interaction of taste and internal state that generates an excitatory neural signal.

D. PALATABILITY IS DISTINCT FROM HEDONIC CONSCIOUSNESS

It is important to be clear that the palatability decision, as we have defined it, does not necessarily refer to the hedonic consciousness of taste that humans experience as they introspect. The palatability decision refers to the association of an entire constellation of behaviors. Human reports of conscious hedonic perceptions, or those perceptions themselves, are only one measure of this decision, and not necessarily the definitive one. It is entirely possible to conceive of a palatability decision, as defined here, existing in the absence of a conscious hedonic perception. Available evidence strongly suggests that this decision can be made in rats, cats, and humans (Miller and Sherrington, 1916; Grill and Norgren, 1978b; Steiner, 1973) that lack a neocortex or even an entire forebrain. The concept of palatability as an intervening variable must therefore be kept conceptually distinct from that of hedonic consciousness. For the sake of clarity, we will refer to the former as the palatability decision in order to emphasize its nature as a functional entity that integrates information about taste, physiological state, and prior associations, and to distinguish it from hedonic palatability as derived from introspection.

II. How Has the Palatability Decision Been Measured?

Measures of the palatability decision have included one-bottle or two-bottle tests, preference choice, and operant tests that provide either long-term (24–48 hr) or short-term (less than 1 hr) access to tastants (Richter and Campbell, 1940; Young, 1948, 1959; Guttman, 1954; Morrison, 1969; Young and Shuford, 1955; Cagan and Maller, 1974). Reflexological measures including integrated lick rate, electromyographic activity of masticatory muscles during licking, and taste reactivity (taste-elicited fixed action patterns) have also been used (Davis, 1973; Yamamoto et al., 1982; Grill and Norgren, 1978a; Berridge et al., 1981). While all of these measures use behavior that depends on the CNS evaluation of taste stimuli, there is considerable discussion about which factors are integrated in this decision for each of these tests and which tests are the best measures of palatability.

Despite many provisos, the general consensus of the field has been to consider palatability as an attribute of the tastant that is invariant. For example, a distinction has been made between what is measured by short- and long-term access tests. Short-term tests, like recordings from peripheral gustatory nerves, show that responses are monotonically related to sucrose concentration (Pfaffmann, 1961). Conversely, with long-term tests there is a reversal in preference as indicated by a decreased intake at higher sucrose concentrations. Such data do not conform to either electrophysiological afferent recordings or short-term test results. For this reason, long-term tests have been regarded as confusing the immediate effects of the taste itself with the effects of a variety of sources of postingestive feedback.

While perhaps tempting, this identification of the palatability decision exclusively with the sensory characteristics of the taste itself is incorrect. First, it is not possible to dissociate taste from internal-state factors no matter how circumscribed the test may be. The logic that the best measures of palatability are those that do not allow changes in postingestive feedback from the meal to modify the behavior being measured has fostered the idea that surgically eliminating postingestive feedback (the sham-feeding preparation, e.g., Mook, 1963) yields a "true" measure of palatability. While the sham-feeding preparation clearly demonstrates that sucrose taste is a potent elicitor of ingestion as well as of gustatory nerve discharge, it must be remembered that this preparation attempts to hold internal-state factors constant rather than eliminating them from consideration entirely. Second, demonstrations of the cephalic reflexes of digestion (Powley, 1977; Berthoud and Jeanrenaud, 1982; Grill et al., 1984) make it unlikely that the sham-feeding preparation can hold the internal state constant. Third, in short-term tests other than sham feeding, where access to tastes is limited to 15 min or less, not only must the internal state of the preparation at the beginning of the test be affected by cephalic reflexes, but there is evidence that glucose absorption occurs within 3 min of intake (Steffens, 1969). Postingestive feedback from mechanical or osmotic signals from the upper GI tract may be equally rapid.

Part of the resistance to modifying the assumption that taste input is the only factor operating in palatability has been the companion assumption that when postingestive feedback does modify the response to taste it does so in a way that does not transform the gustatory signal. For example, Pfaffmann (1982) notes that the reversal of sucrose preference in long-term tests is "only apparent and does not reflect a reduced preference or aversion to the sugar per se." The position that such a reversal reflects other nongustatory, sensory, or physiological factors is shared by others. A variety of experiments, however, have demonstrated that this assumption may be incorrect. Electrophysiological studies suggest that taste signal itself can be transformed early in its central processing. Brush and Halpern (1970) found that inflating the stomach of the frog increased the glossopharyngeal response to NaCl on the tongue and decreased the response to oral quinine. Section of the vagus nerve eliminated the influence of gastric distension. Contreras *et al.* (1984) report that sodium deprivation sufficient to induce salt appetite without changing serum Na levels was correlated with a significant decrease in the suprathreshold response to NaCl in the chorda tympani nerve of the rat. In addition, despite meager evidence for primary afferent convergence of taste and visceral afferent neurons in the first central gustatory relay nucleus, electrophysiological experiments have described alterations in taste cell responses following gastric distension (Glenn and Erickson, 1976; see Norgren, 1983). In addition, many neurons in the rostral medulla that respond to electrical stimulation of peripheral taste nerves such as the chorda tympani also respond to stimulation of visceral afferent nerves such as the cervical vagus (Bereiter *et al.*, 1981). Behavioral data also support an integration among taste input, internal state, and associative factors. For example, measuring human psychophysical judgments of taste pleasantness, Cabanac (1971) has shown that the palatability of a constant glucose stimulus varied as a function of internal state. The same glucose stimulus that was judged pleasant when the subject was food deprived was judged unpleasant when the same subject had just consumed a concentrated glucose solution. Analogously, the palatability evaluation of sucrose taste (measured in a variety of ways) was systematically changed following treatments such as insulin and 2-deoxy-D-glucose injection, which change internal state by altering glucose homeostasis (Thompson and Campbell, 1977; Mayer-Gross and Walker, 1946).

Taste stimuli have a special capacity to be associated by classical conditioning with a variety of states (Garcia *et al.*, 1974; Rozin and Kalat, 1971), and these associations are also factors in determining palatability. For example, Booth (1977) has shown that rats and humans develop associations between tastes and their caloric consequences, and that these associations can produce conditioned preferences that are state dependent for the changes in internal state that occur within a single meal. When rats or humans are offered a choice between a taste that has been associated with the drinking of a rapidly absorbed, concentrated starch and another that has been paired with a dilute starch, the former is ingested at the onset of a meal but rejected at the end of the same meal, while the latter taste is responded to in a reciprocal fashion (Booth *et al.,* 1982). This example clearly illustrates that internal state and classical associations are integrated with taste quality and intensity to yield a decision to respond to taste that we are calling the palatability decision.

Our operating assumption in this article is that the palatability decision represents an integration of taste, internal state, and associative factors and that when each of these variables contributes to modifying the response to a taste stimulus it can do so via a *common* mechanism. In assessing the relative weighting of these factors in other models of ingestive control, experimenters (e.g., Davis and Levine, 1977) have tended to characterize the nature of the internal-state factor as inhibitory and that of the taste factor, especially sugars, as excitatory. We take the perspective that the weighting of each of the integrated variables is not fixed (e.g., osmotic feedback is not solely inhibitory nor is the taste of sucrose solely excitatory), but rather their weighing can vary rapidly between excitatory and inhibitory valences. For example, the same internal-state variable (osmotic feedback) reduces the ingestive reaction to hyperosmotic tastes but increases the ingestive reaction to hypoosmotic taste stimuli (Stellar *et al.,* 1954). Put in other terms, the neural circuit whereby tastes that are hyperosmotic elicit ingestion may be inhibited by the same internal-state signals that excite the circuit whereby tastes that are hypoosmotic lead to ingestion. An additional example is that novel sucrose elicits a pattern of ingestive FAPs in rats. Yet, after a single pairing with the internal-state changes evoked by a LiCl injection, this same sucrose stimulus now elicits a quinine-like aversive pattern of behavior (Grill, 1975). The example of state-conditioned preferences and aversions (Booth, 1977) given in the last paragraph is also relevant here.

A. Taste-Elicited Fixed Action Patterns as a Measure of the Palatability Decision

We take the position that all tests that measure palatability measure an integration of gustatory afferent signals, internal state, and classical associations. The fact all all of these measures reflect the palatability decision, however, does not imply that palatability is the only thing they measure. Other central states might also be expected to affect these measures, and this poses a problem for the study of central-state changes. For example, fear might stop a rat from drinking sucrose, but does fear alter sucrose palatability? Pairing a taste with either footshock or visceral illness results in a subsequent reduction in intake of that taste. Using intake as the measure of palatability would lead to the conclusion that in both types of pairings, the palatability of the taste was decreased. However, this con-

Ingestion
Sequence

Aversion
Sequence

FIG. 1.   Taste-elicited fixed action patterns. Ingestive responses are elicited by oral infusions of glucose, sucrose, and isotonic sodium chloride, and include rhythmic mouth movements, tongue protrusions, lateral tongue protrusions, and paw licking. Aversive responses are elicited by infusions of quinine, caffeine, and sucrose octaacetate solutions, and include gapes, chin rubs, head shakes, paw wipes, forelimb flailing, and locomotion (not shown). (Adapted by permission from Berridge *et al.*, 1981.)

clusion would be incorrect. There may be a degree of overlap in the constellation of effects produced by two functional variables such as fear and palatability; however, this overlap is not complete. When taste reactivity was used as a measure of palatability to compare the effects of taste association with footshock and visceral illness, the results were different. The taste reactivity measure of palatability analyzes the occurrence of nine separate FAPs that can generally be clustered into two patterns of responses: an ingestive sequence and a rejection sequence (see Fig. 1). Following taste–visceral illness pairing there is a shift in the pattern of taste reactivity responses elicited by the paired taste from an ingestion sequence to a rejection or aversion sequence. Taste–footshock pairing produces no such shift in taste reactivity responses (Pelchat *et al.*, 1983). These data suggest that the taste reactivity technique can be used to distinguish between the effects of separate psychological variables (e.g., palatability and fear) that are not distinguished by more traditional measures of palatability.

The taste reactivity measure has another advantage over traditional measures of the palatability decision that require spontaneous intake or appetitive behavior. A variety of neurological lesions and ablations produce aphagic preparations—preparations that do not seek food. A preparation that does not seek food may nevertheless be able to evaluate a taste that is placed directly into its mouth; appetitive and evaluative capacities should not be confused. One goal of our functional analysis of the palatability decision is to empower a neurological investigation of the sites of integration of taste, internal state, and associative factors. This has involved analyzing the palatability decisions made by a variety of aphagic neurological preparations, including chronic supracollicular decerebrate,

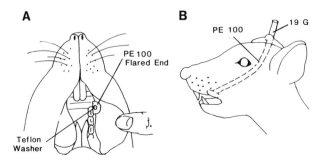

FIG. 2.   Diagram of the intraoral catheter *in situ*. The intraoral end is placed just rostral to the first maxillary molar. The tubing is led out subcutaneously to the skull and secured to a short piece of 19-gauge (19 G) stainless-steel tubing with dental acrylic. (A) Ventral view; (B) lateral view.

thalamic, and decorticate rats. The taste reactivity test enables the palatability decisions of all such aphagic preparations to be examined.

The nonappetitive [in terms of Craig's (1918) original distinction between appetitive and consummatory phases of motivated acts] taste reactivity test makes use of chronic intraoral catheters to deliver calibrated amounts of a taste stimulus directly into the oral cavity, and subsequently to rinse it away without active initiation by or disturbance of the animal (see Figs. 2 and 3). Direct intraoral taste stimulation elicits responses that are videotaped and subsequently analyzed frame by frame. Analysis reveals nine different stereotyped response components that are generally grouped into two different response patterns corresponding to an ingestive and a rejection sequence (as seen in Fig. 1). The ingestive response sequence, seen in Fig. 1, is composed of four response components, while five other components comprise the rejection or aversion sequence. This method of response analysis can also be used in the context of an appetitive test in the neurologically intact animal, without the intraoral fistulae, as in Pelchat *et al.* (1983). Taste-elicited consummatory responses or FAPs share all the characteristics of classic consummatory responses. They are highly stereotyped and represent the final behavioral acts not only in the process of obtaining food, but also in the process of obtaining water and electrolytes.

Use of taste-elicited FAPs as a measure of the palatability decision requires that a number of criteria be met. If these taste-elicited responses do indeed reflect the palatability decision they should (1) represent a general decision to respond to tastes that agrees with other measures of this decision, (2) integrate information from a variety of sources (e.g., taste, internal-state cues, learned associations) to produce demonstrated

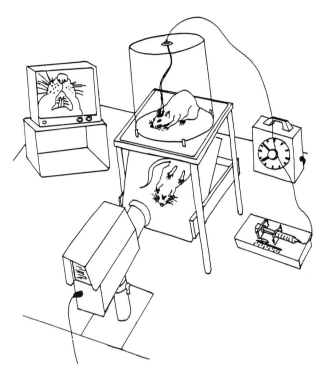

FIG. 3. Apparatus for videotaping taste reactivity responses to taste stimuli injected into the mouth via chronic intraoral catheters. Videotaping is done via a mirror located beneath the Plexiglas floor in the upper right-hand corner of the figure.

shifts or changes in the response to a constant taste, and (3) be organized as functionally related response clusters (e.g., ingestion and rejection sequences) that vary as a group with changes in palatability. This last point is stressed in order to be sure that individual FAPs are not controlled by individual systems and taste properties but rather vary together as functional sequences or clusters according to a more global palatability decision.

All of these criteria are met by existing data. Grill and Norgren (1978a) showed that these responses are elicited by taste stimuli in ways that correspond to other short-term measures of the palatability decision. Ingestive response components are elicited by oral application of sucrose in a graded, concentration-dependent manner. Low concentrations elicit only mouth movements and tongue protrusions. At higher concentrations, the number of tongue protrusions and lateral tongue movements increases as a function of increasing sucrose concentration (Schwartz and

Grill, 1984). Similarly in other short-term tests, intake volume and the number of tongue contacts with a spout have been shown to be dependent on sucrose concentration (Cagan and Maller, 1974; Davis, 1973). In palatability measures that use the amount ingested as a dependent variable, quinine HCl consumption falls off rapidly as concentration exceeds 0.01 mM, the absolute behavioral threshold for quinine (Koh and Teitelbaum, 1961). The threshold for the gape response (0.03 mM) is only one-half log step above this, reflecting the sensitivity of the taste reactivity test. Aversive responses to quinine are also elicited in a concentration-dependent manner. Gapes appear at threshold concentrations, chin rubs are added at slightly higher concentrations, and the three other aversive components are added to the gape and chin-rub sequence at higher concentrations of quinine HCl. Like the magnitude of the peripheral electrophysiological responses, the number of gape and chin-rub components elicited by quinine HCl increases with stimulus concentration (Schwartz and Grill, 1984). Parallel changes in the appearance of aversive components are seen in response to other "bitter" tastes, such as caffeine, sucrose octaacetate, and quinine sulfate (Schwartz and Grill, 1984). Short-term intake of bitter tastes decreases analogously. There is a strong correlation between gape frequency and intake termination for these tastes.

Characteristic consummatory response profiles can be generated for any taste stimulus by recording the total number of rats displaying each of the taste-elicited FAPs during a standardized 1-min intraoral taste infusion (see Fig. 4). These profiles are highly sensitive to the palatability decision. Glucose, isotonic NaCl, ammonium chloride, and quinine HCl can be ranked in that order as a linear palatability hierarchy on the basis of intake (Weiner and Stellar, 1951; Nachman, 1962; Pfaffmann, 1961). Figure 4 shows that taste reactivity profiles exactly parallel this ranking (Berridge et al., 1981). Comparisons between different concentrations of the same taste are best made by quantifying the number of individual taste reactivity response compounds generated rather than by profiles (H. Grill and Spector, unpublished observations).

B. Taste Reactivity Responses Reflect Changes in Internal State and Learned Associations

The second criterion, that the taste-elicited FAPs reflect an integration of taste with internal state and learned associations, is also met. Sucrose-elicited FAPs change as a function of changes in internal-state cues that signal both nutrient depletion and nutrient repletion (Grill and Norgren, 1978d; Grill, 1980; Flynn and Grill, 1983; Grill et al., 1983). If a taste stimulus is continuously infused into a rat's mouth, the volume that is

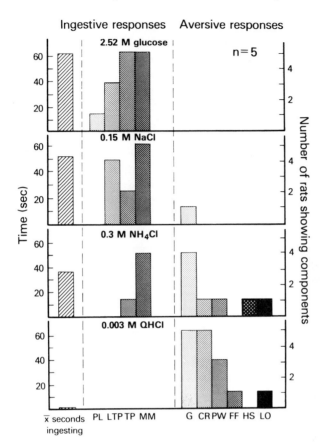

FIG. 4.   Taste reactivity profiles. Taste-elicited responses to oral infusions of four different taste stimuli: glucose (2.52 M), NaCl (0.15 M), NH$_4$Cl (0.3 M), and quinine HCl (0.003 M). Response categories: PL, paw licking; LTP, lateral tongue protrusions; TP, tongue protrusions; MM, mouth movements; G, gapes; CR, chin rubs; PW, paw wipes; FF, forelimb flailing; HS, head shakes; LO, locomotion. Ingestion time is total seconds of stimulus consumption.

consumed can be measured along with the taste-elicited FAPs that it produces. Two different patterns of taste reactivity responses can accompany intake: a sequence of rhythmic movements or a pattern of tongue protrusions and lateral tongue movements interdigitated with mouth movements. Likewise, a taste stimulus can either be rejected passively by fluid dripping from the mouth, or actively by head shakes, chin rubs, paw wiping, or paw shaking. Oral intake is determined by measuring the volume of tastant consumed before it is rejected from the oral cavity. The infusion is stopped at the time of rejection. After a 30-sec interval without infusion, the infusion pump is restarted. If the taste stimulus is rejected again within 30 sec of restarting the infusion, the intake test is terminated and the volume consumed computed. If, however, the rat continues to consume the taste for more than 30 additional seconds, the infusion proceeds until two successive fluid rejection responses occur. Table I demonstrates that when sucrose is continuously infused into the mouths of 24-hr food-deprived intact rats, the volume of sucrose ingested is much greater than when the same rat is tested while food replete (1 hr after a tube-fed meal). The same result is obtained if intraperitoneal insulin injection (regular insulin, 5 U/kg) is substituted for food deprivation in a different group of food-replete rats (see Table I). Water was substituted for the intraorally delivered 0.03 M sucrose in both paradigms, to control for whether alterations in internal state would give rise to a general facilitation of fluid intake. Rats did not increase their intake of orally delivered water when food deprived or insulin treated. It appears that the integration of internal energy-deficit cues and specific types of taste signals is necessary to enhance intraoral intake.

In analyzing the minute-by-minute changes in taste reactivity profiles during sucrose infusion, two interesting parallels between taste reactivity components and intake measures emerged for both food-deplete and -replete conditions. First and most characteristically, the number of sucrose-elicited ingestive FAPs (tongue protrusions, lateral tongue movements, and paw licks) declined with increasing infusion time (Grill, 1984). Second, the number of aversive components like head shakes, paw shakes, and gapes increased in frequency as meal termination approached. The difference between food-deplete and -replete conditions is that food deprivation greatly increases the number of ingestive FAPs emitted at the beginning of the infusion test. In both replete and deplete

TABLE I

EFFECT OF FOOD DEPRIVATION AND INSULIN INJECTION
ON SUCROSE TASTE REACTIVITY

Treatment	Sucrose intake (ml)	Water intake (ml)
Food deprivation		
1-hr deprived	2.74 ± 0.78	2.74 ± 0.82
24-hr deprived	4.45 ± 0.84#	1.97 ± 0.67
Insulin treatment		
Saline control	8.1 ± 1.1	4.7 ± 1.0
Insulin (5 U/kg)	11.3 ± 1.2	5.8 ± 1.9

conditions the number of ingestive responses declines as the test proceeds and is at minimum at the end of the test.

The change in NaCl intake that accompanies alterations in internal sodium state, called salt appetite, is a robust phenomenon in the field and laboratory (Richter, 1956; Denton, 1967). A variety of different explanations for this potent change in NaCl consumption are equally plausible, but traditional palatability measures cannot distinguish among them. Several experiments from our laboratory have addressed the issue of whether the heightened NaCl intake following sodium depletion is accompanied by a shift in the palatability of that substance, that is, in the reaction to its taste. To ensure that any observed shift was truly state dependent, rather than a permanent associative or habituation effect, rats were repeatedly brought in and out of sodium balance. We were thus able to examine NaCl taste reactivity a number of times in each state, and we discovered that FAPs elicited by concentrated NaCl did shift from aversive to ingestive during sodium depletion (Berridge *et al.*, 1984).

At 1.0-ml volume of 0.5 *M* NaCl was infused into a rat's mouth at a constant rate over 1 min. Taste reactivity responses were videotaped for subsequent frame-by-frame analysis. Each week rats were tested both sodium replete and 24 hr after artificial sodium depletion (simultaneous sc injections of 5.0 mg deoxycorticosterone and 7.5 mg furosemide, and 3 hr later an additional 7.5-mg furosemide injection). Each rat was tested five times in each condition and served as its own control. The results of biweekly two-bottle intake tests indicated that a sodium appetite, as traditionally measured, was induced. Sodium depletion dramatically affected taste-elicited FAPs as seen in the weekly data in Fig. 5. A significant increase in ingestive FAPs and reduction in aversive FAPs elicited by a constant NaCl taste is shown in the pooled data. The palatability of a constant 0.5 *M* NaCl taste stimulus was therefore controlled by internal-sodium-state cues.

Classically conditioned associations represent another factor that is integrated with taste and internal state to determine palatability. Of the associative paradigms used to affect the intake of taste stimuli, conditioned taste aversion (CTA) is the most widely used. Despite its name, however, aversive behavior per se is *not* normally measured in this paradigm. What is typically measured is the reduction in taste-elicited intake. The reduction of intake is the measure of taste avoidance. As noted earlier, however, intake tests cannot distinguish between reduced taste intake based on changes in palatability and reduced intake based on anticipated negative consequences (fear or danger). The taste reactivity analysis *does* measure aversive behavior. Using this test we have demonstrated that when a taste has been associated with a certain class of aversive

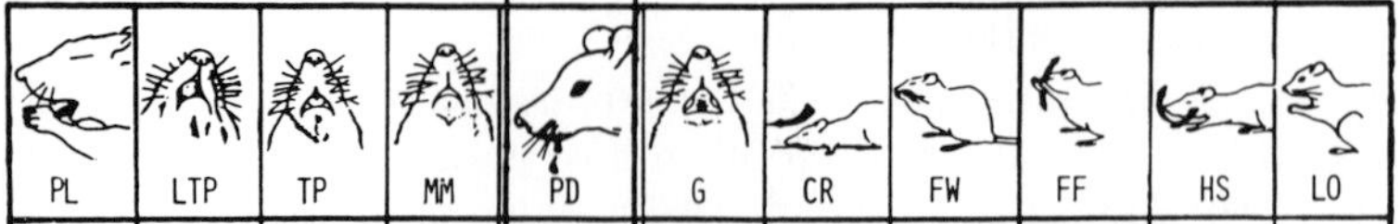

	INGESTIVE					AVERSIVE				
PL	LTP	TP	MM	PD	G	CR	FW	FF	HS	LO
I										
0.6	2.6	1.6	5.3	2.0	3.3	0	0	0.3	1.6	0
3.6	3.3	7.6	3.0	0	0	0	0	0	0	0
II										
0.3	0.6	1.0	4.3	3.0	0	0	1.0	1.6	3.0	0.6
4.3	3.0	7.6	5.3	0	0	0	0	0	0	0
III										
0	0.3	2.3	4.6	4.0	0	0	0	0	2.0	0.3
2.3	1.0	13.0	1.3	0	0	0	0	0	0	0
IV										
0	0	0	2.3	4.0	0.6	0	0	0	3.0	0
3.3	0.6	8.3	4.0	0	0	0	0	0	0	0
V										
0	0	0	4.0	4.3	0	0	0.6	0.6	3.3	0
4.0	1.0	9.3	3.6	0	0	0	0	0	0	0

FIG. 5. Mean number of taste-elicited FAPs per rat for three rats to 0.5 M NaCl when either sodium replete (upper rows) or deplete (lower rows) for weeks I–V. Ingestive responses are paw licking (PL), lateral tongue protrusions (LTP), tongue protrusions (TP), and mouth movements (MM). Failure to show any consummatory response, either ingestive or aversive, results in the passive drip of fluid from the mouth (PD). Aversive responses are gapes (G), chin rubs (CR), face washing (FW), forelimb flailing (FF), head shakes (HS), and locomotion (LO).

unconditioned stimuli (UCSs), its palatability is changed by even a single taste–UCS pairing (Grill, 1975; Berridge *et al.*, 1981; Pelchat *et al.*, 1983). This class of aversive UCSs is exemplified by the action of LiCl. Intoxication with lithium salts produces nausea and vomiting in humans (Baldessarini, 1980), and administration of antiemetic drugs blocks the expression of taste–LiCl paired taste avoidance in the rat (Coil *et al.*, 1978). Other classes of aversive UCSs (including footshock and lactose intolerance) that do not act on the upper gastrointestinal tract reduced taste intake but did not produce a shift in taste reactivity responses (Pelchat *et al.*, 1983).

Figure 6 demonstrates the changes in taste reactivity profiles produced by two taste–LiCl associations. Novel sugars or other tastes that elicit an ingestive response sequence will elicit a quinine-like aversive-response sequence following associative pairings with LiCl injections (Grill, 1975; Berridge *et al.*, 1981; Pelchat *et al.*, 1983). The first association of a taste

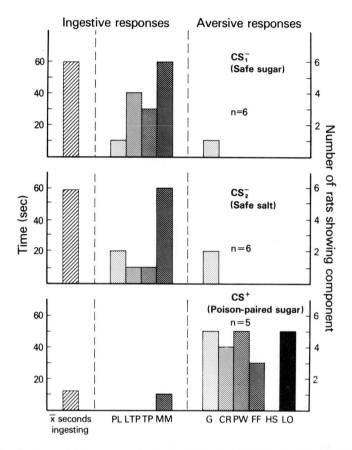

FIG. 6. Taste reactivity responses to discriminative taste CS. Taste-elicited FAPs to oral infusions of the CS_1^- (15% maltose or frutose), CS_2^- (0.15 M NaCl), and CS^+ (15% maltose or fructose). Response categories are as in Fig. 5. Ingesting time is total seconds of stimulus consumption.

with LiCl produces a shift in palatability that is most often typified by a mixed response, that is, a response containing components of both ingestive and rejection sequences. Following additional pairings, the palatability of the paired taste shifts even further to contain a greater percentage of aversive FAPs and a smaller percentage of ingestive FAPs until the response is exclusively aversive.

The CTA paradigm reveals that the association of taste with the internal consequences of certain aversive UCSs produces a change from ingestive to aversive in the palatability of the paired taste. Attempts to reverse taste palatability in the opposite direction, from aversive to ingestive, as a

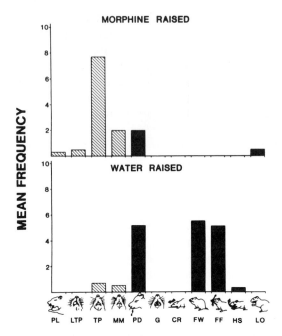

FIG. 7. Mean frequency of ingestive (hatched bars) and aversive (solid bars) FAPs elicited by intraoral infusions of 0.3, 0.6, and 1.5 mg/ml morphine sulfate for morphine-raised (group M) and water-raised (group W) rats maintained on either ad lib access to morphine sulfate or following 72-hr access to water. Response categories are as in Fig. 5.

function of association with the internal consequences of other UCSs have met with much less success (see also Booth *et al.*, 1982). We have made progress on this issue by using a morphine addiction paradigm. Morphine tastes bitter to humans. Rats avoid the taste of morphine when first exposed to it and consume water in preference to it in two-bottle tests. When rats are forced to drink morphine, they reverse their original preference and drink more morphine solution than water (Stolerman and Kumar, 1970; Ternes, 1975c). The question we addressed was whether the association of morphine taste with its potent opiate internal-state changes could change its palatability evaluation.

Taste reactivity to morphine and other tastes was examined in rats that had been raised for several months with morphine solution as their only source of water and in control rats raised with water (Zellner *et al.*, 1984). Taste reactivity was examined in two conditions: during home cage ad lib access to morphine or water, and during periods of its withdrawal. These data are shown in Fig. 7. Oral presentations of morphine elicited aversive FAPs, and the solution was spit out by water-raised rats both during periods of water access and during morphine withdrawal. In contrast, morphine-raised rats displayed ingestive taste reactivity responses (tongue protrusions, lateral tongue movements, and mouth movements) in response to morphine taste, and they swallowed the infused solution following either morphine home cage access or withdrawal. The percentage of ingestive components elicited by oral morphine was significantly greater for morphine-raised than water-raised rats. Sucrose elicited the same ingestive sequences in morphine- and water-raised groups. Quinine taste elicited aversive responses in both groups, and there were no significant differences in the number of aversive components produced by both groups.

In morphine-raised rats, quinine had a tendency to elicit mixed responses that included some ingestive components. These quinine data could therefore be interpreted as indicating that similarities in the tastes of morphine and quinine produced a generalization to the reinforcing qualities of morphine. Alternatively, the morphine-raised rats may simply have habituated to morphine's taste during their prolonged pretest exposure, and their response to quinine might then reflect generalization of the taste habituation. To control for this latter possibility, another group of rats was raised for a number of months on a quinine solution as their only source of water. Quinine is judged bitter by humans and has toxic or aversive postingestional consequences (Scalafani *et al.,* 1979). If habituation to a bitter taste occurs irrespective of the valence of the associated postingestive effects of the bitter taste, then quinine exposure should come to alter quinine taste reactivity similar to the shift in morphine taste reactivity. However, when subsequently examined, these rats did not display any ingestive components to quinine but passively rejected the taste even after a period of quinine withdrawal. It is concluded that the association of morphine taste with its internal consequences produces a change in its palatability.

As mentioned earlier, if the taste reactivity measure does indeed reflect the palatability decision it must satisfy several criteria. The examples just provided on the effects of internal state (e.g., food deprivation, insulin injection, sodium depletion) and classical associations (e.g., CTA, morphine addiction) on the palatability decision satisfy the second criterion, that the taste-elicited FAPs integrate information from a variety of sources to produce changes in the response to a constant taste stimulus. The third criterion, that clusters of taste-elicited FAPs vary together with changes in palatability, is also fulfilled. The use of the terms "ingestive sequence" and "aversive sequence" arose because in the sated intact rat some taste stimuli (e.g., sucrose) tended to elicit one set of FAPs, while another taste stimulus (e.g., quinine) evoked another response sequence composed of different FAPs. During the sucrose response a pattern of mouth movements, tongue protrusions, and lateral tongue movements was elicited and the stimulus was ingested. During the quinine response a pattern of gapes, chin rubs, head shaking, paw wipes, face washes, forelimb shaking, and paw rubs was elicited, and the stimulus was rejected. Each component FAP of the quinine response appears to facilitate removal of the stimulus from contact with the animal and can therefore be defined as aversive responses based on the criteria of Craig (1918). While these data demonstrate that a given stimulus can elicit a characteristic group of FAPs, they do not indicate whether each FAP group is activated by a single mechanism. It is conceivable, for instance, that each FAP is elicited separately from all other FAPs and that each response is under unique control rather than under the control of a more global palatability decision.

Data that address this question come from an analysis of instances in which both ingestive and aversive FAPs are elicited (e.g., by mixtures of sucrose and quinine). Berridge (1983) analyzed the sequence of FAPs generated by tastes producing mixed response patterns. The FAP sequence or FAP transition analysis of these tastes is shown in Table II and reveals the frequency with which each FAP is followed by every other

TABLE II

TASTE REACTIVITY RESPONSES OF RATS TO A TASTE MIXTURE[a]

	Ingestive				Aversive				
	PL	LTP	TP	MM	G	CR	FW	FF	HS
Ingestive									
PL	1	—	—	—	—	—	—	1	—
LTP	1	6	4	6	—	—	—	—	—
TP	—	3	5	7	1	—	—	—	—
MM	—	6	8	45	4	3	—	—	2
Aversive									
G	—	1	—	6	8	3	1	—	3
CR	—	—	—	—	2	3	3	—	4
FW	—	—	—	—	—	1	2	5	2
FF	—	—	—	—	1	—	7	3	—
HS	—	—	—	1	2	5	—	3	3

[a] Mixture consisted of 0.03 M NH$_4$Cl, 1 M glucose, and 0.0003 M quinine HCl. Abbreviations: PL, paw licks; LTP, lateral tongue protrusions; TP, tongue protrusions; MM, mouth movements; G, gapes; CR, chin rubs; FW, face wash; FF, forelimb flail; HS, head shake. Vertical axis denotes first behavior; horizontal axis shows every instance in which a particular behavior followed. Note that transitions typically occur *within* ingestive or aversive subgroups rather than between groups, although some exceptions do exist.

FAP. This analysis reveals strong temporal bonds within ingestive and aversive response groups but very weak associations between these two groups. This temporal clustering suggests that an ingestive decision activates a number of ingestive FAPs together as a unit and that aversive groups likewise function as units. Schwartz (1983) extended the taste reactivity analysis of Grill and Norgren (1978a) by increasing the volume and duration of the oral infusion of taste from 0.05 ml in a single pulse to 1.0 ml infused over 1 min. An analysis involving FAP sequencing was performed. Ranks for every possible pair of taste-elicited FAPs were correlated using a Spearman rank correlation coefficient, and a coefficient of association was obtained. This coefficient represents the likelihood that any two FAPs were followed by the same third component. For example, a coefficient of 0.9 between mouth movements and tongue protrusions would mean that it is highly probable that the same third component, lateral tongue movements, will follow both mouth movements and tongue protrusions. A negative coefficient between gapes and tongue protrusions would mean that components that follow gapes are usually not those that follow tongue protrusions. As can be seen in Table III for sucrose, the same components that follow mouth movements usually follow tongue protrusions and lateral tongue movements. Conversely, the components that follow gapes are not usually followed by tongue protrusions and lateral tongue movements. Similarly, as shown in Table III for quinine, gapes, chin rubs, head shakes, and forelimb shakes (all part of the "aversive" sequence) are highly correlated with each other as a group and negatively correlated with mouth movements and tongue protrusions. These data, as well as those of Berridge, strongly suggest that each FAP is not under separate control but rather that functional clusters of FAPs do exist and can be referred to as ingestive and aversive sequences. It should be noted that in both sequence analyses, the mouth movement component is positively correlated both with gaping, an aversive component, and with tongue protrusions and lateral tongue movements, which are ingestive components. These and other data (e.g., Berridge and Grill, 1983) lead to the conclusion that mouth movements are not strongly weighted toward either ingestion or aversion, and may be best described as a sampling act whose function may be preliminary to evaluation.

III. Fine Structure of Palatability Decisions: A Two-Dimensional Model

An additional advantage of taste reactivity over traditional measures of palatability is that fewer assumptions are built into this measure. Traditional behavioral measures, such as intake, preference, or operants, all use responses that are themselves best described as varying along a single

TABLE III
TASTE REACTIVITY RESPONSES OF RATS[a]

	LTP	TP	MM
Ingestive[b]			
LTP	—	0.65	0.70
TP	—	—	0.82
MM	—	—	—
Aversive[b]			
G	−0.90	−0.90	0.50

	TP	MM	G	CR	FF	HS	LO	R
Ingestive[c]								
TP	—	0.50	—	—	—	—	—	—
MM	—	—	—	—	—	—	—	—
Aversive[c]								
G	−0.70	0.50	—	—	—	—	—	—
CR	−0.90	−0.80	0.80	—	—	—	—	—
FF	−0.80	0.20	0.70	0.75	—	0.25	—	—
HS	−0.90	−0.15	0.75	0.85	—	—	—	—
LO	−0.75	−0.10	0.55	0.40	0.35	0.30	—	—
R	−0.80	−0.70	0.65	0.50	0.43	0.40	0.90	—

[a] Abbreviations: LTP, lateral tongue protrusion; TP, tongue protrusions; MM, mouth movements; G, gapes; CR, chin rubs; FF, forelimb flail; HS, head shake; LO, locomotion; R, rearing. Correlation between the order of taste reactivity responses of rats receiving intraoral infusions of tastants. Each number corresponds to the direction of the relationship between the responses that follow any two taste reactivity responses; positive values mean that the relative frequency of occurrence of behaviors following any response on the horizontal axis is similar to that following any response on the vertical axis. For example, behaviors that follow tongue protrusions have the same relative frequency distribution as behaviors that follow lateral tongue protrusions.
[b] Responses to 0.3 M sucrose.
[c] Responses to 0.0003 M quinine.

continuum, either from high to low or from positive to negative. Using these measures, the palatability evaluation of a given taste under a given testing condition is implicitly characterized as a single point along that continuum (e.g., Young, 1977). This characterization allows the response to a taste to be described as palatable, unpalatable, or neutral, but never as both positive and negative at the same time. The drawback of such measures and of the palatability description they provide is that they are likely to give the impression that palatability itself (apart from its measurement) is a single evaluation produced by the central nervous system. Even if the brain actually generated evaluations of palatability using a mechanism whose output could not be accurately described by a point falling along a single dimension, these measures would not detect it.

Taste-elicited FAPs, on the other hand, can vary along a number of dimensions—as many dimensions as there are FAPs. In fact, however, the FAPs do not appear to vary independently along these many (nine) dimensions. Instead, as just noted, they cluster into two distinct groups of ingestive and aversive responses, as noted earlier. By itself, this clustering appears consistent with the traditional single-dimension model of palatability. Each cluster could correspond to extreme palatability assessments and be plotted at either end of the continuum. A somewhat more difficult observation to reconcile with the one-dimensional model, however, is that the ingestive and aversive clusters occasionally intermesh and that sometimes, especially during infusions of certain taste stimuli, there is a rapid alternation back and forth between ingestive and aversive FAPs (Berridge and Grill, 1983; Schwartz and Grill, 1984).

A. Interpreting Alternating Ingestive and Aversive Responses

Rapid alternation between one behavior and its functional opposite has often been interpreted as revealing conflict between underlying mechanisms (e.g., Tinbergen, 1952; Andrew, 1956; Sevenster, 1961; Hinde, 1970). Such alternation has been termed "ambivalent behavior" (Tinbergen, 1952). The rapid alternation we have observed between ingestive and aversive FAPs could imply an actual conflict between internal decisions to emit these two different kinds of acts. This would imply that the evaluation of palatability actually involves two separate analyses that correspond, respectively, to dimensions of ingestion and aversion (see Fig. 8). Low activation of both dimensions (point A) results in a relatively neutral response such as passive dripping of the infused solution or rhyth-

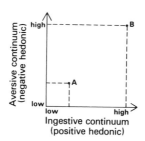

Fig. 8. A two-dimensional model of palatability. Point A represents a taste that weakly activates both ingestion and aversion and results in a passive response. Point B represents a taste that strongly activates both ingestion and aversion and results in active alternation of ingestive and aversive consummatory responses. The palatability of other tastes may be represented by points falling anywhere within the plane described by the axes of ingestion and aversion.

mic mouth movements occurring alone. High activation of both (point B) results in the simultaneous expression of the two extremes, namely the rapid alternation of mixed ingestive and aversive FAPs (Berridge and Grill, 1983).

The interpretation of FAP sequences is complicated, however, by the likely possibility that palatability decisions are not the only decisions that play a role in their production. Additional mediating systems must exist in order to translate palatability decisions into a particular sequence of behavioral responding. These mediating systems, or motor control systems, can be expected to involve rules of their own and are responsible for the actual patterning of movement (similar to the control systems invoked by MacFarland, 1974; Fentress, 1981). Before concluding that a particular pattern of behavior reflects the existence of two separate central nervous decisions about palatability, one must ask whether the same pattern could have been produced instead by a particular motor control system acting secondarily on a single palatability decision. In the case of alternation such a result is easy to imagine. A behavioral alternation between ingestive and aversive FAPs could result from a single palatability decision if the motor control system symmetrically activated responses on either side of the palatibility decision itself: ingestive responses first and then aversive responses and so on.

B. The Use of Isohedonic Tastes to Support a Two-Dimensional Model

To choose between the hypothesis of a motor control system whose output produced alternation operating with a single palatability decision and the hypothesis of a two-dimensional analysis of palatability, we need to know more than the mere fact that behavioral alternation exists. We need to know how the rat behaves under conditions in which the two hypotheses make different predictions. One such situation is when the negative palatability decision elicited by a taste shifts to become either more negative or more positive. According to the single-dimension view, a shift moves the evaluation along the palatability continuum, and one should therefore see a reciprocal change in the behavioral output: as one class of FAPs grows the other should decline reciprocally. According to the two-dimensional view, in contrast, it should be possible to produce an increase in the strength of aversion without changing the strength of ingestion, by moving the decision point in Fig. 8 upward along the aversive axis but keeping it stationary along the ingestive axis. Berridge and Grill (1983) found that the proportion of rats emitting aversive FAPs could be increased without changing the proportion of rats emitting ingestive FAPs by adding quinine HCl together with sucrose to an original solution of ammonium chloride. Subsequent work in our laboratory has used a modified version of Young's isohedonic (equally preferred) taste pairs to show that the number of emitted ingestive and aversive FAPs can be independently manipulated (Berridge, 1983; Berridge and Grill, 1984). Young and Schulte (1963) determined the concentration of sucrose that must be added to a given quinine HCl solution to make the mixture equally preferred to a standard, unadulterated sucrose solution of lower concentration. The resulting taste mixture together with its sucrose standard constitute an isohedonic pair. When a number of different quinine–sucrose mixtures have been identified as isohedonic to a given sucrose standard, a curve may be plotted in a space where the axes denote sucrose and quinine concentrations, respectively. This curve is an isohedonic contour, and all points along it are assumed to be equally preferred (Young and Madsen, 1963).

Two isohedonic contours corresponding to 4 and 8% sucrose standards were chosen from Young and Schulte (1963) for FAP analysis. Both the FAPs that were elicited by these two standards alone and by their isohedonic mixtures that contained 0.01% quinine (7% sucrose plus 0.01% quinine for the lower concentration, and 18% sucrose plus 0.01% quinine for the higher) were examined. Since the primary purpose of the study was to replicate the independent increase in aversive FAPs found by Berridge and Grill (1983), the 8% sucrose standard was also compared to a mixture that should lie on the aversive side of its isohedonic contour, namely, a solution of 18% sucrose and 0.05% quinine. The number of FAPs emitted for each tastant was analyzed using the scoring procedure described in Berridge *et al.* (1984).

In the first isohedonic comparison, the sucrose–quinine mixture elicited both significantly more active aversive responses and significantly more ingestive responses than its 4% sucrose standard (this always refers to tongue protrusions, lateral tongue movements, and paw licking; see Fig. 9). Mouth movements are not included in this analysis, since the performance of other more strongly weighted ingestive components can break up and reduce mouth movement bins by simple intrusion (Berridge and Grill, 1983). This result by itself could suggest either that the taste mixture evokes an increase in nonspecific activation in conjunction with a single palatability evaluation, or that the two separate evaluations of ingestion and aversion are both enhanced by the sucrose–quinine mixture. Interestingly, this effect was not seen in the comparison between the higher concentration isohedonic pair: FAPs remained the same. Since the level of FAPs makes a ceiling effect unlikely, this could reflect the presence of inhibitory relations between the central positive and negative

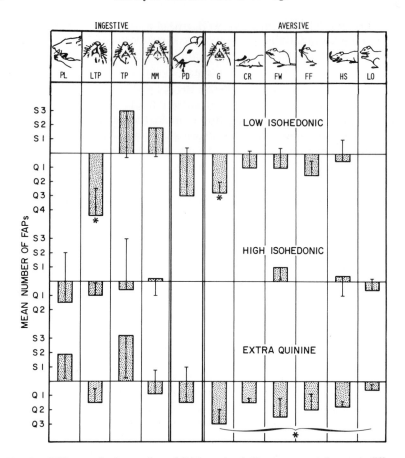

FIG. 9. Difference in the number of FAPs emitted. Bars represent the mean difference (±SEM) in the number of FAPs elicited by the constituents of each taste pair. Extension of the bar above the line represents a greater number of FAPs elicited by the sucrose standard; extension of the bar below the line represents a greater number of FAPs elicited by the sucrose–quinine mixture. Asterisks represent significant difference at $p < 0.05$. FAP symbols are as in Fig. 5.

decisions, or between their motor control systems, at high levels of activation (Fentress, 1973, 1983).

It is important to note that in the comparison between 8% sucrose and its "extra-quinine" mixture (18% sucrose plus 0.05% quinine), there was no significant change in ingestive components, but there was a significant increase in pooled aversive components (Berridge and Grill, 1984; see Fig. 9). This result demonstrates again that changes in the strength of aversive components need not be accompanied by reciprocal changes in ingestive components. These data (Berridge and Grill, 1984) are clearly incompatible with the single-dimension model of palatability, as it has been considered so far.

A modification of the motor control system might be suggested here that would allow these data again to become compatible with a single-dimensional model. A change in aversive FAPs while ingestive components remain constant is compatible with a single palatability decision, only if one supposes that aversive FAPs are more sensitive to changes in the strength of the palatability decision signal than are ingestive FAPs, and that ingestive components have a flat sensitivity curve above a certain low threshold. Put another way, it takes a greater shift of the palatability evaluation to produce a change in ingestive FAPs than to change aversive ones. If this were true, however, aversive responses should always be at least as sensitive as ingestive FAPs to changes in palatability. Other evidence from our laboratory suggests that this is not the case. In the study of the effects of sodium depletion on taste reactivity described earlier, it was found that the FAPs elicited while the animal was sodium replete shift over repeated trials to become less ingestive. Pooled ingestive FAPs elicited from sodium-sated animals gradually declined with repeated trials, while the number of pooled aversive responses remained unchanged as rats were repeatedly brought into and out of sodium balance (Berridge *et al.,* 1984).

Together with the previously discussed experiments, these data suggest that both ingestive and aversive FAP groups can be made to change independently, and they provide further support for the hypothesis of two separate dimensions of palatability evaluation. A motor control system that is differentially sensitive to a single palatability decision will not account for these data unless one supposes that the ingestive production system is more sensitive to palatability shifts under some conditions, but that the aversive group is more sensitive under others.

C. Additional Support for a Two-Dimensional Model

The hypothesis that palatability processing involves two separate decisions finds additional support from other lines of evidence. Rat pups begin to show ingestive consummatory responses to tastes at an earlier age than they do aversive responses (Grill and Norgren, 1978c; Hall and Bryan, 1981). This could reflect a difference in the maturation rate of either gustatory receptors or the decision systems themselves. Studies by Weingarten and colleagues indicate that the well-known "finickiness" of ventromedial hypothalamic (VMH)-lesioned rats is asymmetrical (Weingarten, 1982; Weingarten *et al.,* 1983). These rats are hyperreactive to sweet but not to bitter solutions in sham-feeding analyses compared to weight-paired controls, suggesting that only the positive palatability decision is affected by these lesions. In a similar dissociation of positive and negative responses to taste, Xenakis and Scalafani (1982) have reported that the consumption by nonfasted, obese VMH rats is overinhibited by quinine adulteration relative to normal-weight controls, but that the same animals respond as do controls to the positive reinforcing properties of sweet tastes, as measured by the effects of sweetness dilution. Finally, Ganchrow *et al.* (1981) have reported that rats that tend to self-administer high rates of intracranial electrical stimulation also tend to overconsume saccharin solutions compared to rats that self-stimulate at lower rates, but that they do not differ from low self-stimulators in quinine consumption. This again implies a separation between systems of positive and negative evaluation, and suggests further that the systems mediating the positive evaluations of different stimuli may overlap.

Thus, the hypothesis that palatability processing involves two separate decisions about a taste, corresponding to magnitudes of ingestion and aversion, appears to hold some promise of being an accurate description of how the brain analyzes gustatory information. It also serves as a reminder that new insights often can be gained by a more careful analysis of the stream of behavior, even behavior that at first sight appears quite simple.

IV. Neural Analysis of Palatability

The goal of a functional analysis of palatability is to empower a neurological investigation of the sites of integration of taste, internal state, and associative factors that would (1) suggest how the nervous system organizes its control of palatability and (2) improve the likelihood of reconstructing these events at the neurophysiological level. The approach that we (work begun by H. Grill and R. Norgren in 1974) applied to this neurological analysis was to examine whether a Jacksonian hierarchical organization would adequately explain the way the nervous system organizes the control of palatability. This hierarchical approach involved analyzing the palatability decisions made by classical neurological preparations including chronic decerebrate, thalamic, and decorticate rats. As an organizing principle for this section, the data generated by these neurological preparations will be compared to the palatability decisions made by intact rats.

As discussed earlier, palatability represents the CNS integration of taste, internal state, and associative factors. The relative weighting of these factors, however, is not always the same. A functional hierarchy of palatability decisions is made by determining the number of factors that are integrated to produce the six different examples of palatability decisions discussed previously. Table IV organizes these examples into three levels of palatability decision complexity. Level 1, the simplest type of decision, integrates two factors: present taste and present internal state. In the intact rat, taste is *always* being integrated with state and compared with previous associations between taste and state; however, the weighting of the association and state factors can be reduced in certain instances. For example, in the intact rat, if the comparison of taste and state associations in memory, previously shown to be very rapid (Halpern and Tapper, 1971), yields no match to the present taste or state, then the associative factor would have no weight and would not be included in this particular decision. In contrast, when the comparison does yield a match, association then becomes a weighted factor in the palatability decision (see later). Second, it is possible that neural manipulations may reveal instances where palatability decisions are determined by taste alone. This type of decision will be called level 0 because it is not seen in the intact rat. The respective effects of food deprivation or sodium depletion (internal-state factors) on sucrose or NaCl taste reactivity and intake represent level 1 decisions. In these cases the association factor can be thought of as having no weight.

Association becomes an integrated factor when a previous association between taste and state has occurred. Both level 2 and 3 decisions involve

TABLE IV
THREE LEVELS OF PALATABILITY DECISION COMPLEXITY

Level	Integrated factors	Examples
1	Present taste, present internal state	Effects of food deprivation and insulin treatment on sucrose palatability; effects of sodium depletion on salt palatability
2	Present taste, previous association between what is now present taste and a previous internal state, present internal state	Effects of conditioned taste aversions; effects of morphine addiction on morphine palatability
3	Present taste, previous association between what is now present taste and a previous internal state; correspondence between present state and state previously associated with present taste	Booth's conditioned satiety and hunger effects on palatability

the association factor but differ in their relative weighting of the present internal-state factor. Level 2 and 3 decisions include present taste, present state, and past taste–state associations as factors in the integration of the palatability decision. Level 3 decisions, however, require a correspondence between the present state and the particular state during the previous taste–state association for a change in palatability to be evidenced; in other words, level 3 decisions are state dependent. Level 2 decisions include present state *only* in a nonassociative context (as does level 1), while level 3 decisions include present state as an associative element. The conditioned taste aversion and morphine addiction paradigms represent examples of level 2 decisions, because a correspondence between present state and state previously associated with present taste is not necessary for an alteration in palatability to occur. For example, ingestive FAPs are elicited by the taste of "bitter" morphine when it is presented to an addicted rat or to one that is in morphine withdrawal. Likewise, aversive FAPs are evoked by the taste of a LiCl-paired glucose taste whether it is presented to a sated or to a mildly hungry rat. Present state is included as a factor in level 2 decisions, because its weighting can influence the behavioral outcome. For example, extremes of food or sodium deprivation will alter the degree of taste avoidance when either sucrose or NaCl taste has been a conditioned stimulus in a CTA. In contrast, level 3 decisions require a correspondence between present state and the state of the rat during its previous taste association. For example, a rat prefers a taste that has previously been associated with dilute starch ingestion only when it is tested in a sated condition (Booth, 1977). In fact, if this rat were presented with the dilute starch-paired taste when in a hungry condition, it would avoid the taste, that is, display a reversed preference. The functional hierarchy of the complexity of palatability decisions just noted may be useful in evaluating whether the neural control of palatability is hierarchically organized in the rat's nervous system.

A. CHRONIC DECEREBRATE RATS

1. Level 1 Decisions

The chronic supracollicular decerebrate rat is a caudal brain stem preparation that lacks its forebrain, as shown in Fig. 10. The gustatory system of this preparation contains only the first and second central gustatory relay nuclei, the nucleus of the solitary tract (NTS), and the parabrachial nucleus (PBN). The chronic decerebrate rat is a viable preparation despite its extensive neural damage. It maintains a righted posture, locomotes (albeit sluggishly), and grooms effectively, as shown in Fig. 11.

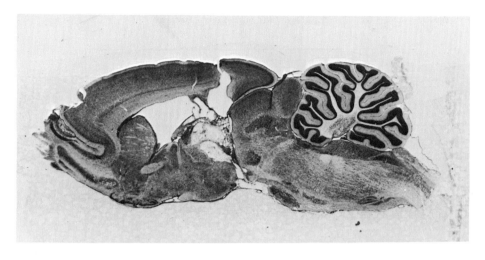

Fig. 10. Sagittal section stained with cresyl violet from the brain of a representative chronic decerebrate rat; survival time, 37 days. The supracollicular plane of section is highly similar for each rat. The tissue posterior to the transection appears normal in the light microscope. A cavity filling the space normally occupied by portions of the thalamus and hippocampus is present anterior to the transections of rats surviving 30 days or more.

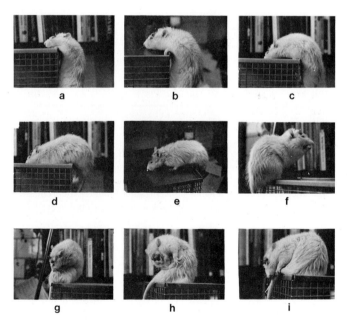

Fig. 11. Chronic decerebrate rats exhibit no spontaneous activity other than grooming but often overreact with well-coordinated movements to seemingly inappropriate stimuli. Tail pinch facilitates a brisk, well-coordinated sequence of cage climbing (a–e). Decerebrate rats maintain their fur; face washing (f) and grooming of the flanks (g and h) and anal (i) and genital areas involve complicated postures that are executed in a coordinated fashion by these rats.

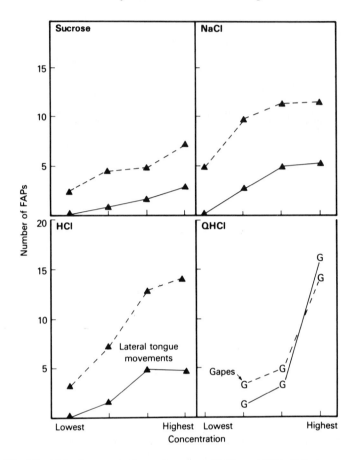

FIG. 12.   The highest concentrations of sucrose, NaCl, and HCl elicited approximately the same number of lateral tongue movements from chronic decerebrates (——) as intact rats (----) performed in response to the lowest concentration of these stimuli. Nevertheless, the slope of the lateral tongue movement–concentration function was roughly parallel for both preparations. The number of gape responses to quinine stimuli were very similar for decerebrate and intact rats.

When tested in the sated condition (1 hr after an intragastric meal), the chronic decerebrate rat displays the same taste reactivity responses as the sated intact rat (Grill and Norgren, 1978b). For example, sucrose, NaCl, and HCl stimuli elicit an ingestive sequence composed of mouth movements, tongue protrusions, and lateral tongue movements, while quinine stimuli evoke an aversive sequence including gapes, chin rubs, head shakes, and forelimb shakes. As seen in Fig. 12, increasing sucrose con-

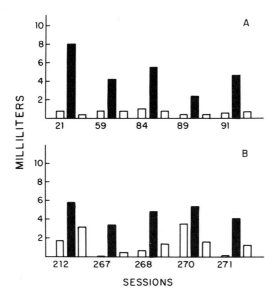

Fig. 13.   (A) Internal sucrose (0.03 *M*) intake of chronic decerebrate rats and (B) pair-fed control rats for just-fed (open bars) and 24-hr food-deprived (solid bars) conditions. Rat code numbers are shown below the abscissa.

centrations result in greater numbers of lateral tongue movements for both chronic decerebrate and intact rats. The decerebrate rat's threshold for the gape response (0.03 m*M* quinine HCl) is identical to that of the intact rat, as is the number of gapes elicited by increasing concentrations of quinine (see Fig. 12).

Palatability decisions are directly affected by changes in the internal metabolic state of the decerebrate rat. Figure 13 displays the intraoral sucrose intake of decerebrate rats tested in sated and food-deprived conditions. When sucrose is infused into the mouths of 24-hr food-deprived decerebrate rats they, like their pair-fed intact controls, double their sucrose intake over sated levels (Grill and Norgren, 1978d; Grill, 1980). The specific types of internal-state factors that are integrated with gustatory afferent signals (present taste) to produce state-dependent alterations in decerebrate palatability decisions are an important issue. Simple 24-hr food deprivation will affect a great many internal-state factors, while other internal metabolic manipulations may be more specific in their action. For this reason we have examined the effect of insulin injection on the palatability decisions of sated decerebrate rats. Figure 14 demonstrates that insulin injection produces the same reduction in plasma glu-

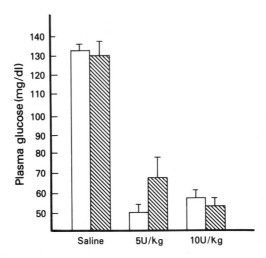

FIG. 14. Mean plasma glucose concentrations (±SEM) of control (open) and chronic decerebrate (hatched) rats at the time of intraoral intake tests, that is, 3 hr after treatment with saline and insulin (5 and 10 U/kg).

cose level for decerebrate and pair-fed intact rats. Figure 15 reveals that insulin's effect on plasma glucose, like the more general effects of 24-hr food deprivation, results in a significant increase in sucrose intake but not water intake for both decerebrate and intact rats (Flynn and Grill, 1983). Decerebrate and pair-fed intact rats increase their ingestion of sucrose but not water, in response to the internal-state deficits posed by insulin injection and food deprivation. Since both groups of rats discriminated between the taste of these solutions, the enhanced ingestion of sucrose following internal-state changes in fuel availability does not reflect a general facilitation of fluid intake. It appears that a combination of internal fuel-deficit signals together with specific types of taste signals is necessary to change the intake and palatability of the sucrose taste stimulus. The isolated, caudal brain stem mechanisms of the chronic decerebrate rat are therefore sufficient to integrate these signals into a level 1 palatability decision. But, does this preparation demonstrate its integration of other internal-state changes in the palatability decisions it expresses for other tastes?

We have examined two other examples of level 1 decisions in the chronic decerebrate rat: the effects of hyperosmotic signals on the palatability evaluation of water, and the effects of sodium loss on the evaluation of NaCl palatability. In both instances in chronic decerebrate rats integration had taken place; that is, they did not respond differentially to

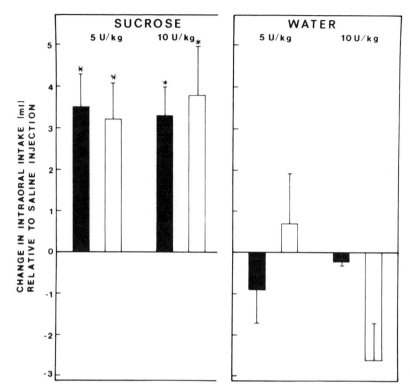

Fig. 15. Change in intake (milliliters) relative to intake during saline injection condition; solid bars, decerebrate; open bars, control. Asterisks denote $p < 0.05$; paired t-test comparisons, significantly different from saline of that group. Sucrose = 0.03 M.

water or NaCl taste as a function of internal-state changes. Figure 16A–C demonstrates that changing the internal osmotic state of decerebrate rats using a variety of treatments (subcutaneous injections of hypertonic NaCl, intragastric NaCl, or water deprivation) does not lead to an immediate or even a delayed increase in the palatability of water as measured by intraoral intake (Grill and Miselis, 1981). The same treatments dramatically elevated intraoral water intake in pair-fed intact rats. The chronic decerebrate, like the intact rat, conserves urinary sodium after sodium loss and excretes sodium during salt loading. Despite this physiological similarity, however, sodium loss, effected by the combination of a diuretic (furosemide) and high doses of a mineralocorticoid (deoxycorticosterone acetate), did not result in either an increase in 0.5 M NaCl intake or a change in the pattern of taste reactivity to NaCl (Grill and Schulkin, 1984). As noted before, pair-fed intact rats dramatically alter both their

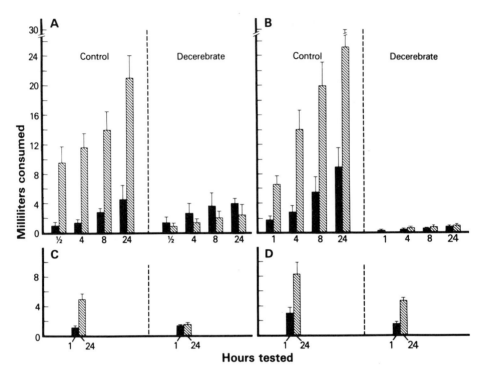

FIG. 16.   (A) Intraoral water intake following a 2-ml sc injection of either isotonic saline (control test, solid bars) or 10% saline (experimental test, hatched bars) administered 30 min after intragastric meal. Water was administered remotely via fistulas at 0.5, 4, 8, and 24 hr after the injection; rats did not receive any additional meals during this period. Bars indicate cumulative water intakes from first ingestion test. (B) Intraoral water intake following intra-gastric administration of 12 ml of regular diet (control test, solid bars) or diet osmotically enhanced with 3% NaCl (experimental test, hatched bars). Testing paradigm was same as in (A) except that first administration of water was given 1 hr after intragastric meals. No additional meals were given during the testing period. (C) Intraoral water intake following intragastric diet deprivation of either 1 hr (solid bars) or 24 hr (hatched bars). (D) Intraoral sucrose (0.03 M) intake following intragastric diet deprivation of 1 hr (solid bars) and 24 hr (hatched bars). Testing paradigm was same as in (C) except that rats were infused with 0.03 M sucrose instead of distilled water.

taste reactivity and intake responses to 0.5 M NaCl as a function of internal sodium state (see Fig. 5).

   The sodium-depleted or osmotically challenged decerebrate rat re-sponds to intraorally delivered water or NaCl as it did when tested in the nondeprived state; that is, it consumes the same volume of these tastants irrespective of internal state (level 0 integration, see earlier). Since decerebrate rats can differentially respond to the taste of NaCl and water, their lack of level 1 capacity for integrating taste and internal-state information in response to water or sodium deprivation appears to derive from either a lack of internal-state information available to the caudal brain stem or a lack of an integration of these signals with taste afferent input at this level.

At present the sites of osmotic and other relevant interoceptors and the integration of these signals into the neural mechanisms for the achievement of water balance by ingestive responses are presumed to require the forebrain (Grill and Miselis, 1981; however, see also Rogers and Novin, 1983). With respect to sodium appetites, it is interesting to note that sodium deficit leads to an alteration in primary afferent discharge to NaCl (Contreras *et al.*, 1984). Important questions for the neurology of sodium appetite and the neural control of palatability are whether this change in peripheral nerve response is (1) sufficient to account for the altered behavioral response and (2) dependent or independent of centrifugal control. It is interesting to consider these questions in the light of the decerebrate data. If the peripheral nerve change is behaviorally sufficient and independent of centrifugal influence, then why does the decerebrate not alter either its intake of or taste reactivity to saline? It will be necessary to examine the chorda tympani's electrophysiological response to NaCl in sodium-depleted decerebrate rats to clarify this point.

2. Level 2 Decisions

Garcia *et al.* (1974) have suggested that the association of gustatory and visceral stimuli that results in conditioned taste aversions may reflect the intimate relationship between gustatory and visceral afferent neurons within the NTS of the caudal brain stem. Therefore, one might predict that a chronic decerebrate rat could alter its response to a taste that had been associated with visceral illness. We have found just the opposite (Grill and Norgren, 1978d). Intact rats display a palatability shift for a LiCl-paired sucrose stimulus after a single association (an aversive sequence replaces an initial ingestive one). In contrast, chronic decerebrate rats do not alter their response to sucrose following as many as 12 sucrose–LiCl pairings. Sucrose continued to elicit an ingestive pattern in these rats that was in no way modified by the 12 sucrose–LiCl pairings. Decerebrate and pair-fed intact rats were retested at 24-hr intervals in this paradigm. To examine the possibility that decerebrate rats require an ongoing visceral stimulus in order to display a palatability shift, in a manner analogous to the effects of food deprivation and insulin injection,

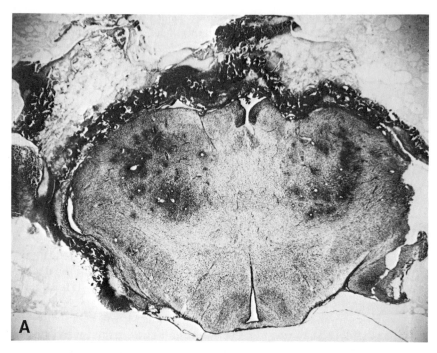

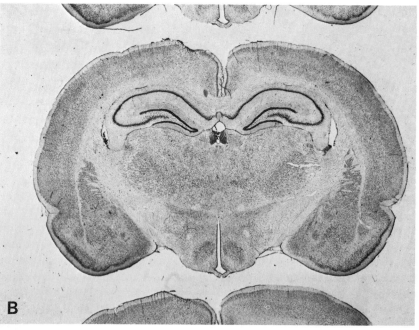

we have retested these rats 1 hr after taste–LiCl pairing. While intact rats display a palatability shift in this paradigm, decerebrates do not (R. Norgren and H. Grill, unpublished observations).

Decerebrate rats display level 0 decisions for CTA, osmotic challenge, and sodium appetite paradigms, while they demonstrate level 1 decisions for meal and energy challenge paradigms. We have extended the list of the decerebrate's level 1 capacity by showing that when this preparation is treated with cholecystokinin after 24 hr of food deprivation, it (like the intact rat) will reduce both its intake of sucrose and the ingestive taste reactivity responses it elicits (Grill *et al.*, 1983).

B. Chronic Thalamic Rats

1. Level 1 Decisions

The chronic thalamic rat is a diencephalic preparation whose telencephalon has been removed by aspiration and therefore whose thalamus is effectively disconnected from its reciprocal neocortical connections (see Fig. 17). Like the decerebrate, the thalamic rat is permanently aphagic. The gustatory system of the thalamic rat is more complete than that of the decerebrate. The brain of this preparation contains two more relay nuclei than the decerebrate's, the parabrachial nucleus' projection to sites in the ventral forebrain and the PBN's bifurcated dorsal projection to the ventral posteromedial thalamus (Norgren, 1976). In the sated condition (1 hr after tube feeding), however, thalamic rats respond aversively to 50-μl intraoral applications of *all* taste stimuli and therefore are quite different from intact and chronic decerebrate rats. As shown in Fig. 18, tongue protrusions and lateral tongue movements are not elicited by NaCl, HCl, water, or sucrose taste stimuli in the sated thalamic rat. In contrast to the taste reactivity of sated decerebrate and intact rats, sated thalamic rats display a pattern of mouth movements, rearing, gaping, chin rubbing, and paw wiping in response to a variety of taste stimuli (Grill and Norgren, 1978b). During the execution of this response sequence the stimulus is actively or passively rejected rather than swallowed. The same pattern of response is also elicited by orally applied quinine taste stimuli. While the sated thalamic rat does not display an ingestive sequence of response as a

---

Fig. 17. Coronal section of a representative thalamic (A) and intact (B) preparation at the level of the ventromedial nucleus of the hypothalamus. Sections are stained with cresyl violet; survival time of the thalamic rat, 20 days. There is extensive retrograde degeneration within the thalamus in each case. In this brain, there is gliosis within the thalamus that is probably vascular in origin.

Fig. 18.   Every taste stimulus tested elicited the same stereotyped response sequence from thalamic rats. The response began with gaping (a), which was coincident with rearing (a–c), and assuming bipedal posture. In this posture additional gapes were followed by paw wiping (d) and face washing (e). The thalamic rat then resumed the initial quadrupedal posture and performed chin-rubbing (f) and paw-pushing (g) responses. The entire response sequence was repeated up to four times as a function of stimulus concentration and category. Eyes were closed and facial muscles tightly contracted in all components except paw pushing.

function of taste quality, it does alter the number of repetitions of its basic aversive response sequence shown in Fig. 18. Therefore, the duration of its response to taste increases with increasing taste concentration (see Fig. 19).

The capacity of the chronic thalamic rat to alter its response to sucrose taste as a function of metabolic-state change is of great interest but has not yet been examined. Pfaffmann (personal communication) points out that the sated chronic thalamic preparation is the first example of a neurological lesion that completely eliminates positive responses to taste. Since chronic decerebrates have the capacity to execute ingestive response sequences, it seems that neural mechanisms rostral to the midbrain in some way suppress (or depotentiate) the production of ingestive responses of the sated thalamic rat.

One other neural manipulation appears to eliminate positive responses to food, if only temporarily: lesions of the lateral hypothalamus. Teitel-

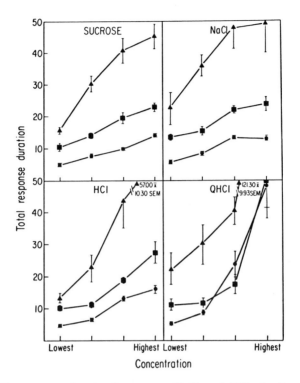

FIG. 19. The response duration for sucrose, NaCl, and HCl stimuli was longer for decerebrates (■) than intact rats (●) for all concentrations tested. Furthermore, the decerebrate's increased response duration was consistent, approximately 7.5 ± 2.1 sec within and between these stimulus categories. Thalamic rats (▲) response duration slope, for all taste stimuli, resembled the rapidly accelerating quinine slopes of intact and decerebrate rats. The quinine-like response duration slope was consistent with the general aversive response of the thalamic preparation. Brackets, SEM.

baum and Epstein (1962) mention that depositing a normally preferred taste into the mouths of stage I lateral hypothalamically lesioned (LHX) rats elicits an aversive pattern of response that includes chin rubbing and forelimb shaking. In an effort to document further and extend these observations, our laboratory has performed additional experiments (Fluharty and Grill, 1980). Assessment of sucrose, NaCl, and quinine taste reactivity and intraoral intake of 1.0 *M* sucrose and distilled water (1 ml infused during 1 min) began 2 days after rats received large bilateral LH lesions. When tested sated (1 hr after tube feeding), LHX rats, like sated thalamic rats, actively or passively rejected all taste stimuli. Presentations (50 μl) of sucrose, NaCl, and water stimuli, as well as quinine, were rejected. These taste stimuli elicited either an aversive pattern that included gapes, chin rubbing, and paw wiping, or passive fluid rejection. In contrast, when the same LHX rats were tested in the deprived condition their taste reactivity was normal. When these rats were tested food and water deprived (24 hr after intragastric liquid diet), sucrose, NaCl, and water stimuli all evoked an ingestive sequence (like that of intact and chronic decerebrate rats) that included lateral tongue movements and tongue protrusions. Deprived LHX rats, like intact and decerebrate rats, responded to quinine HCl concentrations at or above 0.03 mM with an aversive sequence. Like taste reactivity, the intake measure of palatability was also affected by the internal state of the LHX rat. Intake of 1.0 M sucrose and distilled water was 0.98 ± 0.01 and 0.73 ± 0.10 ml (a total of 1.0 ml was presented) when tested deprived, and 0.36 ± 0.08 and 0.05 ± 0.02 ml, respectively, when the LHX rat was tested sated. To clarify which aspects of the tube-fed meal procedure contributed to the inhibition of ingestive responses, the effects of the tubing procedure itself as well as the volumetric, osmotic, and caloric effects of the liquid diet meal were separately analyzed. As can be seen in Fig. 20, the results of these experiments demonstrate that the suppression or depotentiation of ingestive responses in LHX rats following a tube-fed meal derives from an exaggerated sensitivity to the caloric consequences of the meal.

C. Chronic Decorticate Rats

The chronic decorticate rat is a striatal preparation whose neocortex has been removed via aspiration as seen in Fig. 21. The central gustatory system of the decorticate is complete except for its cortical component. Decorticate rats are not permanently aphagic, unlike the thalamic and decerebrates. While deficits in ingestive tasks are short lived or minimal, some transient and permanent deficits in tongue and forelimb use that could contribute to food consumption have been noted (Castro, 1975; Kirwin et al., 1978; Whishaw et al., 1981). Despite the loss of the entire neocortex and its cortical gustatory area, decorticate rats seem capable of displaying both level 1 and 2 palatability decisions (see Wirsig and Grill, 1982).

1. Level 1 Decisions

Using the intake measure of palatability, sated gustatory decorticate rats have been shown to display normal taste thresholds for sucrose, NaCl, HCl, and quinine tastes (Benjamin, 1959; Braun and Kiefer, 1975). Decorticate rats respond to alterations in internal metabolic, osmotic, and

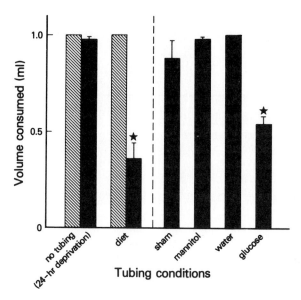

FIG. 20. The effect of six randomly presented intragastric intubation conditions on intra-oral sucrose intake. The conditions are 12 ml of liquid diet, 0.2 M mannitol, 1.4 M glucose, 8 ml of distilled water (the portion of 12-ml diet that is water); passing the tube but not delivering any liquid (sham); or neither passing the tube nor any liquid (24-hr deprived). At 90 min after each intubation condition, 1 ml of 1.0 M sucrose (1 ml/min) was intraorally infused into the mouths of lateral hypothalamically lesioned (solid bars) and yoked control (hatched bars) rats. The volume of the sucrose ingested is shown as the amplitude of each histogram. Analysis of variance reveals that sucrose intake following diet and glucose-tubed conditions is significantly lower (★, $p > 0.01$) than other conditions for the lesioned rat.

sodium state by altering their intake of liquid diet, water, and NaCl, respectively (Wolf *et al.*, 1970; Schulkin and Grill, 1980).

2. Level 2 Decisions

While there is some disagreement over the effect of gustatory cortical ablation on the rat's ability to acquire and retain a conditioned taste aversion, this may be explained by a lack, until recently, of an adequate anatomical description of this region (Kosar *et al.*, 1984; Norgren, *et al.*, 1982). Using physiological feedback first to determine the boundaries of this region and then to ablate it bilaterally, Yamamoto *et al.* (1980) have determined that while these rats do not retain a prelesion CTA, they can acquire a postlesion CTA and therefore possess what appears to be level 2 decision capacity (Kiefer *et al.*, 1984). As a proviso to the data presented on the complete or gustatory decorticate rat, it should be noted that only

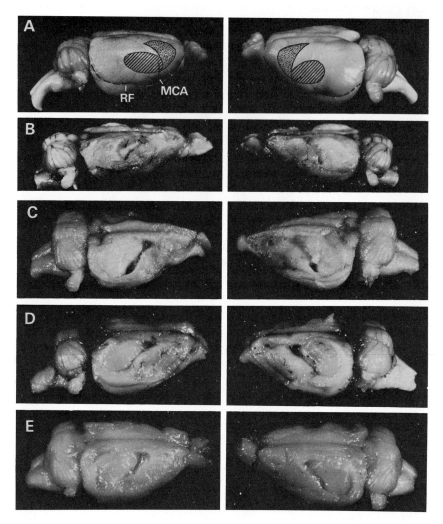

FIG. 21. Lateral views of each hemisphere of four representative decorticate and one intact brain. The upper pair of photographs (A) of an intact brain focuses the reader's attention on the position of the rhinal fissure (RF) and the fissure within which the middle cerebral artery (MCA) courses. The crossing of these two fissures just dorsal to RF is the approximate center of the gustatory neocortical representation. The two outlined regions of neocortex in (A) represent the approximate position of oromotor (dotted pattern) and oro-sensory (striped pattern) neocortical representations (Hall and Lindholm, 1974). The slightly different appearance of these regions in the two lateral views relates to the different rotations of the brain in the two photographs. As can be seen from comparing (A) with (B–E), oromotor and orosensory regions have been bilaterally removed in the brains shown.

intake responses and not taste reactivity responses have thus far been measured. Since intake responses do not distinguish between taste avoidance and taste aversion (see earlier and Pelchat *et al.* 1983), it will be important to reexamine these experiments using the taste reactivity measure of palatability.

Operating on the assumption that while the neocortex does not seem to contribute to level 1 or 2 palatability decisions, its preeminent position in the neural hierarchy should be revealed by deficits in more complex palatability decisions, Wirsig and Grill (1982) examined decorticate rats for their ability to express a salt appetite by latent learning. Using the paradigm of Krieckhaus and Wolf (1968), groups of water-deprived decorticate rats were trained to perform a bar-pressing task to obtain either water or isotonic NaCl. After daily bar-pressing rates had stabilized, groups of rats were first allowed ad libitum access to water (water deprivation ameliorated), then were treated with furosemide and deoxycorticosterone acetate to elicit salt appetite (sodium deficit facilitated), and then were returned to the operant situation and were allowed to press a bar that did not yield fluid reward (extinction). Decorticate rats that were trained with isotonic NaCl reward (for as little as 1 min!) resisted extinction, while water-trained decorticates extinguished rapidly. In this paradigm, present taste was eliminated as a factor by the extinction condition, but present state (sodium deficit) and the previous association between taste (NaCl) and the behavioral act of procuring that particular taste (bar pressing) were integrated to yield the resistance to extinction in the NaCl-trained group. These data indicate that decorticate rats are capable of demonstrating the output of complex palatability integrations that are even more complex that those comprising levels 2 and 3, suggesting a fourth level.

V. Neural Control of Palatability: The Adequacy of a Hierarchical Model

There are many ways in which the functional palatability decision could be theoretically mapped onto the brain. For instance, the various inputs (taste, internal-state cues, prior associations) could converge onto a single neural integrator that would decide on the appropriate response for the whole system. This single integrator could be an anatomically compact nucleus or region (e.g., hypothalamus, see Grill, 1980) or could be distributed as a network throughout the brain. The defining feature of a single-integrator model is that its complex integration would produce only a single decision that would direct all responses to a taste. A disruption of the system should likewise affect all responses equally. At the other theoretical extreme, there might exist myriad neural entities, each making separate decisions unrelated to one another, that sum together equally to produce an output (cf. Dethier, 1982). The unitary appearance of such an output might be misinterpreted according to this view; the behavioral output would not need to correspond to any one of the decision-making entities but only to their interaction in the final common path.

We believe that the data just described suggest that neither of these models is accurate, and that palatability is instead processed by the brain in a neural hierarchy characterized by a number of neural decision-making entities. The presence of these multiple decisions is revealed both by the data from surgical transections and lesions, and by the detailed analysis of the FAP sequences of intact animals discussed earlier in this article. These decision-making entities are not equal, however. Some of the decisions revealed by decerebrate transections, for example, are overruled by the forebrain in intact animals. For example, sucrose paired with LiCl injection results in the substitution of an aversive pattern for an ingestive pattern in intact rats but not in decerebrate rats. Likewise, the separate decisions that are displayed in the taste-elicited FAPs may be combined into a single one to direct instrumental appetitive behavior. This implies that the multiple components are organized hierarchically: some entities integrate more factors and are the "boss of" other decision makers (Dawkins, 1976), being able to overrule them.

As a caveat, it should be noted that this interpretation holds only if we assume that the caudal brain stem mechanisms that make decisions in the decerebrate and thalamic rats continue to make those same decisions in the intact rats but are overruled by the rostral mechanisms. In other words, in order to reject the hierarchical hypothesis of palatability processing, it would be necessary to show that the processing and integration of taste within the caudal brain stem is completely different in decerebrate and intact animals, and that the decisions shown by the decerebrate are simply not made in a caudal brain stem that has an attached forebrain. However, there is currently no reason to assume that the caudal brain stem functions differently when isolated from its forebrain connections. In fact, decerebration is often employed in physiological experiments concerned with demonstrating the physiological function of *intact* caudal brain stem function (e.g., Lund and Dellow, 1971; Kawamura and Yamamoto, 1978).

The hypothesis that palatability is organized hierarchically within the brain carries definite implications. First, discrete neural manipulations such as transections or lesions should not eliminate the intervening variable entirely but instead should either fragment it by destroying the hierarchical connections between components, or unbalance it by eliminating

certain components of the hierarchy or inputs to the components. The fragmentation of behavior is exemplified by the decerebrate, in which only a limited subset of the causal factors are processed and only FAPs and neuroendocrine responses are activated, and by the demonstrations of Teitelbaum and colleagues of the deterioration of goal-directed movement into its component (and often antagonistic) reflexes following lateral hypothalamic lesions. The discovery of such fragmentation has led to the suggestion that the purposiveness of directed behavior in intact animals and the apparent unity of intervening variables are "visual illusions" (Teitelbaum, 1982). This suggestion is based on the belief that when behavior can be broken into parts, the parts may be more real than the whole. It is important to recognize, however, that this is not true if the nervous system is organized hierarchically. The relations between the parts, the direction in which information flows, and the relative priority of each part's output are as important as the parts themselves. The importance of these interpart relations make the whole as real an entity as the parts themselves. A goal-directed action may utilize many movement subsystems. However, these systems are not allowed to operate independently in the integrated nervous system of an intact animal. They are selectively overruled and combined by higher rules of connection that are extrinsic and superordinate to the subsystems themselves. It is the reality and importance of these rules that is revealed by neural manipulations that fragment behavior, not their "illusory" nature.

A second implication of neural hierarchies concerns the procedures for validating intervening variables in behavioral analyses. An intervening variable is defined by a high degree of correlation between a constellation of different behaviors: they vary together within an animal and they are influenced in the same ways by the same things (Miller, 1959). The question is, how good must such a correlation be before one can conclude that a single decision is controlling a group of behaviors? If the single variable exerts a direct and exclusive control over each behavior, then the correlation between different behavioral measures should be perfect (Miller, 1959, 1982). In a hierarchical mechanism, a perfect correlation between outputs is possible as long as each component is controlled by only one higher component. But not all hierarchies are organized in this way. In many hierarchies, called branching (Dawkins, 1976) or lattice (Gallistel, 1980a) hierarchies, the descending networks of separate high-level components overlap. In these hierarchies, a given low-level component appears to have multiple controls. Two low-level components may share certain higher controls with one another but not share others, and therefore may not correlate perfectly with one another. Since the evidence for multiple controls over behavioral acts is quite strong (e.g., Premack,

1962; Fentress, 1968; Hinde, 1970; Gallistel, 1980b), we should expect that when the nervous system controls behavior in a hierarchical fashion the hierarchies involved will be lattice ones. Agreement between different behavioral outputs that are influenced by the same high-level controls should be probabilistic rather than perfect. This should be kept in mind when considering what constitutes a valid empirical test for intervening variables.

A. ANATOMICAL MODELS

The model of brain organization suggested by Hughlings Jackson incorporates a functional hierarchy into a neural framework (in Taylor, 1958). This hierarchy is a lattice hierarchy: the principle of "descending control" allows low-level motor elements to be activated by a variety of high-level entities. For example, tongue movements, whose final common path neurons are contained within the hypoglossal nucleus, may be utilized in different constellations of behavior such as speech and food intake. The cortical lesion accompanying aphasia interferes with tongue movements in speech without affecting the tongue movements of food ingestion (as noted by Jackson in 1878). That is, the final common path is preserved, but some aspects of its control by higher-level structures have been disabled.

Jackson's hierarchical model carries a very salient feature that has influenced our present conception of the nervous system: it is organized rostrocaudally. Higher functions are assumed to be the province of rostral entities, and the more complex the integration, the more rostral the corresponding structure is thought to be. Thus, the neocortex sits at the apex of this neurofunctional hierarchy. Caudal mechanisms can integrate and control simple behaviors but not complex ones, and even the simple integrations of caudal mechanisms are performed again in (and may be overruled by) more rostral structures.

To a large degree, the data we have described here are compatible with Jackson's longstanding model. Decisions about palatability are made at several levels of the nervous system. Even the supracollicular decerebrate can integrate taste with the internal-state cues arising from food deprivation or insulin injection, to produce the appropriate behavioral responses. The ability to integrate other sources of information, such as learned associations, emerges only in rats possessing more rostral structures. And these additional structures and integrations are capable of entirely reversing the decisions made by the isolated caudal brain stem. For example, while a single oral infusion of sucrose will always elicit ingestive FAPs in a decerebrate rat, even one that has repeated treatments in which LiCl has been paired with sucrose, taste aversion conditioning can eliminate all traces of ingestion and replace it completely with aversive FAPs in the intact rat. Sodium depletion similarly changes the pattern of taste reactivity for intact but not chronic decerebrate rats.

B. Evaluating Jackson's Hierarchical Model

There are two observations from our data, however, that strongly contradict Jackson's model and suggest that modifications of his schema must be made. The first is that the behavioral competence of the decorticate rat in tasks involving higher integrations is nearly identical to that of the rat that possesses a neocortex (e.g., Braun, 1975; Oakley, 1979; Braun et al., 1981; Wirsig and Grill, 1982). The decorticate is responsive to all of the internal-state variables that affect the responses of intact rats to tastes, and can associate tastes with their postingestive consequences and act accordingly. The deficits of decorticate rats, while undeniably real, appear to have more to do with low-level acts of sensorimotor integration (e.g., fine tongue movements and place orientation; Whishaw et al., 1981) and with certain memorial or retentive processes (in taste aversion learning; Yamamoto et al., 1980). The low-level nature of these deficits is striking considering that one has removed what ought to be the prime integrator of behavior (highest level). To date, the only thing the neocortex seems to give the rat is a number of relatively simple integrations. Vanderwolf (1983) has summarized a variety of work with his colleagues that suggests that decortication can produce more severe behavioral deficits in rats than we have indicated here; however, differences in surgical procedures, involving most notably their removal of pyriform cortex and hippocampus, and damage to subcortical structures may account in large part for the increased severity of the deficits they report.

A hierarchical model of the nervous system is compatible with these data only if one is willing to reject the assumption that the cortex dominates the functional hierarchy. Unless future tests can be developed to show that the decorticate rat lacks specifically high-level functions, it appears that the cortex plays a functional role of no greater complexity than the caudal brain stem in the control of ingestive behavior and that, instead, it is the subcortical forebrain that exerts the highest functional controls on palatability processes. Our view of the cortex as a functionally low- or middle-level component in the control of palatability is compatible with trends in the study of the controls of complex voluntary movement in primates (cf. Phillips, 1973; Evarts, 1975) and with human clinical data (Penfield and Rasmussen, 1950). A similarly non-Jacksonian role has been suggested for the entire forebrain of the less encephalized teleost fish (cf. Aronson, 1970, for review). Forebrain ablation typically eliminates no single complex integration in these animals. Instead, it slightly impairs performance on a great many behavioral tests in ways that are not compatible with the loss of specifically high-level integrations.

A second difficulty for Jackson's model comes from a comparison of the thalamic and decerebrate preparations. The decerebrate rat is capable of producing both ingestive and aversive FAPs in response to the same tastes as the intact rat, and of modifying these responses on the basis of its caloric state. The thalamic rat, in contrast, shows only aversive FAPs (even to sucrose), and if it is capable of modifying its response at all, it certainly is less flexible than the decerebrate rat. The presence of the substriatal forebrain combined with a caudal brain stem appears to produce a less sophisticated behavioral product than the caudal brain stem alone, in direct contradiction to Jackson's predictions. The hierarchical model of the nervous system can be saved, however, if we assume (1) that the separate positive and negative decisions reflected in the FAPs of the intact rat are also separately embedded in the neural decision-making systems of the forebrain, and (2) that the mechanisms of the negative decision predominate in the substriatal forebrain. This argument will be convincing, and the Jacksonian hierarchical model can be retained, only if it eventually can be shown that all of the integrations and decisions (positive as well as negative) made by the decerebrate are also made by the thalamic rat, but that the positive ingestive decisions are simply overruled by the additional rostral circuitry in this preparation. If this is true, then the thalamic preparation can be viewed as unbalancing the hierarchy at the level at which the positive and negative assessments of palatability still persist as separate entities. This still contradicts Jackson's model to some degree (because an animal that possesses part of a forebrain remains less flexible than one that has none), but it does at least allow the nervous system to become functionally more complex as one ascends rostrally. It is simply that the functional lopsidedness of the remaining circuitry prevents some of its potential sophistication from being expressed behaviorally.

C. HIERARCHIES OF INFORMATION PROCESSING

The degree to which taste information may be transformed as it is conveyed rostrally along the functional hierarchy is a separate issue, concerning which little empirical evidence exists at present to guide us. Two extremes are possible: on the one hand, taste information might be preserved in its original form at every level. Each level would then separately carry out all of the analyses relevant to its particular decision. This is the state of affairs envisioned by Jackson. In his model, the elementary integrations performed by lower levels are carried out again by higher mechanisms (the principle of rerepresentation; in Taylor, 1958). This requires sensory information to be unchanged by initial processing if it is to arrive at higher mechanisms in its original "raw" form. It also requires that a tremendous amount of redundancy be built into the system. Some elementary integrations may have to be performed many times on the same sensory data.

An alternative possibility is that of a two-way transfer of information between different levels of the hierarchy. In this model, not only are lower levels controlled by the decisions of their superiors, but also the outputs of those lower levels are themselves the objects on which higher levels base their decisions. If higher mechanisms can delegate simple processing to lower elements, then "raw" sensory data need not be conveyed unchanged to every level of the hierarchy. This is a two-way hierarchy in the sense that there is a hierarchy of information processing, as well as a hierarchy of control. In sensory systems there are numerous examples of reciprocal projections from rostral levels to the preceding one(s). For example, the whole gustatory system receives feedback from the cortical relay (Norgren and Grill, 1976), and this arrangement is not unique to the taste system but seems to be a feature of all sensory systems. In addition to this possibility of descending control, there are, as noted earlier, several suggestions that the "purity" of the taste signal is not preserved as it is processed successively by the central gustatory system. Rather, there is some evidence to suggest that the taste signal is altered in its early central processing by its integration with visceral afferent signals (see Norgren, 1983).

These two models are theoretical extremes, and intermediates could also exist. Higher levels could use unfiltered sensory information for some decisions but rely on the outputs of lower levels for others. It is also possible that functionally identical decisions could be made using different sources of information under different behavioral conditions. For example, Fentress (1972) has found that while tactile sensory feedback is crucial to sequencing decisions in normal mouse grooming, the same decisions are made without sensory feedback during displacement grooming under conditions of high behavioral arousal. The resolution of these issues will require a better understanding of the degree to which taste as well as visceral information is transformed and how it is used by different levels of the nervous system hierarchy. Both behavioral studies in conjunction with neural manipulations and electrophysiological data will be relevant to deciding between these possibilities.

D. Alternatives to Brain Hierarchies

This discussion has focused entirely on a hierarchical model of nervous function, because it is most useful for predictions about how various manipulations should affect behavior, and because the data gathered by us so far are compatible with such predictions, given the modifications to the model discussed earlier. We wish to stress, however, that this need not always continue to be the case. Other models of neural function are conceivable, for example, the single-integrator and distributed equal systems models mentioned earlier. More sophisticated alternatives have also been suggested under the label of heterarchies or other systems of distributed control (Winston, 1972; Nelson, 1973; Mountcastle, 1978; Dethier, 1982). Dynamic systems in which the rules of control are not fixed but instead vary are also possible, so that some models obtain under certain conditions but others are more suitable in different behavioral situations (Fentress, 1983). As a general rule, however, these models are defined primarily in opposition to hierarchies or simpler models (cf. Dawkins, 1976). The precise details of their operation are unclear and not susceptible to definite prediction. Until specific versions of these models can be constructed that suggest testable predictions for ingestive behavior, it is difficult to think about them with the same degree of rigor that one can bring to bear on the hierarchical model. Advances in this direction therefore await theoretical rather than empirical development.

Acknowledgments

We dedicate this article to Professor Curt Richter, whose work continues to inspire us. We wish to thank our colleagues Ralph Norgren, Bill Flynn, Gary Schwartz, and Eva Kosar for their assistance in generating these data. Randy Gallistel, Eva Kosar, and John Fentress provided critical reviews and helpful comments on earlier drafts. Our research has been supported by NIH Grant AM-21397.

References

Andrew, R. J. (1956). Some remarks on behavior in conflict situations with special reference to *Emberiza spp. British Journal of Animal Behavior* **4**, 41–45.

Aronson, L. R. (1970). Functional evolution of the forebrain in lower vertebrates. *In* "Development and Evolution of Behavior: Essays in Memory of T. C. Schneirla" (L. R. Aronson, E. Tobach, D. S. Lehrman, and J. S. Rosenblatt, eds.). Freeman, San Francisco, California.

Baldessarini, R. J. (1980). Drugs and the treatment of psychiatric disorders. *In* "The Pharmacological Basis of Therapeutics" (A. G. Gilman, L. S. Goodman, and A. Gilman, eds.), 6th Ed. Macmillan, New York.

Benjamin, R. M. (1959). Absence of deficits in taste discrimination following cortical lesions as a function of the amount of preoperative practice. *Journal of Comparative and Physiological Psychology* **52,** 255–258.

Bereiter, D. A., Berthoud, H. R., and Jeanrenaud, B. (1981). Chorda tympani and vagus nerve convergence onto caudal brain stem neurons in the rat. *Brain Research Bulletin* **8,** 261–266.

Berridge, K. C. (1983). Palatability processing and production rules in the ingestive fixed action patterns of rats. Unpublished doctoral dissertation, University of Pennsylvania.

Berridge, K. C., and Grill, H. J. (1983). Alternating ingestive and aversive consummatory responses suggest a two-dimensional analysis of palatability in rats. *Behavioral Neuroscience* **97,** 563–573.

Berridge, K., and Grill, H. J. (1984). Isohedonic tastes support a two-dimensional hypothesis of palatability. *Appetite* **5,** 221–231.

Berridge, K., Grill, H. J., and Norgren, R. (1981). Relation of consummatory responses and preabsorptive insulin release to palatability and learned taste aversions. *Journal of Comparative and Physiological Psychology* **95,** 363–382.

Berridge, K. C., Flynn, F. W., Schulkin, J., and Grill, H. J. (1984). Sodium depletion enhances salt palatability in rats. *Behavioral Neuroscience* **98,** 652–660.

Berthoud, H. R., and Jeanrenaud, B. (1982). Sham feeding-induced cephalic phase insulin release in the rat. *American Journal of Physiology* **238,** E336–E340.

Booth, D. A. (1972). Conditioned satiety in the rat. *Journal of Comparative and Physiological Psychology* **81,** 457–471.

Booth, D. A. (1977). Food intake and chemical senses. *In* "Metabolic Expectancies" (Y. Katuski, M. Sato, S. F. Takagi, and Y. Oomura, eds.), pp. 317–330. Univ. of Tokyo Press, Tokyo.

Booth, D. A. (1980). Conditioned reactions in motivation. *In* "Analysis of Motivational Processes" (F. M. Toates and T. R. Halliday, eds.), pp. 77–102. Academic Press, New York.

Booth, D. A., Mather, P., and Fuller, J. (1982). Starch content of ordinary foods associatively conditions human appetite and satiation, indexed by intake and eating pleasantness of starch paired flavours. *Appetite* **3,** 163–184.

Braun, J. J. (1975). Neocortex and feeding behavior in the rat. *Journal of Comparative Physiological Psychology* **89,** 507–522.

Braun, J. J., and Kiefer, S. W. (1975). Preference-aversion functions for basic taste stimuli in rats lacking gustatory neocortex. *Bulletin of the Psychonomic Society* **6,** 438–439.

Braun, J. J., Kiefer, S. W., and Ouellet, J. V. (1981). Psychic ageusia in rats lacking gustatory neocortex. *Experimental Neurology* **72,** 711–715.

Brush, A. D., and Halpern, B. P. (1970). Centrifugal control of gustatory responses. *Physiology and Behavior* **5,** 743–746.

Cabanac, M. (1971). Physiological role of pleasure. *Science* **173,** 1103–1107.

Cagan, R. H., and Maller, O. (1974). Brief exposure single-stimulus behavioral method. *Journal of Comparative and Physiological Psychology* **87,** 47–55.

Castro, A. J. (1975). Tongue usage as a measure of cerebral cortical localization in the rat. *Experimental Neurology* **47,** 343–352.

Coil, J. D., Hankins, W. G., Jenden, D. J., and Garcia, J. (1978). The attenuation of a specific cue-to-consequence association by anti-emetic agents. *Psychopharmacology* **56,** 21–25.

Contreras, R. J., Kosten, T., and Frank, M. E. (1984). Activity in salt taste fibers: Peripheral mechanism for mediating changes in salt intake. *Chemical Senses* **8,** 275–288.

Craig, W. (1918). Appetites and aversions as constituents of instincts. *Biological Bulletin* **34,** 91–107.

Cruz, S. E., Perelle, I. B., and Wolf, G. (1977). Methodological aspects of sodium appetite: An addendum. *Behavioral Biology* **20,** 96–103.

Davis, J. D. (1973). The effectiveness of some sugars in stimulating licking behavior in the rat. *Physiology and Behavior* **11,** 39–45.

Davis, J. D., and Levine, M. W. (1977). A model for the control of ingestion. *Psychological Review* **84,** 379–412.

Dawkins, R. (1976). "Hierarchical Organisation: A Candidate Principle for Ethology," pp. 7–54. Cambridge Univ. Press, London and New York.

Denton, D. A. (1967). Salt appetite. *In* "Handbook of Physiology," Vol. 1. Amer. Physiol. Soc., Washington, D.C.

Dethier, V. G. (1976). "The Hungry Fly: A Physiological Study of the Behavior Association with Feeding." Howard Univ. Press, Cambridge, Massachusetts.

Dethier, V. G. (1982). The contribution of insects to the study of motivation. *In* "Changing Concepts of the Nervous System" (A. R. Morrison and P. L. Strick, eds.), pp. 445–455. Academic Press, New York.

Evarts, E. V. (1975). Changing concepts of central control of movement. *Canadian Journal of Physiology and Pharmacology* **53,** 191–201.

Fentress, J. C. (1968). Interrupting ongoing behavior in voles (*Microtus agrestis* and *Clethrionomys britannicus*): I and II. *Animal Behavior* **16,** 135–167.

Fentress, J. C. (1972). Development and patterning of movement sequences in inbred mice. *In* "The Biology of Behavior" (J. A. Kiger, ed.), pp. 83–132. Oregon State Univ. Press, Corvalis.

Fentress, J. C. (1973). Specific and nonspecific factors in the causation of behavior. *In* "Perspectives in Ethology" (P. P. G. Bateson and P. H. Klopfer, eds.), pp. 155–224. Plenum, New York.

Fentress, J. C. (1980). How can behavior be studied from a neuroethological perspective? *In* "Information Processing in the Nervous System" (H. M. Pinsker and W. D. Willis, Jr., eds.). Raven, New York.

Fentress, J. C. (1981). Order in ontogeny: Relation dynamics. *In* "Behavioral Development" (K. Immelman, G. Barlow, M. Main, and L. Petrinovich, eds.), pp. 338–371. Cambridge Univ. Press, London and New York.

Fentress, J. C. (1983). Ethological models of hierarchy and patterning of species-specific behavior. *In* "Handbook of Behavioral Neurobiology" (E. Satinoff and P. Teitelbaum, eds.), Vol. VI, pp. 185–233. Plenum, New York.

Fluharty, S. J., and Grill, H. J. (1980). Taste reactivity of lateral hypothalamic lesioned rats: Effects of deprivation and tube feeding. *Neuroscience Abstracts* **6,** 28.

Flynn, W. F., and Grill, H. J. (1983). Insulin elicits ingestion in decerebrate rats. *Science* **221,** 188–190.

Gallistel, C. R. (1980a). "The Organization of Action: A New Synthesis." Erlbaum, Hillsdale, New Jersey.

Gallistel, C. R. (1980b). From muscles to motivation. *American Scientist* **68,** 398–409.

Gallistel, C. R. (1983). Self-stimulation. *In* "The Physiological Basis of Memory" J. A. Deutsch, ed.), pp. 269–349. Academic Press, New York.

Gallistel, C. R., Shizgal, P., and Yeomans, J. S. (1981). A portrait of the substrate for the self-stimulation. *Psychological Review* **3,** 228–273.

Ganchrow, J. R., Lieblich, I., and Cohen, E. (1981). Consummatory responses to taste stimuli in rats selected for high and low rates of self-stimulation. *Physiology and Behavior* **27,** 971–976.

Garcia, J., and Koelling, R. A. (1966). Relation of cue to consequence in avoidance learning. *Psychonomic Science* **4,** 123–124.

Garcia, J., Hankins, W. G., and Rusinak, K. W. (1974). Behavioral regulation of the milieu interne in man and rat. *Science* **185**, 824–831.

Glenn, J. and Erickson, R. (1976). Gastric modulation of gustatory afferent activity. *Physiology and Behavior* **16**, 561–568.

Grill, H. J. (1975). Sucrose as an aversive stimulus. *Neuroscience Abstracts* **1**, 525.

Grill, H. J. (1980). Production and regulation of ingestive consummatory behavior in the chronic decerebrate rat. *Brain Research Bulletin* **5**, 79–87.

Grill, H. J., (1984). In preparation.

Grill, H. J., and Miselis, R. R. (1981). Lack of ingestive compensation to osmotic stimuli in chronic decerebrate rats. *American Journal of Physiology* **240**, 81–86.

Grill, H. J., and Norgren, R. (1978a). The taste reactivity test. I. Mimetic responses to gustatory stimuli in neurologically normal rats. *Brain Research* **143**, 263–279.

Grill, H. J., and Norgren, R. (1978b). The taste reactivity test. II. Mimetic responses to gustatory stimuli in chronic thalamic and chronic decerebrate rats. *Brain Research* **143**, 281–297.

Grill, H. J., and Norgren, R. (1978c). Neurological tests and behavioral deficits in chronic thalamic and chronic decerebrate rats. *Brain Research* **143**, 299–312.

Grill, H. J., and Norgren, R. (1978d). Chronically decerebrate rats demonstrate satiation but not bait-shyness. *Science* **201**, 267–269.

Grill, H. J., and Schulkin, J. (1984). Sodium homeostasis in chronic decerebrate rats. *Behavioral Neuroscience* (in press).

Grill, H. J., Ganster, D., and Smith, G. P. (1983). CCK-8 decreases sucrose intake in chronic decerebrate rats. *Neuroscience Abstracts* **9**, 903.

Grill, H. J., Berridge, K. C., and Ganster, D. J. (1984). Oral glucose is the prime elicitor of preabsorptive insulin secretion. *American Journal of Psychology* **246**, R88–R95.

Guttman, N. (1954). Equal reinforcement values for sucrose and glucose solutions compared with equal sweetness values. *Journal of Comparative and Physiological Psychology* **47**, 358–361.

Hall, W. G., and Bryan, T. E. (1981). The ontogeny of feeding in rats: IV. Taste development as measured by intake and behavioral responses to oral infusions of sucrose and quinine. *Journal of Comparative and Physiological Psychology* **95**, 240–251.

Halpern, B. P., and Tapper, D. N. (1971). Taste stimuli: Quality coding time. *Science* **171**, 1256–1258.

Hawkins, R. D., Abrams, T. W., Carew, T. J., and Kandel, E. R. (1983). A cellular mechanism of classical conditioning in *Aplysia*: Activity-dependent amplification of presynaptic facilitation. *Science* **219**, 400–404.

Hebb, D. O. (1949). "The Organization of Behavior." Wiley, New York.

Hinde, R. A. (1970). "Animal Behaviour: A Synthesis of Ethology and Comparative Psychology." McGraw-Hill, New York.

Kandel, E. R., and Schwartz, J. H. (1982). Molecular biology of learning: Modulation of transmitter release. *Science* **218**, 433–442.

Kawamura, Y., and Yamamoto, T. (1978). Studies on neural mechanisms of the gustatory–salivary reflex in rabbits. *Journal of Physiology* **285**, 35–47.

Kiefer, S. W., Cabral, R. J., and Garcia, J. (1984). Neonatal ablations of the gustatory neocortex in the rat: Taste aversion learning and taste reactivity. *Behav. Neurosci.* **98**, 804–812.

Kirwin, J. D., Parkenson, S. P., and Watkins, D. W. (1978). Effects of lingual nerve section on neocortical ablations on rat's licking response. *Neuroscience Abstracts* **4**, 382.

Koh, S. D., and Teitelbaum, P. (1961). Absolute behavioral taste thresholds in the rat. *Journal of Comparative Physiological Psychology* **54**, 223–229.

Krieckhaus, E. E., and Wolf, G. (1968). Acquisition of sodium by rats: Interaction of innate mechanisms and latent learning. *Journal of Comparative and Physiological Psychology* **65,** 197–201.

Lund, J. P., and Dellow, P. G. (1971). The influence of interactive stimuli on rhythmical masticatory movements in rabbit. *Archives of Oral Biology* **16,** 215–223.

McFarland. D. J. (1974). Time-sharing as a behavioral phenomenon. *In* "Advances in the Study of Behavior" (D. S. Lehrman, J. S. Rosenblatt, R. A. Hinde, and E. Shaw, eds.), Vol. 5, pp. 201–225. Academic Press, New York.

Mayer-Gross, W., and Walker, J. W. (1946). Taste and selection of food in hypoglycaemia. *Br. J. Exp. Pathol.* **27,** 297–305.

Meehl, P. E. (1950). On the circularity of the law of effect. *Psychological Bulletin* **47,** 52–75.

Miller, F. R., and Sherrington, C. S. (1916). Some observations on the buccopharyngeal stage of reflex deglutition in the cat. *Quarterly Journal of Experimental Physiology* **9,** 147–186.

Miller, N. E. (1959). Liberalization of basic S-R concepts: extensions to conflict behavior, motivation, and social learning. *In* "Psychology: A study of a Science" (S. Koch, ed.), Vol. 2, pp. 196–292. McGraw-Hill, New York.

Miller, N. E. (1982). Motivation and psychological stress. *In* "The Physiological Mechanisms of Motivation" (D. W. Pfaff, ed.). Springer-Verlag, Berlin and New York.

Mook, D. (1963). Oral and postingestional determinants of the intake of various solutions in rats with esophageal fistulas. *Journal of Comparative and Physiological Psychology* **56,** 645–659.

Morrison, G. R. (1969). The relative effectiveness of salt stimuli for the rat. *Canadian Journal of Psychology* **23,** 35–40.

Mountcastle, V. B. (1978). An organizing principle for cerebral function: The unit module and the distribution system. *In* "The Mindful Brain" (V. B. Mountcastle and G. M. Edelman, eds.). MIT Press, Cambridge, Massachusetts.

Nachman, M. (1962). Taste preference for sodium salts by adrenalectomized rats. *Journal of Comparative Physiological Psychology* **55,** 1124–1129.

Nelson, K. (1973). Does the holistic study of behavior have a future? *In* "Perspectives in Ethology" (P. P. G. Bateson and P. H. Klopfer, eds.). Plenum, New York.

Norgren, R. (1976). Taste pathways to hypothalamus and amygdala. *Journal of Comparative Neurology* **166,** 17–30.

Norgren, R. (1983). Afferent interactions of cranial nerves involved in ingestion. *Journal of the Autonomic Nervous System* **9,** 67–77.

Norgren, R., and Grill, H. J. (1976). Efferent distribution from the cortical gustatory area in rats. *Neuroscience Abstracts* **5,** 124.

Norgren, R., Kosar, E., and Grill, H. J. (1982). Gustatory cortex in the rat delimited by thalamocortical projections, physiological properties, and cytoarchitecture. *Neuroscience Abstracts* **8,** 201.

Oakley, D. A. (1979). Cerebral cortex and adaptive behavior. *In* "Brain, Behavior, and Evolution" (D. A. Oakley and H. C. Plotkin, eds.). Methuen, London.

Pelchat, M. L., Grill, H. J., Rozin, P., and Jacobs, J. (1983). Quality of acquired responses to tastes by *Rattus norvericus* depends on type of associated discomfort. *Journal of Comparative Psychology* **97,** 140–153.

Penfield, W., and Rasmussen, T. (1950). "The Cerebral Cortex of Man." MacMillan, New York.

Pfaffmann, C. (1961). The sensory and motivating properties of the sense of taste. *Nebraska Symposium on Motivation,* 71–110.

Pfaffmann, C. (1982). Taste: A model of incentive motivation. *In* "The Physiological Mechanisms of Motivation'' (D. W. Pfaff, ed.), pp. 61–97. Springer-Verlag, Berlin and New York.

Phillips, C. G. (1973). Cortical localization and ''sensorimotor processes'' at the ''middle level'' in primates. *Proceedings Review of Social Medicine* **66**, 987–1002.

Powley, T. L. (1977). The ventromedial hypothalamic syndrome, satiety, and cephalic phase hypothesis. *Psychology Review* **84**, 89–126.

Premack, D. (1962). Reversibility of the reinforcement relation. *Science* **136**, 235–237.

Richter, C. P. (1956). Salt appetite of mammals: Its dependence on instinct and metabolism. *In* ''L'Instinct dans le Comportement des Animaux et de l'Homme'' (M. Autori, ed.). Masson, Paris.

Richter, C. P., and Campbell, K. H. (1940). Taste thresholds and taste preferences of rats for five common sugars. *Journal of Nutrition* **SU20**, 31–46.

Rogers, R. C., and Novin, D. (1983). The neurological aspects of hepatic osmoregulation. ''The Kidney in Liver Disease,'' 2nd Ed., pp. 337–450. Elsevier, Amsterdam.

Ross, G. R. T., ed. and trans. (1906). ''Aristotle: De Sensu and De Memoria.'' Cambridge Univ. Press, London and New York.

Rozin, P. (1967). Specific aversions as a component of specific hungers. *Journal of Comparative and Physiological Psychology* **64**, 237–242.

Rozin, P., and Fallon, A. (1980). The psychological categorization of foods and non-foods: A preliminary taxonomy of food rejections. *Appetite* **1**, 193–201.

Rozin, P., and Kalat, W. (1971). Specific hungers and poison avoidance as adaptive specializations of learning. *Psychological Review* **78**, 459–486.

Scalafani, A., Aravich, P. F., and Schwartz, J. (1979). Hypothalamic hyperphagic rats overeat bitter sucrose octaacetate diets but not quinine diets. *Physiol. Behav.* **22**, 759–766.

Schiffman, H. R. (1976). ''Sensation and Perception: An Integrated Approach.'' Wiley, New York.

Schulkin, J., and Grill, H. J. (1980). Compensatory ingestion in the decorticate rat: Timing or motor deficits. Paper presented to the *International Conference on the Physiology of Food and Fluid Intake,* Warsaw, Poland, July.

Schwartz, G. J. (1983). Temporal patterns in the behavioral topography of the oro-facial response. Unpublished master's thesis, University of Pennsylvania.

Schwartz, G., and Grill, H. J. (1984). Relationship between taste reactivity and intake in neurologically intact rats. *Chemical Senses* **9**, 249–272.

Sevenster, P. (1961). A causal analysis of a displacement activity (fanning in *Gasterosteus aculeatus* L.). *Behaviour Supplement* **9**, 1–170.

Steffens, A. B. (1969). Rapid absorption of glucose in the intestinal tract of the rat after ingestion of a meal. *Physiology and Behavior* **4**, 829–832.

Steiner, J. E. (1973). The gustofacial response: Observation of normal and anencephalic newborn infants. *Oral Sensation and Perception,* **17**, 254–278.

Stellar, E., Hyman, R., and Samet, S. (1954). Gastric factors controlling water and salt solution drinking. *Journal of Comparative and Physiological Psychology* **47**, 220–226.

Stolerman, I. P., and Kumar, R. (1970). Preferences for morphine in rats: Validation of an experimental model of dependence. *Psychopharmacologia* **17**, 137–150.

Taylor, J., ed. (1958). ''Selected Writings of John Hughlings Jackson,'' Vols. 1 and 2. Staples Press, London.

Teitelbaum, P. (1982). Disconnection and antagonistic interaction of movement subsystems in motivated behavior. *In* ''Changing Concepts of the Nervous System'' (A. R. Morrison and P. L. Strick, eds.), pp. 467–485. Academic Press, New York.

Teitelbaum, P., and Epstein, A. N. (1962). The lateral hypothalamic syndrome: Recovery of feeding and drinking after lateral hypothalamic lesions. *Psychological Review* **69**, 74–90.

Teitelbaum, P., Schallert, T., and Wishaw, I. Q. (1983). Sources of spontaneity if motivated behavior. *In* "Handbook of Behavioral Neurobiology, Vol. 6: Motivation" (E. Satinoff, and P. Teitelbaum, eds.), pp. 23–26. Plenum, New York.

Ternes, J. W. (1975a). Conditioned aversion to morphine with naloxone. *Bulletin of the Psychonomic Society* **5**, 292–294.

Ternes, J. W. (1975b). Naloxone-induced aversion to sucrose in morphine-dependent rats. *Bulletin of the Psychonomic Society* **5**, 311–312.

Ternes, J. W. (1975c). Induced preference for morphine in rats. *Bulletin of the Psychonomic Society* **5**, 315–316.

Ternes, J. W. (1975d). Conditioned aversion to morphine with lithium chloride in morphine-dependent rats. *Bulletin of the Psychonomic Society* **5**, 331–332.

Thompson, D. A., and Campbell, R. G. (1977). Hunger in humans induced by 2-deoxy-D-glucose: Glucopyruvic control of taste preference and food intake. *Science* **191**, 1065–1068.

Tinbergen, N. (1952). "Derived" activities: Their causation, biological significance, origin and emancipation during evolution. *Quarterly Review of Biology* **27**, 1–32.

Tolman, E. C. (1932). "Purposive Behavior in Animal and Men." Century, New York.

Uttal, W. R. (1981). "A Taxonomy of Visual Processes." Erlbaum, Hillsdale, New Jersey.

Vanderwolf, C. H. (1983). The role of the cerebral cortex and ascending activating systems in the control of behavior. *In* "Handbook of Behavioral Neurobiology, Vol. 6: Motivation" (E. Satinoff, and P. Teitelbaum, eds.). Plenum, New York.

von Holst, E., and von Saint Paul, U. (1963). On the functional organisation of drives. *Animal Behaviour* **11**, 1–20.

Weiner, I. H., and Stellar, E. (1951). Salt preference in the rat determined by single-stimulus method. *Journal of Comparative and Physiological Psychology* **44**, 394–401.

Weingarten, H. P. (1982). Diet palatability modulates sham feeding in VHM-lesion and normal rats: Implications for finickiness and evaluation of sham-feeding data. *Journal of Comparative and Physiological Psychology* **96**, 223–233.

Weingarten, H. P., Chang, P., and Jarvie, K. R. (1983). Reactivity of normal and VMH-lesioned rats to quinine-adulterated foods: Negative evidence for finickiness. *Behavioral Neuroscience* **97**, 221–233.

Whishaw, I. Q., Schallert, T., and Kolb, B. (1981). An analysis of feeding and sensorimotor abilities of rats after decortication. *Journal of Comparative Physiological Psychology* **95**, 85–103.

Winston, P. H. (1972). The M.I.T. robot. *In* "Machine Intelligence" (B. Meltzer and D. Michie, eds.), Vol.7. Edinburgh Univ. Press, Edinburgh.

Wirsig, C. R., and Grill, H. J. (1982). Contribution of the rat's neocortex to ingestive control: I. Latent learning for the taste of Sodium Chloride. *Journal of Comparative and Physiological Psychology* **96**, 615–627.

Wolf, G., DiCara, L. V., and Braun, J. J. (1970). Sodium appetite in rats after neocortical ablation. *Physiology and Behavior* **5**, 1265–1269.

Xenakis, S., and Scalafani, A. (1982). The dopaminergic mediation of a sweet reward in normal and VMH hyperphagic rats. *Pharmacology, Biochemistry and Behavior* **16**, 293–302.

Yamamoto, T., Matsuo, R., and Kawamura, Y. (1980). Localization of cortical fustatory area in rats and its role in taste discrimination. *Journal of Neurophysiology* **4**, 440–455.

Yamamoto, T., Matsuo, R., Fujiwara, T., and Kawamura, Y. (1982). EMG activities of masticatory muscles during licking in rats. *Physiology and Behavior* **29**, 905—913.

Young, P. T. (1948). Appetite, palatability, and feeding habit: A critical review. *Psychological Bulletin* **SU45,** 289–320.

Young, P. T. (1959). The role of affective processes in learning and motivation. *Psychological Review* **66,** 104–125.

Young, P. T. (1967). Palatability: The hedonic response to foodstuffs. *In* "Handbook of Physiology," pp. 353–366. Amer. Physiol. Soc., Washington, D.C.

Young, P. T. (1977). Role of hedonic processes in the development of sweet taste preferences. *In* "Taste and Development: The Genesis of Sweet Preference" (J. M. Weiffenbach, ed.), pp. 399–417. U.S. Dept. of Health, Education and Welfare, Bethesda, Maryland.

Young, P. T., and Greene, J. T. (1953). Quantity of food ingested as a measure of relative acceptability. *Journal of Comparative and Physiological Psychology* **46,** 288–294.

Young, P. T., and Madsen, C. H., Jr. (1963). Individual isohedons in sucrose-sodium chloride and sucrose-saccharin gustatory areas. *Journal of Comparative and Physiological Psychology* **56,** 903–909.

Young, P. T., and Schulte, R. H. (1963). Isohedonic contours and tongue activity in three gustatory areas of the rat. *Journal of Comparative and Physiological Psychology* **56,** 465–475.

Young, P. T., and Shuford, E. H., Jr. (1955). Quantitative control of motivation through sucrose solutions of different concentrations. *Journal of Comparative and Physiological Psychology* **48,** 114–118.

Zeigler, H. P. (1983). The trigeminal system and ingestive behavior. *In* "Handbook of Behavioral Neurobiology, Vol. 6: Motivation" (E. Satinoff and P. Teitlebaun, eds.), pp. 265–327. Plenum, New York.

Zellner, D. A., Berridge, K. C., Grill, H. J., and Ternes, J. W. (1984). Rats learn to like the taste of morphine. *Behavioral Neuroscience,* in press.

Trigeminal Orosensation and Ingestive Behavior in the Rat

H. Philip Zeigler

Biopsychology Program
Hunter College
City University of New York
New York, New York

Mark F. Jacquin

Department of Anatomy
UMDNJ—Rutgers Medical School
Piscataway, New Jersey

Maria G. Miller

Division of Nutrition
Food and Drug Administration
Washington, D.C.

PROGRESS IN PSYCHOBIOLOGY AND PHYSIOLOGICAL PSYCHOLOGY, VOL. 11

Trigeminal Orosensation and Ingestive Behavior in the Rat

H. Philip Zeigler

I. Introduction: Orosensorimotor Mechanisms and the Study of Ingestive Behavior

The oral region of vertebrates is served by two major sensory systems, gustation and somatosensation (taste and the general skin senses). Of the two, the somatosensory innervation is by far the largest, as judged by the proportion of CNS tissue devoted to its central representation. Yet in our thinking about orosensation and appetite we have emphasized gustation to such an extent that the word "taste" has come to serve as a generic term for orosensation in general (e.g., Pfaffmann, 1960). As a result we have almost completely ignored the contribution of oral somatosensation to ingestive behavior.

Furthermore, in focusing on the mouth as a source of orosensations, we have tended to forget that it is also a response system. The oral region is the source not only of an array of complex sensations but of the stimuli that mediate the sensorimotor control of eating and drinking movements. Ingestive behavior, like all organized movement, requires for its control a continuous flow of information. The monitoring of that orosensory input, as well as the organization of oromotor outputs, is largely under the control of the trigeminal system.

II. The Trigeminal System in Comparative Perspective

While it may be an exaggeration to claim that the vertebrate brain evolved to serve the vertebrate mouth (Young, 1968), it is a fact that a well-developed trigeminal system is characteristic of all vertebrates from fish to primates. Its phylogenetic ubiquity reflects the importance of stimuli from the orofacial region and the role of the oromotor system in many types of species-typical behaviors, including eating, drinking, exploration, aggression, and reproduction.

The pattern of trigeminal innervation suggests at least three general groups of trigeminal sensory functions: (1) exploration of the external environment, (2) characterization of objects within the mouth, and (3) sensory modulation of the organized flow of efferent impulses generating patterns of movement in the orofacial musculature. The organization of these functions in different species will vary both with the ecology of the species and with its phyletic position.

> The predominant sensory function of the trigeminal system . . . is that of relaying to the forebrain precise information about the changing environment as the animal enters and explores new territory. . . . In nocturnal or burrowing animals [trigeminal input] may well furnish most of the information about the immediate milieu. [With] the development of the vibrissae . . . the animal can actively explore the environment well beyond its facial profile. . . . The exploratory function of the face and mouth become of much less importance in the higher mammals, particularly in the primates, as the hand evolves. . . . In amphibia, reptiles and birds, the jaws are used to shape and position food in the pharynx ready for swallowing. . . . In mammals, sucking in the newborn and mastication in the adult . . . depend greatly upon trigeminal input to the CNS from the lips and intraoral structures, particularly the tongue [Darian-Smith, 1973, pp. 1271–1273].

Our comparative studies of trigeminal mechanisms in the rat and pigeon provide an excellent illustration of the commonality of trigeminal function in two vertebrate classes differing markedly in structure, ecology, and phyletic position. Indeed, it is difficult to think of two species whose sensory worlds and modes of feeding are more different. The pigeon's feeding behavior (Zeigler *et al.*, 1980) involves a pecking response during which the eyes are closing and the mouth is opening, terminating in a sequence of grasping, mandibulation, and swallowing. Pecking appears to be a ballistic response, visually elicited but independent of visual feedback once initiated. Grasping and mandibulation involve somatosensory inputs. Furthermore, the pigeon is a granivorous bird, so that its chemical senses (olfaction and taste) are unlikely to play a major role in its feeding behavior. In contrast, the rat is an omnivore and its sensory world is often assumed to be dominated by smell.

Despite these differences, both species have highly developed trigeminal systems. The beak of birds is richly endowed with somatosensory receptors, as is the oral region of the rat. In both species the innervation of the oral region involves primarily the sensory and motor divisions of the trigeminal nerve, and in both the trigeminal system plays a critical role in mediating the relationship between mouth, brain, and appetite.

Several studies of trigeminal mechanisms and ingestive behavior suggest that, in addition to these sensorimotor functions, the trigeminal system also makes a critical contribution to the motivational control of eating and drinking (Jacquin and Zeigler, 1982, 1983; Miller, 1981; Zeigler, 1976, 1983). Our studies of trigeminal mechanisms and ingestive behavior in the pigeon have been reviewed at length elsewhere (Zeigler, 1976, 1983). The present article reviews a program of research on trigeminal contributions to eating and drinking in the rat.

III. Ingestive Behavior in the Rat: Spatiotemporal Organization and the Role of Trigeminal Inputs

Even cursory observations of eating and drinking in the rat strongly suggest that somatosensory inputs from both head and body are used to guide ingestion. In the course of eating or drinking the rat adopts one of a number of characteristic postures to facilitate ingestion. The forefeet may be used to steady the object while the head is lowered, or the food (or sipper tube) may be held between the forepaws with the rat squatting on its haunches. Thus typical ingestive sequences involve the synergistic coordination of orofacial and forepaw movements. Such coordination is a characteristic of many mammalian manipulative behaviors (e.g., Breno-witz, 1980) and may be reflected in patterns of CNS organization (see Section IV,B,5,b).

The oromotor portion of the ingestive sequence begins with contact of the object by the oral region. The specific nature of the oral behaviors used to transfer a commodity from the external environment to the oral cavity depends on the stimulus properties of the commodity. Hard, brittle materials (such as lab chow pellets) are broken into bite-size pieces by the "chipping" actions of the mandibular and maxillary incisors. Softer foods, such as mashes, are ingested by lapping, which, like the licking of water, involves repetitive protraction and retraction of the tongue. Movements of the tongue and molar teeth are involved, successively, in mastication, preparing a bolus of food for swallowing.

The tongue plays a critical role in the ingestion of liquids, and the process of licking has been described in detail by Halpern (1977; Maro-witz and Halpern, 1973). The extent to which licking is modifiable by environmental factors has often been noted (Weijnen and Mendelson, 1977), and it has been suggested that the essential features of the licking response are controlled largely by the tactile properties of the drop (Hulse and Suter, 1968, 1970). These authors have shown that burst size and intraburst lick rate are unrelated to gustatory stimulus dimensions and directly proportional to drop size. A contribution of thermal stimuli to the control of drinking was demonstrated in studies of licking elicited by air

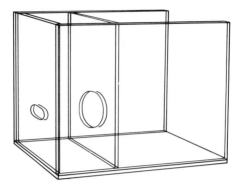

Fig. 1.   Diagram of the testing apparatus used in the cinematographic analysis of ingestive behavior movement patterns. The circular aperture cut in the barrier allows access to
either the paw or the snout, but not to both. A sipper tube or chow pellet is mounted on the
rear wall of the chamber, facing the aperture.

streams or cool metal surfaces (Mendelson, 1977). Kissileff (1973) has
shown that oral somatosensory stimuli play an important role in the acquisition of intragastric self-injection of water. Thus the process of ingestion
in the rat, whether of food or water, involves a continuous flow of somatosensory (trigeminal) input from the oral region that is used to guide grasping, licking, biting, lapping, mastication, and transport into the pharynx
prior to swallowing.

This flow of trigeminal orosensory input presumably begins with first
contact of the food or water source with the rat's perioral region and
continues until the food or water is removed from the oral cavity. The
intraoral portions of the ingestive sequence (mastication, transport, swallowing) have been extensively analyzed using electromyography (Weijs
and Dantuma, 1975) and cinefluorography (Hiiemae and Ardran, 1968),
and responses to intraorally delivered gustatory stimuli have also been
examined (Grill and Norgren, 1978). However, there are no systematic
data on the role of *perioral* stimuli in the initial phases of ingestion. Such
data can suggest useful behavioral units for the analysis of neural mechanisms of ingestion and indicate loci for the stimulus control of ingestive
movement patterns (Zeigler *et al.*, 1980).

To obtain such data for the rat we studied eating and drinking under
testing conditions that enabled us to focus exclusively on the role of
perioral inputs and orofacial movements by constraining ingestive behavior to successive acts of biting or licking (Zeigler *et al.*, 1984).

Observations were carried out using an apparatus (Fig. 1) designed to
provide controlled access to food and water while excluding the use of the

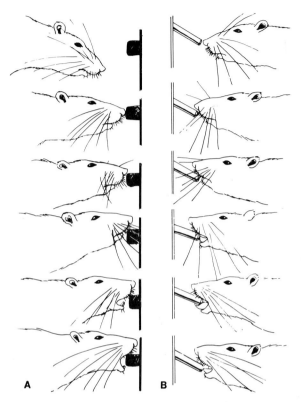

FIG. 2. Schematic representation of ingestive behavior sequences in the rat. (A) Eating a chow pellet; (B) drinking from a sipper tube. (From Zeigler *et al.*, 1984.)

forepaws. A rectangular Plexiglas chamber was divided into runway and observation compartments by a transparent Plexiglas panel. The panel contained a hole large enough to permit the entrance of *either* the rat's snout or its paws, but not both simultaneously. The wall directly opposite the panel contained a small hole in which either a block of lab chow or a sipper tube could be mounted so as to project into the observation chamber. The apparatus was mounted on the front of the rat's home cage, accessible through an opening in the cage. Subjects were tested under moderate food and water deprivation, and videotape recordings were made of eating and drinking in the test situation.

Figure 2 illustrates, schematically, the detailed spatiotemporal organization of eating and drinking sequences in the rat. Note that these sequences, each of which consists of several distinct movement patterns, are completed in less than 1 sec.

A. EATING

The eating sequence begins with the rat's snout tilted toward the floor so that its rhinarium is below the lower edge of the pellet and its mouth is completely closed. Approach to the pellet is quite variable in topography and time course. It is often not a smooth, continuous movement but sometimes involves pauses and reversals of direction. As the snout advances it is elevated, brushing the frontal perioral hairs across the surface of the food pellet and bringing the rhinarium opposite to and parallel with the pellet. At this point, the rat often pauses in its forward motion and carries out a series of orotactile "scans" (in the horizontal plane), during which the vibrissae emit their characteristic "whisking" movements and their tips may be seen curling and uncurling around the pellet. At the end of this period the snout is moved forward and upward, bringing the upper lip line into contact with the pellet edge. This forward movement overlaps with the initiation of mouth opening. It continues until the pellet is within the oral cavity and pressed up against the upper lip, and it concludes with the initiation of jaw closure (Fig. 2A).

B. DRINKING

The drinking sequence also begins with a ventrally tilted snout that is gradually elevated during approach to the sipper tube. The vibrissae are seen to palpate the tube, curling and uncurling around it in successive "whisking" cycles. The mouth is closed during the period of approach and remains closed throughout a prolonged period of contact with the perioral region. The start of mouth opening coincides with a forward movement of the snout that brings the tube into contact with the upper lip line. Ingestion is accomplished by successive cycles of tongue protraction and retraction that bridge the gap between the tip of the sipper tube and the inside of the mouth (Fig. 2B).

Frame-by-frame analysis of videotape records suggested that ingestive sequences could be divided into three components: approach, perioral contact, and mouth opening. As Fig. 3 indicates, there is considerable variability in the duration of all three phases but it is greater for eating than for drinking. Variations in the approach phase probably reflect such factors as adaptation to the test situation and distraction. The mouth-opening phase, in both eating and drinking, is more stereotyped in form and duration. Once initiated, it continues without pause or reversal, presumably until appropriate intraoral inputs from the food or water source elicit closing. Differences between the durations of mouth opening during

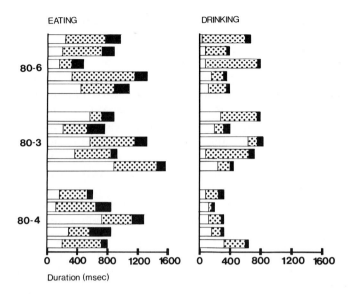

FIG. 3. Temporal relations among three phases of ingestive behavior (open bars, approach; dotted bars, perioral contact; closed bars, mouth opening) for three normal rats (numbers 80-3, 80-4, 80-6) during eating and drinking. (From Zeigler *et al.*, 1984.)

eating and drinking may reflect differences in the cross-sectional size of the pellet and sipper tube. Moreover, the stimulus configuration presented by the pellet changes after each bite, while that of the sipper tube remains constant. Thus, the fact that perioral contact durations are generally shorter and less variable for drinking may reflect the greater stereotypy of the stimulus array presented by the sipper tube.

The focus of these observations was on the period of perioral contact immediately preceding mouth opening and ingestion. Our formal analysis confirms the impression gained from examination of dozens of recorded ingestive behavior sequences. *Mouth opening in the rat does not occur during the approach phase of eating or drinking but always follows a relatively prolonged period of perioral contact with the food or water source.*

These observations suggest that, under normal conditions, the mouth-opening phase of ingestive behavior is elicited, not by distal stimuli (vision, olfaction), but by proximate somatosensory stimuli originating in the perioral region. Moreover, the close temporal relation between perioral stimulation and mouth opening suggests that these stimuli may engage reflex mechanisms of jaw movement control. The modality mediating these perioral inputs is, of course, the trigeminal system.

IV. Neurobiology of the Trigeminal Sensorimotor System

A. AFFERENT MECHANISMS

The orofacial region of mammals is richly supplied with receptors sensitive to touch, pressure, vibration, temperature, and pain. Our primary interest is in *mechanoreceptors,* structures that vary in their sensitivity and adaptive characteristics across a wide range of stimulus properties and act as detectors of position, velocity, and acceleration (e.g., Burgess and Perl, 1973). Many of these receptors are associated with various types of specialized structures, located within various portions of the intraoral and perioral regions (Fig. 4).

The *furry buccal pads,* for example, are continuous with the perioral hairs and, by virtue of their location, are strategically placed to monitor the properties of objects passing through the rat's oral cavity. Similarly, the morphology of the rat's *rhinarium* suggests that it plays some role in somatosensory discrimination. It is located at the tip of the rat's snout, comprising two rounded pads separated in the midline by a vertical groove (philtrum) that bisects the upper lip. Ultramicroscopic observa-

 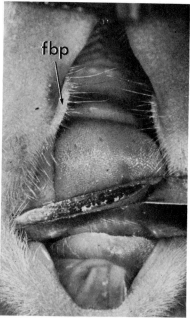

FIG. 4. Two views of the orofacial region of the rat, illustrating some of the trigeminally innervated areas discussed in the text: fbp, furry buccal pad; r, rhinarium; v, vibrissae.

tions reveal that the epidermis covering each pad has a pattern of surface ridges similar to those in human and primate digital skin. On the basis of its morphology and the density of its innervation, MacIntosh (1975) has suggested that there may be functional parallels as well. The most familiar of these structures, the whiskers (mystacial vibrissae) have obvious exploratory or orientation functions (Welker, 1964). The characteristic "whisking" behavior of these large hairs is generated by neurons in the facial motor nucleus. However, the continuous feedback about the environment provided by the vibrissae is monitored by trigeminal afferents carried in the infraorbital nerve. Unfortunately, the behavioral functions of the rhinarium and furry buccal pad have been totally unexplored, and there have been no systematic studies of vibrissae function since the classic account by Vincent (1912).

Three additional receptor loci within the orofacial region should be noted. The first, the periodonteum, is the tissue surrounding the teeth and containing a variety of receptor types sensitive to temperature, touch, pain, and pressure. Second, there are a set of specialized receptors in the capsule and ligaments of the temporomandibular joint, similar to those found in other joints and, like them, specialized for the detection of variations in the static position and displacement of the mandible. Finally, there are the muscle receptors (muscle spindles and Golgi tendon organs), which signal, respectively, stretch and contraction of the jaw muscles. Muscle receptors are found in large numbers in the jaw closers, where they are linked to specific oromotor reflexes (see later) but appear to be sparsely distributed in the jaw openers. The functional significance of this difference is not clear.

All the receptors just described are innervated by sensory branches of the trigeminal (cranial V) nerve. The cell bodies of these trigeminal primary afferents are located within the trigeminal (Gasserian) ganglion, which lies in a bony depression at the base of the skull, separated from the brain dorsally by the dura mater. The ganglion is continuous rostrally with the three divisions of the trigeminal nerve—ophthalmic, maxillary, and mandibular—and is connected to the brain by the trigeminal sensory root (Fig. 5). The development of sensitive histochemical techniques has made it possible to privide a relatively unproblematic account of the organization of trigeminal afferents within the Gasserian ganglion and of their central projections within the brain stem (e.g., Jacquin *et al.*, 1983b).

B. CENTRAL CONNECTIONS

The somatosensory system has two major divisions—cranial and spinal—conveying inputs, respectively, from the head and body regions.

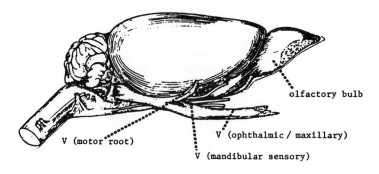

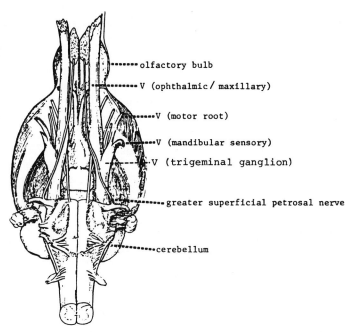

FIG. 5.   Lateral and ventral views of the rat brain illustrating the location of the trigeminal sensory nerves, the Gasserian (V) ganglion, and the trigeminal sensory and motor roots. Note that the maxillary and ophthalmic nerves are fused into one sensory division. (Modified from Greene, 1968, Fig. 140.)

The organization of the trigeminal system (Fig. 6) is similar in many respects to that of its spinal counterpart. The cell bodies of its primary afferents are located in a peripheral sensory ganglion, outside the CNS, so that the trigeminal ganglion may be analogized with the dorsal root (sensory) ganglia of the spinal cord. The one exception to this analogy is jaw muscle proprioception, since the cell bodies of afferents innervating mus-

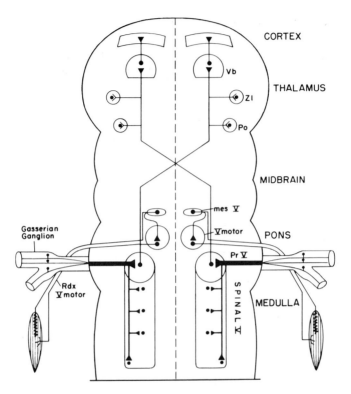

FIG. 6.   Organization of the trigeminal sensorimotor system in the rat. A highly simplified schematic diagram showing the projection of primary afferents upon the trigeminal brain stem nuclear complex (Pr V, Spinal V, Mes V) and the projection of the trigeminal lemniscus upon the forebrain. Not shown are other primary afferents to the brain stem as well as projections to the superior colliculus and cerebellum (see text). (From Zeigler, 1983.)

cle stretch receptors lie not in a peripheral sensory ganglion but within a central trigeminal structure, the trigeminal mesencephalic nucleus (n Mes V).

Some degree of somatotopic organization is characteristic of all levels of the somatosensory system, reflecting that fact that receptors in adjacent peripheral orofacial regions project to adjacent regions within central trigeminal nuclei. As a consequence, the orofacial region is represented at successive levels from the trigeminal ganglion to the neocortex. Differential innervation densities of specific peripheral structures (e.g., lips, mystacial vibrissae, furry buccal pads) will therefore be reflected in the organization of this somatotopic pattern, presumably reflecting, in turn, the functional significance of specific orofacial regions. Furthermore, the receptive field properties of single neurons within the somatotopic projection are submodality specific, preserving the representation of inputs from somatosensory submodalities such as touch, pressure, and joint rotation. Thus the projection of the orofacial region upon successive central nuclear areas is both a spatial and a functional representation of those regions (Fig. 7).

1. Trigeminal (Gasserian) Ganglion

Somatotopic organization is already evident at the level of the primary afferent neuron. Within the ganglion, ophthalmic and maxillary nerve cells and fibers are combined to form a single mass occupying its more anteromedial portions, while the mandibular division forms its posterolateral portion. Somata from the mandibular nerve, innervating the lower third of the face and the ventral half of the oral cavity, are located within the posterolateral region; those from the ophthalamic nerve, serving the dorsal third of the face, are found anteromedially, while the somata of maxillary branches, innervating upper lip, vibrissae, facial pads, and dorsal oral cavity, are interposed (e.g., Gregg and Dixon, 1973; Jacquin *et al.,* 1983b; Marfurt, 1981; Mazza and Dixon, 1972). Somatotopic organization is seen not only across the three divisions of the trigeminal nerve but within a given division as well. Within the posterolateral division of the ganglion, nerve branches innervating rostral oral and perioral fields have their cell bodies in the ventral portion, while branches subserving posterior orofacial fields have somata in more dorsal parts of this region (Jacquin *et al.,* 1983b).

2. Projections of Primary Trigeminal Afferents

Axons of primary afferents collect in the large trigeminal sensory root that enters the brain stem at pontine levels and forms a trigeminal spinal tract. It has been suspected for some time that trigeminal primary afferents project upon a variety of "nontrigeminal" structures, that is, upon structures that are not traditionally regarded as components of the brain stem trigeminal nuclear complex. Confirmation and extension of the earlier work has been obtained in experiments employing HRP treatment of the trigeminal ganglion and of individual trigeminal sensory branches (Jacquin *et al.,* 1982b). "Nontrigeminal" projections include the dorsal horn, the gracile and cuneate nuclei, the solitary nucleus, the cerebellar nuclei and cortex, and the lateral (parvocellular) reticular formation. The functional significance of many of these projections is unclear.

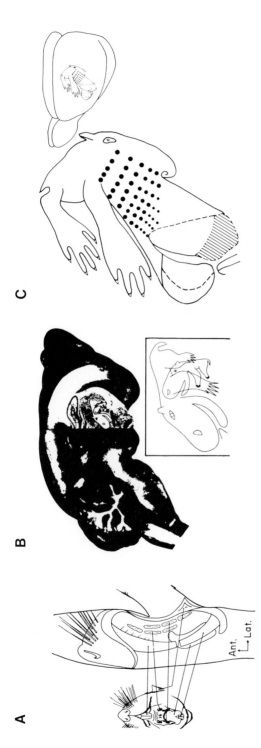

FIG. 7. "Rodentunculi" illustrating the projection of the orofacial regions at successive levels of the CNS. (A) Gasserian ganglion (from Mazza and Dixon, 1972); (B) thalamus (Emmers, 1965); (C) neocortex (from Welker, 1971). The projections upon thalamus and cortex were defined by electrophysiological recording; that for the Gasserian ganglion is based on analysis of chromatolytic changes after section of individual trigeminal nerve branches.

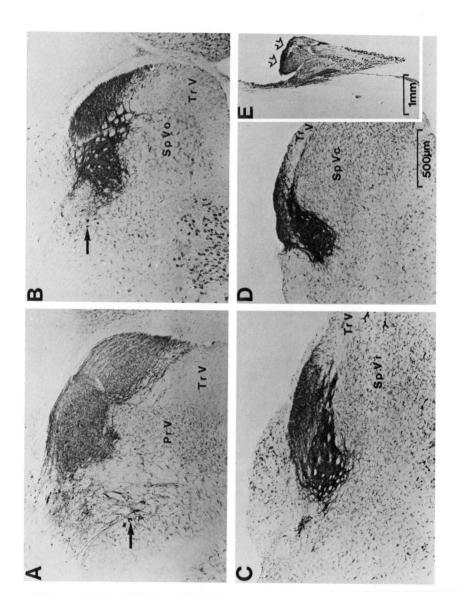

3. Trigeminal Nuclear Brain Stem Complex

The majority of primary trigeminal afferents project upon a group of trigeminal nuclei at various levels of the brain stem. Myelinated fibers in the sensory root bifurcate on entering the brain stem, giving off a rostral branch that ascends to terminate within the principal sensory trigeminal nucleus (Pr V) and a caudal branch that descends variable distances within the tract to terminate in one or more divisions (oralis, interpolaris, caudalis) of the spinal trigeminal nucleus (Sp V). Together with the trigeminal mesencephalic nucleus (n Mes V), these structures make up the trigeminal brain stem nuclear complex.

By contrast with the trigeminal ganglion, the somatotopic organization of the orofacial region within the brain stem nuclear complex reflects an inverted dorsal-to-ventral sequence: mandibular afferents lying most dorsally, maxillary and ophthalamic divisions, ventrally. This organization was first delineated electrophysiologically (Nord, 1967, 1968), but a more detailed description is now available based on anatomical studies. As Fig. 8 indicates, HRP applied to the transected mandibular division of the ganglion labels the dorsal one-third of Pr V and Sp V (oralis) and the dorsomedial one-third of the interpolaris and caudalis nuclei (Jacquin *et al.,* 1983b). Subsequent experiments by these workers have provided detailed descriptions of the somatotopic organization of the ophthalmic–maxillary divisions as well. As is the case at all levels of the rat's trigeminal system, the representation of the oral cavity and vibrissae dominate the projection.

4. Thalamocortical Projection

The bulk of the ascending projections from the more rostral components of the brain stem nuclei terminate upon the ventrobasal (Vb) complex of the thalamus (see Fig. 6) via a trigeminal lemniscus (LTr). As Fig. 9 indicates, LTr originates in Pr V (1). It decussates at the level of the

---

FIG. 8.   Brain stem labeling produced by application of HRP to the right, whole mandibular V ganglion (and motor root). Sections counterstained with thionin. (A) Region of Pr V. The dorsal one-third of Tr V and Pr V contain anterogradely labeled primary afferent fibers; arrow denotes a retrogradely labeled V motoneuron in Mot V. (B) Region of Sp V oralis. Ovoid unlabeled areas within the mandibular terminal field are acellular fiber pathways. Arrow indicates a retrogradely labeled salivatory neuron; darkly counterstained Mot V cells do *not* contain HRP. (C) Region of Sp V interpolaris. (D) Region of Sp V caudalis. (E) Site of HRP application (arrows) in the distal mandibular portion of the V ganglion at midhorizontal level; up is rostral. Note that at all levels HRP applied to the ganglion labels the dorsal portions of the trigeminal nuclei. (From Jacquin *et al.,* 1983b.)

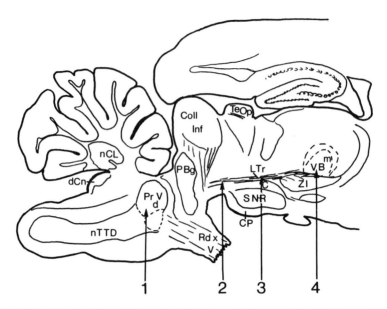

FIG. 9. Sagittal section through the rat brain illustrating the trajectory of the trigeminal lemniscus (LTr) in the rat. (1) Origin of the tract in the principal trigeminal sensory nucleus. (2) Decussation of the tract. (3) Location of LTr at the level of the substantia nigra. (4) Diencephalic terminations in zona incerta and ventrobasal nucleus of the thalamus. Rdx V, trigeminal sensory root; nTTD, spinal trigeminal nucleus; PBg, parabigeminal nuclei; nCL, cerebellar nuclei. (From Zeigler and Karten, 1974.)

interpeduncular nucleus (2) and continues through the mesencephalon, lying immediately dorsal to the medial portion of the substantia nigra at the level of the ventral tegmentum (3). At the diencephalic level the lemniscus gives off collaterals to the posterior thalamic region and to zona incerta before terminating (4) in the thalamic ventrobasal complex (Smith, 1973). Because the trigeminal lemniscus lies medial to the medial lemniscus within the diencephalon, the two lemnisci distribute, respectively, to the medial and lateral portions of the ventrobasal complex. The projection of the orofacial region upon the thalamus is somatotopically organized in a continuous fashion (Fig. 7B), with oral and perioral regions located most medially, adjacent to the thalamic gustatory areas.

The trigeminothalamic projection is of considerable interest because it represents the "lemniscal" component of the somatosensory projection for the head region, relaying information that complements that provided for the body by the medial lemniscal pathway. It has the functional properties of other "lemniscal" systems, conveying the information provided by the primary afferents in a rapid and highly secure fashion to the thalamus and cortex (Darian-Smith, 1973). The receptive fields of trigemino-thalamic neurons are restricted in extent, activated primarily by receptors responsive to skin displacement or hair movement, and they function as position or velocity detectors. As Fig. 7B indicates, the ventrobasal projection in the rat includes both head and body projections, a duality of somatosensory representations and the domination of the somatosensory projection by orofacial (trigeminal) representation.

A very similar situation is illustrated in Fig. 7C, which shows the somatosensory projection upon the neocortex of the rat. The orofacial region accounts for a major portion of the dual representation, and within that region the furry buccal pad and the mystacial vibrissae are prominently represented.

5. "Sensorimotor" Connections of the Trigeminal System

In addition to its ascending "lemniscal" connections, the trigeminal system has direct and indirect connections with a large number of "non-trigeminal" CNS structures at several brain levels, including the reticular formation, the cerebellum, and the superior colliculus. Little is known about the significance of these connections. However, since all these structures have more or less direct links with efferent mechanisms, they may contribute to the "sensorimotor" functions of the trigeminal system.

a. Reticular Formation. It is now well established that reticular neurons may serve as premotor elements in the control of eye, neck, and limb musculature as well as in the generation of patterned movements such as locomotion and mastication (Hobson and Scheibel, 1980; Nakamura, 1980). Direct connections with oromotor nuclei have been demonstrated in both birds (Arends and Dubbeldam, 1982; Berkhoudt *et al.*, 1982) and mammals (Holstege *et al.*, 1977; Travers and Norgren, 1983). Trigeminal inputs reach the reticular formation both via the projection of primary afferents (Jacquin *et al.*, 1982b) and via secondary projections from spinal V, which lies adjacent to it. Trigeminoreticular connections may be involved in oromotor reflexes as well as in the generation of masticatory rhythms (see Section IV,C). Moreover, the reticular formation has been shown to mediate the state-dependent modulation of jaw reflexes, facilitating them during wakefulness and inhibiting them during quiet sleep (Hobson and Scheibel, 1980).

b. Cerebellum. A series of "micromapping" studies by Welker and colleagues (e.g., Shambes *et al.*, 1978) has revealed some organizing principles underlying the trigeminal projection upon the cerebellar cortex and suggested a hypothesis regarding the functional significance of the projection. Cutaneous stimulation of the body surface evokes short latency responses from neurons in the granule cell (GC) layer, with a very dense projection from the orofacial region. The projections terminate upon columns of granule cells and, unlike the neocortical projection, the representation of the body surface upon the cerebellar cortex is organized as a group of individual "patches." Each such patch represents a specific body region (e.g., upper lip, lower lip, vibrissae, furry buccal pad, incisors, forepaw). The overall array of individual patches within any cerebellar folium makes up a mosaic representing the body surface. While the cutaneous somatotopic representation *within* each patch is continuous and precise (like that of the trigeminal lemniscal projection), the patch boundaries are discrete. Moreover, in many cases receptive fields "that are peripherally *disjunctive* or spatially separated project to adjacent GC patches in the cerebellar cortex" (Shambes *et al.*, 1978, p. 115). Thus, for example, the receptive field patches for lower lip, upper lip, forepaw, hind limb, vibrissae, and forelimb may lie contiguously within a very small area of the cerebellar cortex, producing a "fractured somatotopy." The situation is illustrated in Fig. 10, which should be compared with the neocortical representation of the orofacial region presented in Fig. 7C.

Many of the patches represent body structures that "may act as a unit in discriminative and/or instinctual behavior sequences" (Shambes *et al.*, p. 127), and the largest patches are from the furry buccal pad, the mystacial vibrissae, and the upper and lower lips, all of which "have striated facial muscle insertions and are active in many palpating, mobilizing and prehensile labial and facial exploratory actions" (Shambes *et al.*, p. 128). The short latency of the trigeminal inputs (3–5 msec), the differential representation of movable parts, and the specific spatial nature of the "fractured" somatotopy led these investigators to hypothesize that trigeminal inputs to the cerebellum were involved in neural circuits controlling species-typical movement sequences requiring coordinations among oromotor structures and guidance by a continuous flow of sensory input from the oral region.

> We propose . . . that adjacent cerebellar GC patchlike inputs from two different peripheral structures provide a substrate for the subsequent inhibitory and facilitatory intracortical circuit operations necessary to effect integral or conjoint actions of the two separate body structures in active touching of objects or surfaces in specific ways; e.g., the handling of food particles by teeth and lips, or by lips and hands or upper and lower lips, etc. [Shambes *et al.*, 1978, p. 128].

c. Superior Colliculus.   The mammalian superior colliculus (SC) consists of several concentric laminae that may be functionally characterized in terms of the origin of their inputs. The more superficial layers receive a retinotopically organized visual input, while the intermediate and deeper

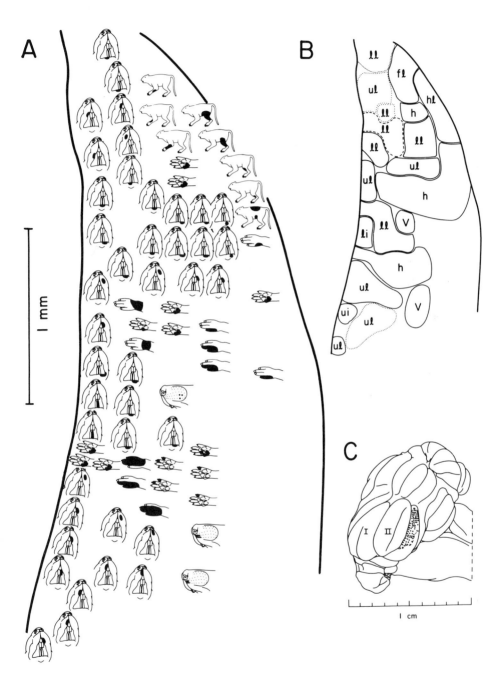

FIG. 10. Examples of "fractured somatotopy" in the granule cell areas of the rat cerebellum, based on multiple-unit recordings. (A) Figurines illustrating the location of receptive field of units recorded from points in the cerebellar cortex. (B) Areal maps of the same cortical area to illustrate the spatial relations among receptive field "patches" (see text for description). (C) Location of the recording sites on the cortical surface corresponding to the individual figurines in (A). (From Shambes *et al.*, 1978.)

layers are responsive to auditory and somatosensory stimulation. Orofacial somatosensation is especially well represented. Trigeminal projections to the SC arise from several regions of the trigeminal brain stem nuclear complex, and the trigeminocollicular projection terminates largely in the intermediate gray layers (Huerta *et al.*, 1981; Killackey and Erzurumlu, 1981).

Physiological studies in the rat indicate that most of the contralateral body surface is represented in the SC in an organized somatotopic fashion. However, the bulk of the SC tactile area is occupied by vibrissae representation, with only a small area devoted to hindquarters and with no representation of intraoral structures (Kassel, 1980). By contrast with the cerebellar tactile projection, which displays a "fractured somatotopy," the SC tactile representation is continuously organized. However, stimulation–recording studies of SC–cerebellar projections show that the two regions are interrelated in a very precise fashion. SC stimulation evokes responses only in those cerebellar patches whose receptive fields include vibrissae representation, but not in forelimbs or lower lip patches.

That SC somatotopic representation is devoted mainly to the vibrissae is undoubtedly of functional significance. Previous studies of the organization of the SC (Chalupa and Rhoades, 1977; Drager and Hubel, 1975) indicated that the retinotopic and somatotopic projections are in "spatial register," suggesting a critical role for trigeminocollicular inputs in the control of the rat's orienting behavior.

It is clear from this brief review that trigeminal inputs from the oral region will influence the activity of neurons at all levels of the brain from medulla to neocortex. Since the function of a set of neurons is likely to be determined by its connectivity patterns, we may assume that trigeminal projections to different brain regions reflect corresponding differences in function. Thus, while the generation of reflex mastication may involve trigeminal inputs to brain stem structures (Dellow and Lund, 1971), trigeminal inputs to the basal ganglia may be involved in the coordination of head position and oropharyngeal movements necessary for efficient ingestion of food (Levine *et al.*, 1971; Lidsky *et al.*, 1978).

C. Efferent Mechanisms

Considered as an effector system, the mouth of mammals has a variety of functions related to food and water intake, including prehension, mastication, licking, sucking, manipulation, transport, and swallowing. The structures mediating these movement patterns are innervated by branches of cranial nerves V, VII, IX, X, XI, and XII. The cell bodies of the motoneurons involved lie in a column of motor nuclei stretching from the caudal medulla to the rostral pons. The functional anatomy and neural control of the orofacial region have been reviewed in considerable detail (e.g., Halpern, 1977; Dubner *et al.*, 1978), and the present section will be restricted to an overview of the neural control of the jaw.

The muscles controlling the position and movements of the mandible ("muscles of mastication") include a group of jaw-opener (digastric, lateral pterygoid, and mylohyoid) and jaw-closer (masseter, temporalis, and medial pterygoid) muscles. All of the jaw muscles (with the exception of the posterior belly of the digastric) are innervated by the mandibular (motor) division of the trigeminal nerve. The cell bodies of jaw motoneurons are located in the trigeminal motor nucleus (Mot V) at about the level of Pr V in the pons (see Fig. 11). Their axons form a trigeminal motor root that emerges from the pons slightly medial and dorsal to the sensory root. It then moves more ventrally and laterally, encircling the sensory root in its peripheral trajectory, joining the mandibular sensory division just caudal to its junction with the trigeminal ganglion. Physiological studies (Pelletier *et al.*, 1974) indicate that the trigeminal motor root carries both efferents to and proprioceptive afferents from the muscles of mastication. Recent anatomical studies of the retrograde labeling seen after application of HRP to individual trigeminal motor nerves reveals a precise somatotopic representation of each of the jaw muscles within the trigeminal motor nucleus (Jacquin *et al.*, 1983b; Mizuno *et al.*, 1975).

These jaw motoneurons represent the "final common path" for all jaw movements and are under the influence of a wide variety of peripheral and central controls. With the exception of the monosynaptic projections of muscle spindle afferents upon Mot V, all these influences are indirect. They are mediated through a number of interneuronal premotor pools located either in the reticular formation itself or in nuclear regions forming a continuous interneuronal system intercalated between the trigeminal sensory and motor neurons: intertrigeminal, intratrigeminal, juxtatrigeminal, and supratrigeminal areas (Holstege *et al.*, 1977; Mizuno *et al.*, 1974; Travers and Norgren, 1983). Similar, discrete interneuron pools are found in close proximity to other cranial nerve nuclei involved in oromotor activity. Given their innervation by both central and peripheral afferents and their termination upon cranial motoneurons, such interneurons are in a position to function as sensorimotor "integrating" elements—channeling diverse inputs and modulating levels of responsiveness in functionally organized groups of oromotor neurons.

A traditional starting place for the study of efferent mechanisms of ingestive behavior has been the analysis of oromotor reflexes, particularly the jaw reflexes. The emphasis on reflex analysis reflects both conceptual and methodological assumptions. First, reflexes (e.g., jaw opening and

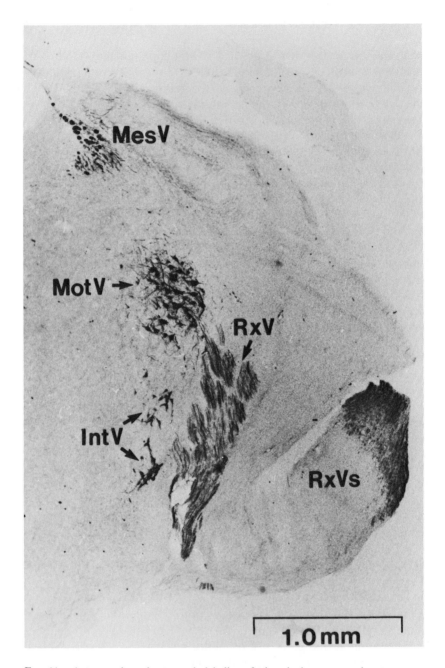

Fig. 11. Anterograde and retrograde labeling of trigeminal sensory and motor components of the brain stem seen after application of HRP to the cut end of the mandibular nerve.
Photomicrograph of a 50-μm, uncounterstained section through the pons at the level of the
rostral V motor nucleus (Mot V). Retrograde labeling is seen in Mot V, the trigeminal
mesencephalic nucleus (Mes V), the trigeminal motor root (Rx V), and the intertrigeminal
area (Int V). Anterogradely labeled mandibular primary afferent fibers are visible in the
trigeminal sensory root (Rx Vs). (From Jacquin *et al.,* 1983a.)

closing, tongue protraction and retraction) are viewed as the elements providing the motor substrates from which more complex response patterns (e.g., chewing, biting) are assembled. Second, reflex activity may be used as an indicator response to assess changes in responsiveness in the oromotor system produced by the activity of higher brain levels (central reflex modulation).

The jaw reflexes have been studied since Sherrington (1917), and one of them (the jaw-closing reflex) has played a role in the analysis of oromotor activity paralleling that of the myotatic (stretch) reflex in studies of spinal cord physiology. Stretch of the jaw muscles produces a reflex whose cellular basis has been analyzed in detail. Muscle stretch activates spindle receptors in the jaw closers innervated by axons with cell bodies in ipsilateral Mes V nucleus. These unipolar neurons send their central processes directly to the trigeminal motor nucleus, producing a monosynaptic excitatory postsynaptic potential (EPSP) in the jaw-closing motoneurons. Like all "simple" reflexes, the jaw jerk reflects an artificially simplified situation, since the jaw closers are rarely activated in this "phasic" manner. Moreover, there is evidence that, in addition to spindle receptors, a variety of intraoral and perioral afferents (from gums, teeth, and palate) with cell bodies in Mes V contribute to the peripheral controls of jaw closing via their connections with Mot V neurons (see Fig. 5).

The jaw-opening reflex may be elicited by electrical or mechanical stimulation of intraoral and perioral regions (see Section VII) and is generally measured as the activity of digastric or mylohyoid (opener) motoneurons. Its latency indicates disynaptic elicitation via an excitatory interneuron that excites the opener motoneurons and simultaneously produces an inhibitory postsynaptic potential (IPSP) in closer (antagonist) motoneurons (Kidokoro et al., 1968). The interneurons responsible have been identified as lying within the supratrigeminal region, a rostral extension of the lateral reticular formation (Jerge, 1963). This region also receives a substantial primary afferent projection from the mandibular and maxillary divisions of the trigeminal nerve (Jacquin et al., 1982b, 1983b).

Reticular premotor neurons are also involved in the coordinating mechanisms that underlie the bilateral symmetry typical of oromotor activity. Stimulation of these interneurons, in addition to its effects on ipsilateral motoneurons, also produces appropriate patterns of inhibition and facilitation of trigeminal motoneurons in Mot V via a system of commissural fibers crossing the brain stem at the level of Vm (Mizuno et al., 1978). In addition to these systems, Mes V neurons, acting via collateral connections to the hypoglossal motor nucleus, provide a basis for the continuous integration of jaw and tongue movements that are a feature of oromotor activity. (For detailed reviews of peripheral reflex control of the jaw see

Dubner *et al.,* 1978; Luschei and Goldberg, 1981; Nakamura *et al.,* 1980; Nakamura, 1980.)

In addition to all of these peripheral influences, the jaw muscle reflexes are also under central control by structures at various brain levels. The loci from which central modulatory effects may be obtained has been determined by measuring the reflex facilitation and inhibition produced by central (electrical) stimulation. Jaw-closing reflexes are elicited by stimulation of Mes V, jaw opening by stimulation of intraoral and perioral afferents. The magnitude of the modulatory effect is indicated by increases or decreases in the amplitude of evoked reflex activity.

Using such procedures, modulation of jaw-opening and -closing reflexes has been obtained from stimulation of a wide variety of regions, including the brain stem reticular formation, cerebellar cortex, hypothalamus, and amygdala. The reticular modulation is state dependent; that is, its effectiveness varies with changes in brain stem excitability from sleep through wakefulness (Chase *et al.,* 1968). The most striking effects of cerebellar or cerebral cortex stimulation are obtained from those areas to which oral and perioral afferents project (Sessle, 1977; Olsson and Landgren, 1980), suggesting the existence of rapid cerebellar and cerebral trigeminal sensorimotor loops for the control of movement sequences. Cortical outputs also appear to have access to the "masticatory rhythm generator" in the lower brain stem, modulating but not patterning its rhythmic output (Nakamura *et al.,* 1979; Gary-Bobo and Bonvallet, 1975; Luschei and Goldberg, 1981). A possible "limbic system" involvement in oromotor control is suggested by the modulatory effects on jaw reflexes obtained from stimulation of the amygdala (Bonvallet and Gary-Bobo, 1975; Sessle, 1977) and hypothalamus (Landgren and Olsson, 1980).

The pathways by which these diverse influences on oromotor activity are brought to bear are only slowly being delineated. The important point to be noted is that efferent control mechanisms are likely to involve functionally differentiated circuits imposing an array of patterned outputs on final common path motoneurons mediating oromotor activity.

This brief discussion cannot do justice to the voluminous body of anatomical and physiological literature on the trigeminal system. However, it does indicate some of the potential contributions of that system to the control of ingestive behavior. Contact of the perioral surfaces with food objects and their movement within the oral cavity produce patterns of input reflecting the size, shape, and texture characteristics of the food important for eliciting grasping and for driving mastication and swallowing. The trigeminal system is specialized for the rapid and accurate transmission to the CNS of these spatiotemporal patterns of stimulation and for the generation of appropriate movement patterns. However, the functional significance of trigeminal sensory, central, and motor components can only be assessed by neurobehavioral experiments that examine the role of these components in ingestive behavior.

V. Trigeminal Denervation and Ingestive Behavior: Conceptual and Methodological Considerations

In initiating research on trigeminal mechanisms of ingestive behavior in the rat, we have chosen to begin at the periphery rather than study the effects of central lesions. Several considerations have dictated this strategy. First, there is the formidable problem of making extensive bilateral lesions restricted to the *orosensory* portion of the central trigeminal projection while avoiding damage to the projections of adjacent sensory structures that might also be involved in ingestive behavior (e.g., vibrissae, gustatory projections). Second, components of major catecholamine systems lie in close proximity to central trigeminal nuclei and pathways. This is a particularly vexing problem at mesencephalic and diencephalic levels, since deficits in ingestive behavior produced by lesions at these levels may reflect damage to either trigeminal or neurochemical pathways (Zeigler and Karten, 1974; Stricker and Zigmond, 1976). Finally, a detailed analysis of the effects of deafferentation would provide a foundation for further studies designed to analyze the contribution of trigeminal structures at various levels of the neuraxis.

A. Deafferentation Procedures and the Study of Ingestive Behavior

Interruption of orosensory pathways can be produced either directly, by sectioning the sensory nerves involved, or indirectly, by intragastric or intravenous infusion procedures (e.g., Epstein and Teitelbaum, 1962; Nicolaidis and Rowland, 1977). While the indirect (functional deafferentation) procedures have been extremely informative, they eliminate both gustatory and trigeminal inputs indiscriminately, obscure the possible contribution of feedback from the consummatory response itself, and are subject to a variety of methodological problems (e.g., Holman, 1969; Oakley, 1965). The deafferentation procedure, on the other hand, leaves the consummatory responses intact and allows us to discriminate between the contributions of trigeminal and gustatory inputs as well as among the various trigeminal sensory subdivisions. Furthermore, an analysis of the relation between the effects of deafferentation on consummatory behav-

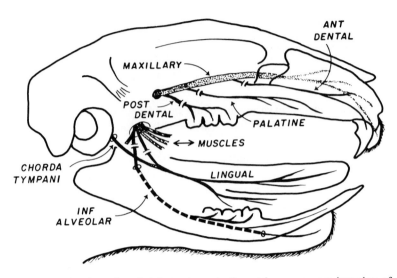

FIG. 12. Innervation of orofacial structures in the rat by orosensory branches of the trigeminal nerve. Structures labeled "ant dental" and "post dental" are equivalent, respectively, to nerve branches labeled anterior superior alveolar and posterior superior alveolar in Table I. (From Miller, 1981.)

ior and its effects on intake control may help clarify the extent to which mechanisms mediating each of these aspects of ingestive behavior share similar neural substrates.

However, trigeminal deafferentation has the major disadvantage that it disrupts the sensorimotor control of eating and drinking. We took a variety of precautions to avoid the confounding effects of such disruptions.

1. We used measures that enabled us to distinguish consummatory impairments from effects on responsiveness.

2. We employed a wide variety of behavioral paradigms from intake measures to operant indices of hunger and thirst.

3. We carried out systematic comparisons with orosensory and oromotor controls.

B. SURGICAL AND HISTOLOGICAL PROCEDURES

Figure 12 illustrates the innervation of orofacial structures by sensory branches of the trigeminal nerve in the rat, and Table I indicates the areas innervated by each of the nerve branches sectioned and the combinations

TABLE I
SURGICAL PROCEDURES AND TREATMENT GROUPS

Trigeminal nerves sectioned	Areas of innervation
1. Anterior superior alveolar	Upper incisors, upper rostral gums, nasal mucosa
2. Posterior superior alveolar	Upper molars, upper caudal gums, cheeks, maxillary sinus
3. Sphenopalatine	Soft and hard palates, cheeks, nasal mucosa
4. Lingual	Anterior two-thirds of tongue, gums, mucous membrane of mouth, sublingual glands
5. Inferior alveolar	Lower lip, lower teeth (incisors, molars), gums, floor of mouth, chin, chin hairs
6. Infraorbital nerve	Upper lip, rhinarium, vibrissae, facial pads
7. Ethmoid nerve	Nasal mucosa
8. Trigeminal motor root	Jaw muscles

Experimental groups	Control groups
Complete trigeminal orosensory deafferentation (nerves 1, 2, 3, 4, 5)	Sensory Infraorbital
Lingual intact (nerves 1, 2, 3, 5)	Ethmoid
Alveolar (nerves 1, 5)	Motor
Unilateral complete (nerves 1, 2, 3, 4, 5)	Motor root V
	Hypoglossal XII
	Procedural
	Sham surgical
	Teeth clipping
	Deprivation

of sections employed to produce the various treatment groups used in our experiments. The surgical procedures involved have been described in detail elsewhere (Jacquin and Zeigler, 1983; Miller, 1981).

1. Experimental Groups

A complete trigeminal orosensory deafferentation interrupted sensory input from the following oral and perioral structures: inferior and superior molars and incisors, floor of the mouth, gums, furry buccal pads, cheeks, palate, anterior two-thirds of the tongue, lower lip, chin, and some nasal mucosa. It is important to keep in mind that even the most complete orosensory deafferentation was designed to *spare* trigeminal inputs from several important orofacial structures including the *vibrissae,* the *rhinarium,* and the *upper lip.* Both chemosensory systems (olfaction and taste) were largely intact. Proprioceptive afferents from and efferents to the jaw muscles were spared, as was the motor control of the tongue. The autonomic system was also spared. In summary, vision, audition, olfaction, and taste, as well as jaw and tongue movement and proprioception, were intact in the deafferented subjects.

2. *Control Groups*

To evaluate the contribution of other orosensory structures and to control for sensorimotor impairments, a variety of surgical control groups were prepared. These included *orosensory* controls with sections of the infraorbital, ethmoid, and gustatory nerves, and *oromotor* controls with section of the trigeminal motor root to the jaw muscles or of the hypoglossal nerve to the tongue. In several cases, HRP was applied to the cut ends of nerve branches sectioned in the deafferentation procedure to label their cell bodies within the trigeminal ganglion. Analysis of the histological data indicates that our deafferentation procedure spared axons of the trigeminal motor root that carry afferents from and efferents to the jaw muscles (Jacquin and Zeigler, 1983, Fig. 1).

C. Behavioral Procedures

We used an array of foods, varying in texture, taste, and ease of manipulation, to explore the relation between deafferentation deficits and the sensory properties of the diet. Pablum (cereal) and rat chow mash provided two diets of similar texture and manipulability that differed in taste. To assess the effects of deafferentation on mastication, we used two types of bite-size foods, one soft and one hard, which are approximately the same size but differ in their requirements for mastication (Purina Tender Vittles and Cat Chow). Purina Rat Chow pellets were used to provide a diet that makes the most extensive demands on the rat's orosensorimotor abilities, since its ingestion requires a complex sequence of oral grasping, manipulation with the mouth and forepaw, shaving, chewing, and mandibulation.

Two conditions of food presentation were used. In the "five-diet" condition, rat chow pellets were available ad lib and the special diets were offered in amounts that required the additional ingestion of rat chow to gain weight. In the "single-diet" condition, a single food was presented ad lib as the animal's entire diet. The solid foods were presented individually in heavy glass bowls (10.5 cm wide × 1.3 cm deep), while shallow plastic Petri dishes (9 × 1.3 cm) were used for mash and pablum. Water (presented in 100-ml calibrated glass bottles with sipper tubes) was available ad lib.

VI. The Trigeminal Syndrome: Intake, Weight Regulation, and Ingestive Behavior after Trigeminal Orosensory Deafferentation

Interruption of trigeminal orosensory inputs by deafferentation (Fig. 12; Table I) produces an array of morphological and behavioral effects related to the condition of the mouth, the sequential organization of ingestive behavior, the quantitative control of food and water intake, and the regulation of body weight.

A. CONDITION OF THE MOUTH

Both Miller's study (1981) and our own observations indicate that when deafferentations involve disruption of inputs to the upper and lower incisors (i.e., section of the inferior and superior anterior alveolar nerves), they produce several types of deterioration of the oral region. These include malocclusion and overbiting, which, in combination with a reduction in the rat's typical gnawing behavior, may result in incisor overgrowth and in abrasions of the anterior palate. Lingual nerve section alone is followed by damage to the tongue, ranging from mild abrasions to biting off its tip (Mendelson and Zec, 1972). However, naturally occurring malocclusions of comparable severity are sometimes found in normal rats (Jacquin, 1980) but are not accompanied by reduced food or water intake. Similarly, deafferentation produces reduced intake even in rats in which the lingual nerve is spared. These observations indicate that effects on the general condition of the mouth cannot account for the intake deficits produced by trigeminal orosensory deafferentation (see Jacquin, 1980).

B. SENSORIMOTOR CAPACITIES

During the immediate postoperative period, rats with bilateral orosensory deafferentation are alert and show no obvious impairments of posture or locomotion. They orient to visual stimuli and display rapid and well-oriented tactile placing responses (forepaw extension) to vibrissal stimulation.

The deafferented rat is clearly capable of biting, licking, chewing, and swallowing in response to *intraoral* stimuli such as liquid food, a cotton swab, or the presence of an intragastric feeding tube. Biting can also be elicited by tail-pinch or paw-pinch stimulation, and bites made under these conditions can have considerable force. Similarly, licking and swallowing can easily be elicited by liquid food or water placed in the mouth. However, in contrast to the ease with which licking and biting could be elicited by *intraoral* stimuli, deafferentation reduced the ease with which they could be elicited by *perioral* stimulation. Tactile stimulation of perioral areas (e.g., lower lip line) with a cotton swab in these animals elicits few attempts to bite, and such bites as do occur are often disoriented and lacking in vigor. The oromotor response sequence to paw-pinch was severely disrupted in extensively deafferented subjects. There were many instances of incomplete sequences (i.e., head turning without mouth contact, mouth contact without mouth opening, mouth opening without biting). Recovery of the sequence tended to take place in the order: mouth contact, mouth opening, biting.

The oromotor behavior of rats with section of the trigeminal motor root or hypoglossal nerve is much more seriously impaired. After unilateral V motor sections, incisor overgrowth and malocclusions were frequent and the teeth required regular clipping. Mouth opening and biting were impaired for several weeks. After a bilateral V motor section, the mandible is fixed in an almost closed position, similar to that of the mouth at rest. Mouth closing in this situation probably reflects "elasticity" in the jaw-closing musculature or connective tissue in the cheek region (Weijs and Dantuma, 1975, p. 12). Tongue movements within the mouth are possible, since rats will lap and swallow food inserted within the oral cavity. However, the fixed jaw position precludes grasping, biting, or tongue extension to any kind of stimulation. Animals with bilateral section of the hypoglossal nerve could open their mouths, bite, and chew but were unable to transport food to the back of the mouth and dropped large amounts of crumbs on the cage floor. Animals with V or XII motor sections thus make ideal controls for any disruptive effects of trigeminal deafferentation on oromotor behavior.

Deafferentation of the snout and vibrissae (by infraorbital section), although it produced the typical hunched posture of these preparations (Vincent, 1912; Zeigler, 1976), produced only a transient disruption of oromotor behavior. No disruptive effects were seen after ethmoid or gustatory nerve sections.

C. CONSUMMATORY BEHAVIOR IN THE DEAFFERENTED RAT

Trigeminal orosensory deafferentation disrupted both eating and drinking response sequences, the greatest disruption occurring in the most extensively deafferented groups ("complete," "lingual intact"). In those subjects that eventually recovered preoperative intake levels, the recovery sequence described here was frequently observed.

In the immediate postoperative period, such approaches to the food as did occur were hesitant, infrequent, and often incomplete. Although the snout was properly oriented and sniffing/whisking was evident, the head was often not lowered sufficiently to make contact with the food. Even when snout contact took place, mouth opening usually failed to occur. Paw swipes through the solid food were observed, and rats often walked right through the dish of mash, departing with food on their paws.

During this period, approaches to water in a dish or sipper tube were infrequent and hesitant. The initial orientation of the snout and lower lip was normal, yet neither mouth opening nor tongue extension occurred. Instead, the snout hovered over the water dish or circled the sipper tube until the drinking sequence was broken off. After a few seconds of such activity, many rats grasped the sipper tube with both paws, turned the head 90°, and pushed the upper lip against the metal sipper tube. However, mouth opening and tongue extension failed to occur and the rat would leave the water bottle.

The return of mash intake was accompanied by the development of alternative modes of feeding such as "shoveling" or "scooping." Shoveling consisted of pushing the snout through the mash and involved the immersion of almost the entire perioral region up to the upper lip. This behavior was often combined with swiping movements of the paw over the food, which provided an edge to the mash surface or coated the sides of the dish with food, presumably increasing the ease of ingestion. In scooping, a paw was used to obtain a small amount of mash, which was then lifted to the mouth and pushed through the teeth, eliciting weak lapping movements and minimal mouth opening. Both modes of feeding facilitated ingestion without normal mouth opening and tongue extension, and both involved the coordination of mouth and paws. The selection of one or the other mode was idiosyncratic and seemed to be shaped by incidental reinforcement. Once acquired, these behaviors were performed with speed and proficiency. Not surprisingly, mash was found between the lips and gums as well as on the body surface and floor of the cage; for this reason, measurements of mash intake during this period were likely to be considerably inflated. Solid foods were occasionally removed from a dish with the forepaws but were dropped and remained uneaten.

The recovery of solid food and water intake was accompanied by the return of mouth opening and biting elicited by contact with food. It was also marked by the gradual return of oral grasping, rather than the use of the forepaws, to remove solid food from the dish. Rats were frequently seen hovering over a pellet, making chewing movements, then partial mouth-opening movements, before finally achieving a gape sufficiently large to grasp the pellet. Removal of the pellet frequently required several such grasps. Ingestion of the mashes continued to involve the alternative behaviors described previously.

Water intake during this period was accomplished without normal tongue extension. Rats assumed contorted postures, freeing water from the bottle by rubbing either their upper or lower lips against the sipper tube. When tongue extension and licking returned, they were slow and weak, and many instances of licking without contact with the tube were observed. A few rats were seen to bite or yank the sipper tube and then turn the head, letting the water trickle down the throat. (Surprisingly little water spillage was produced by this type of drinking behavior.)

Many of the more extensively deafferented rats never recovered normal levels of intake over a 6-month period of postoperative observation. Those that did so exhibited apparently normal consummatory behavior when ingesting solid foods and water, but many of them continued to employ alternative behaviors for eating the two mashes.

By contrast with these subjects, rats with more restricted denervations (e.g., alveolar nerves only) did not show the immediate postoperative aphagia and adipsia but began to ingest cereal and mash immediately and to eat solid foods shortly thereafter. From this point on their temporal sequence of recovery was comparable to that of the "complete" and "lingual intact" cases.

Infraorbital nerve sections produced quite different effects on the organization of ingestive behaviors. While the orally deafferented rats reliably immersed their lower lip in mash during feeding, the infraorbitals always immersed the upper lip and rhinarium as well. This made sustained feeding on mash difficult because of respiratory impairments. Infraorbitals also assumed drinking postures that facilitated lower lip or cheek contact with the sipper tube. Tongue movements and biting seemed normal. Water and food intake recovered within a few days. However, intake and body weight remained below preoperative levels for almost a month postoperatively, by contrast with the other control groups (see Fig. 17).

D. EFFECTS ON INTAKE AND BODY WEIGHT

Figures 13 and 14 present intake and weight data for representative subjects in the "lingual intact" and "alveolar" groups. They illustrate some characteristic effects of orosensory deafferentation, including a disruption in food intake whose persistence varied with diet type, and a reduction in water intake. The return of water intake tends to parallel the return of solid food, and there appears to be a characteristic order of recovery through the different diet types.

All bilateral trigeminal orosensory deafferentations were followed by a disruption of food intake whose magnitude and persistence were a joint function of the locus and extent of the denervation and of the sensory

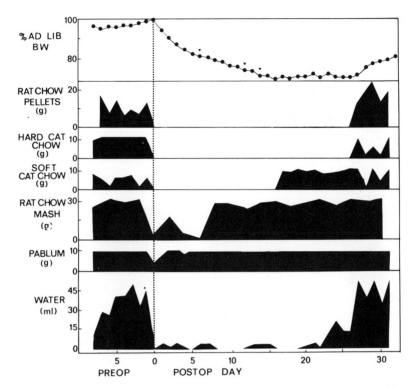

FIG. 13. Food and water intake and body weight (BW) in a representative rat subjected to bilateral section of all trigeminal orosensory nerves except the lingual and maintained on the five-diet regimen. The arrowheads indicate incisor clipping. (From Jacquin and Zeigler, 1983.)

properties of the diet (Fig. 15). Table II illustrates the order of recovery of each diet. Statistical analyses indicate that intakes of the two mashes do not differ, that intake of rat chow mash occurs before soft cat chow, soft cat chow recovers before hard cat chow, and that the durations of aphagia on hard cat chow and hard rat pellets do not differ.

Figure 16 illustrates the relation between diet type, intake, and weight for subjects maintained on a single diet. When a diet of rat chow pellets was the sole food available, deafferented rats exhibited a persistent aphagia and had to be sacrificed to avoid death from starvation. However, even when given unlimited access to a highly palatable food (cereal or mash), deafferented subjects lost considerable weight and did not recover their preoperative weights within a 40-day period of postoperative observations.

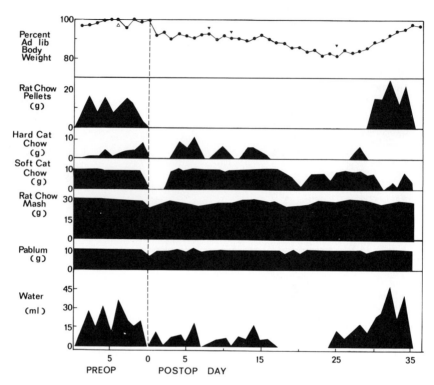

FIG. 14. Intake and body weight in a rat subjected to bilateral section of the inferior alveolar (mandibular sensory) and anterior superior alveolar (maxillary sensory) branches of the trigeminal nerve. Five-diet regimen. Arrowheads as in Fig. 13. (From Jacquin and Zeigler, 1983.)

TABLE II

ORDER OF RECOVERY OF FIVE DIET TYPES IN 17 BILATERAL OROSENSORY
DEAFFERENTED RATS THAT RESUMED EATING EACH OF THE DIETS

Diet	Order of recovery[a]				
	First	Second	Third	Fourth	Fifth
Pablum	88	12	0	0	0
Rat chow mash	65	24	6	6	0
Soft cat chow	6	12	65	12	6
Hard cat chow	6	0	24	53	18
Rat chow pellets	0	0	18	24	59

[a] Data are percentages of the total cases in which intake of that diet recovered first, second, and so on.

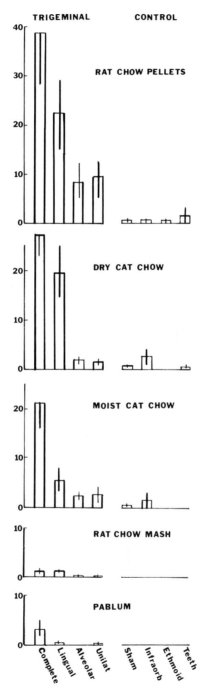

FIG. 15.   Aphagia as a joint function of diet type and surgical treatment (horizontal axis). Number of days is represented on vertical axis. Means ± SEs are indicated. (From Jacquin and Zeigler, 1983.)

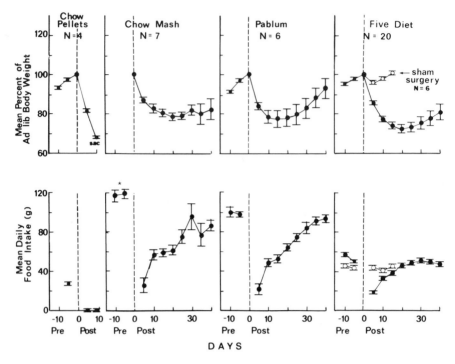

FIG. 16.   Relations among diet type, food intake, and body weight in subjects maintained on a single diet. For comparison, data on sham operates and subjects in the "five-diet" condition are also presented. Star indicates that preoperative intake data were not available and were taken from another experiment. (From Jacquin and Zeigler, 1983.)

Figure 17 summarizes data on solid food intake, water intake, and body weight for all subjects except the oromotor controls (see Table III). Unilaterals did not differ from shams on any intake measure, while all three bilateral orosensory groups exhibited significant reductions in intake and weight followed by a gradual recovery.

Of the four control groups, only the infraorbital controls showed a deficit that, though small relative to the experimental subjects, was persistent. Since the major source of infraorbital afferents is the vibrissae, our findings suggest that, despite their prominence, these structures play a relatively minor role in the control of food intake. Gustatory deafferentation also produced a relatively minor effect on intake and body weight (Jacquin, 1983). As Fig. 18 indicates, the removal of almost all taste afferents produced a persistent reduction in intake but the magnitude of the deficit did not approach that of even the least extensive (alveolar only) trigeminal orosensory denervation (compare Figs. 17 and 18).

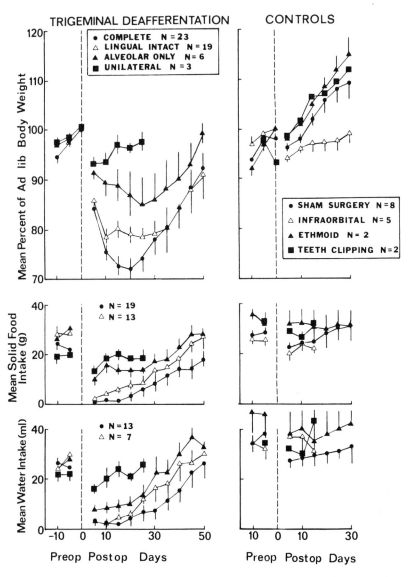

FIG. 17. Solid food and water intake and body weight for experimental, sham surgery, sensory (infraorbital, ethmoid), and procedural control groups. (From Jacquin and Zeigler, 1983.)

TABLE III

EFFECTS OF OROMOTOR DENERVATION ON SOLID FOOD INTAKE
AND RESPONSIVENESS TO FOOD

Group and rat number	Intake[a,c]		Responsiveness[b,c]	
	Preoperative	Postoperative	Preoperative	Postoperative
Motor V (unilateral)				
76-89	33	15	91	64
76-92	32	16	75	54
76-104	41	12	88	38
Mean % of preoperative result	—	40	—	62
Hypoglossal (bilateral)				
78-35	37	14	90	69
78-53	45	9	95	88
78-55	25	13	84	86
Mean % of preoperative result	—	34	—	90

[a] Mean daily grams of solid food eaten.

[b] Percentages of solid food removed.

[c] Comparisons are based on 10 days of intake data preoperatively and postoperatively.

Total water intake was significantly reduced in all three bilateral groups for prolonged periods. The disruption of water intake (adipsia) was most persistent in both the "complete" and "lingual intact" groups. However, even after intake had resumed, these subjects showed occasional days of adipsia.

E. DEAFFERENTATION EFFECTS ON WATER INTAKE: DIRECT VERSUS INDIRECT EFFECTS

Since water and food intake are interdependent in the rat (Adolph, 1947; Bolles, 1961; Collier, 1969), it is possible that the adipsia and hypodipsia of deafferented subjects are due to the abolition and/or reduction in solid food intake and their increased proportional intake of semiliquid foods. To clarify this issue we compared the water intake of deafferented subjects with that of a group of yoked-for-food-intake controls. Throughout the study, the control member of each pair was offered only the diets ingested by its deafferented partner in amounts that matched the intake of the deafferented rat.

Figure 19 compares the water intake of the two groups. Control subjects did not show an immediate adipsia. They decreased their intake

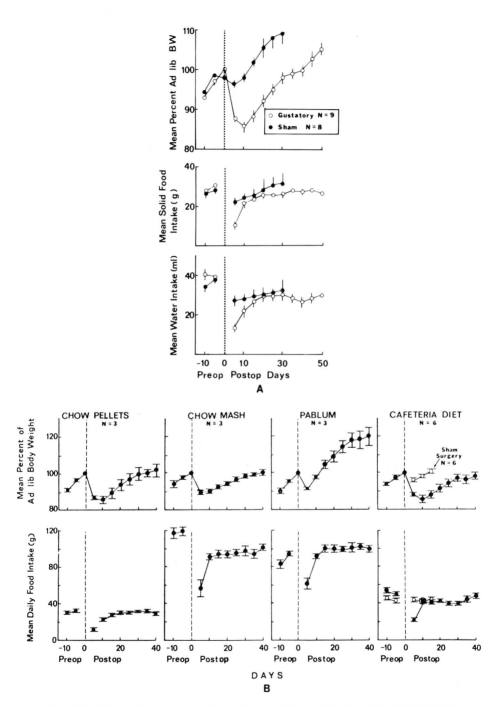

FIG. 18. Effects of gustatory deafferentation on intake and body weight. (A) Solid food and water intake and body weight in the five-diet group. (B) Food intake and body weight in the single-diet groups. Conventions as in Fig. 16. (From Jacquin, 1983.)

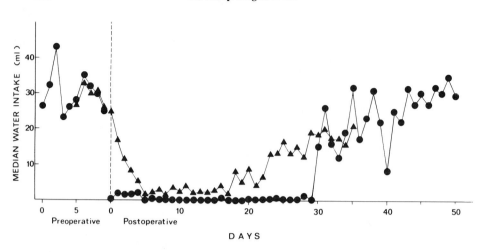

FIG. 19.   Water intake in deafferented rats (●, $N = 6$) and yoked-for-food-intake controls
(▲, $N = 6$). Yoked subjects were maintained on the same types and amounts of food as
deafferented subjects. Note the difference in the rate of decline of intake and the time course
of recovery in the two groups. (From Jacquin and Zeigler, 1983.)

more slowly than the deafferented subjects during the immediate postoperative period and began to ingest substantial amounts of water at times
when the deafferented rats were still adipsic. Differences between the two
groups were significant throughout the 30-day period preceding the recovery of the deafferented subjects.

F. Effects on Body Weight Regulation

Deafferented rats lost weight during a 5-day period of aphagia at the
same rate as normal rats deprived of food and water for an equivalent
period. However, the recovery of lost body weight in deafferented animals was significantly retarded, and body weight remained below free-
feeding levels for more than a month following the resumption of solid
food intake.

The retardation of body weight seen in Fig. 16 is striking, since it occurs
in rats that are ingesting substantial amounts of solid food and show no
obvious consummatory impairments. It suggests that trigeminal orsen-
sory deafferentation produces a reduction in the level at which body
weight is regulated. However, all these animals had undergone a prolonged period of reduced food and water intake, and such treatment has
been shown to depress significantly the level at which weight is subsequently regulated (Armstrong *et al.*, 1980). To clarify this issue we com-

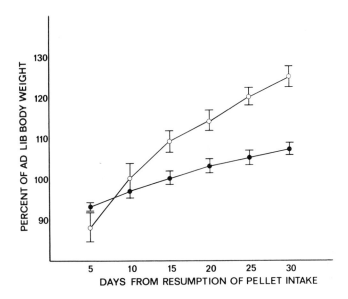

FIG. 20. Effects of deafferentation on long-term body weight. Data were recorded starting with the day on which a subject resumed the eating of rat chow pellets. Six of the
subjects had previously served as "yoked" controls (○). Note that even though the control
group starts at a slightly lower body weight, it continues to increase weight throughout the
30-day period, while the deafferented group (●, $N = 8$) asymptotes at a significantly lower
weight. (From Jacquin and Zeigler, 1983.)

pared the weight regulation of deafferented subjects with that of the
yoked-for-food-intake controls described earlier. Yoking began at least 5
days preoperatively and continued until the deafferented rat began to
ingest rat chow pellets at preoperative levels. At this point the control rat
was unyoked and both animals were given unlimited access to rat chow
pellets only. Water was continuously available.

Figure 21 illustrates the time course of body weight changes in four of
the yoked pairs. After they were unyoked, both groups showed an initial
increase in body weight and their rate of weight gain was similar, indicating that under the challenge of deprivation deafferented rats can substantially increase their intake *on a short-term basis*. However, even though
the deafferented rats were capable of ingesting substantial quantities of
rat chow, their body weights tended to asymptote at values significantly
lower than those of the yoked controls. This is evident in Fig. 20, which
compares group data on weight gain in the two groups for a 30-day period
beginning with the resumption of solid food intake. Taken together, these
data suggest a reduction in the *long-term* level at which body weight was

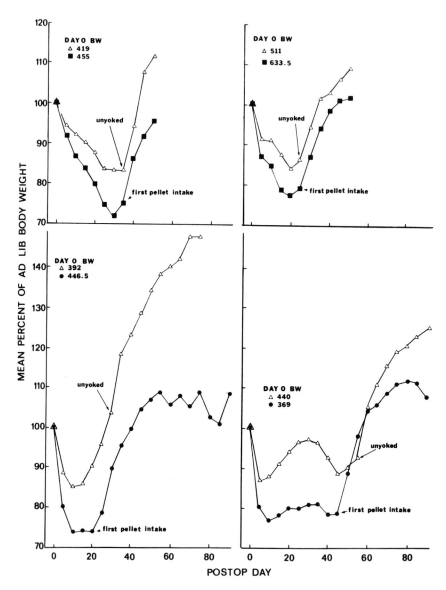

FIG. 21. Body weight changes in individual subjects of the deafferented (●, complete; ■, lingual intact) and "yoked" (△) groups. Body weight at surgery is taken as the ad lib weight. Control subjects were unyoked at the point at which their deafferented partners began to eat rat chow pellets (arrows), and all subjects were maintained only on chow pellets from that point on. (From Jacquin and Zeigler, 1983.)

regulated. Since both groups had undergone equivalent periods of reduced intake, the effect is not attributable solely to prolonged deprivation but must reflect some long-term consequence of orosensory deafferentation. Similar effects are seen after trigeminal deafferentation in the pigeon (Zeigler, 1975)

G. FEEDING EFFICIENCY AND RESPONSIVENESS TO FOOD: A PRELIMINARY ANALYSIS

Our home cage observations of deafferented rats suggest that, in addition to their consummatory impairments, they were also less responsive to food. To assess the differential contribution of these two factors to the reduced intake of the trigeminal rat, we used measures of responsiveness and feeding efficiency that are based on the characteristic organization of the rat's feeding behavior sequence. The first phase of that sequence involves removal of the food from the dish, either with the incisors or with the forepaw. A second phase consists of grasping the pellet and biting or shaving bits of food from its surface; in the third phase, food is moved from the front to the back of the mouth before swallowing. Within this sequence (*removal, grasping, transport*) there are several pivotal junctures where either reduced efficiency or reduced responsiveness will produce a disruption of the sequence and a reduction of food intake. Our three consummatory measures were chosen to sample performance at each of them to distinguish between responsiveness and efficiency deficits.

The measures selected are based, in part, on our observations of the behavior of the oromotor controls. Rats with such impairments, which have difficulty with mouth opening or tongue movement, nevertheless removed substantial quantities of food using a combination of snout and forepaws. The trigeminal motor subjects are unable to open the mouth, cannot grasp or chew the pellets, and leave this food on the cage floor. The hypoglossal controls cannot transport it and leave large amounts of crumbs. As Table III indicates, oromotor controls, although they show marked reduction in intake, still show relatively high levels of postoperative responsiveness to food.

Responsiveness to food was assessed by recording the total amount of food removed from the dish. Two measures of efficiency were employed. Disruptions of "grasping" (mouth opening or biting) were measured by recording the ratio of food intake to food removed from the dish. Deficits in transporting the food were measured by examining the ratio of uningested crumbs to total food intake.

Figure 22 presents data on the two measures of feeding efficiency in the

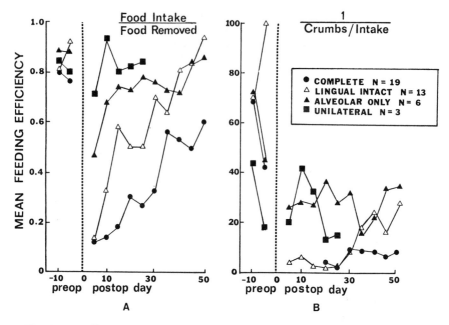

Fɪɢ. 22. Deafferentation effects on two measures of feeding efficiency. (A) Efficiency of grasping (mouth opening, biting); (B) deficits in moving the food from the front to the back of the mouth. (From Jacquin and Zeigler, 1983.)

experimental groups. A reduction in "grasping" efficiency (food intake/ food removed) as well as a considerable degree of recovery was observed in the three bilateral groups. A reduction in "transport" efficiency (crumbs/intake) was also characteristic of the orosensory animals, but this deficit was still apparent more than 6 weeks postoperatively.

Figure 23 presents data on responsiveness to food in the experimental and control groups as measured by the amount of solid food removed from the dish. Orosensory subjects showed a reduction and then a gradual return in responsiveness, and the effect was approximately proportional to the extent of the deafferentation. Except for a slight reduction in the infraorbital group, no such effect was evident in the controls.

As Fig. 24 indicates, the relations among intake, efficiency, and responsiveness measures in the deafferented rat are complex. One measure of efficiency (transport) does not recover to preoperative levels even in animals whose intake does recover, a result indicating that reduced efficiency is compatible with normal intake. Similarly, subjects in the alveolar group showed relatively efficient grasping behavior from about day 10, but continued to show considerably reduced intake and responsiveness.

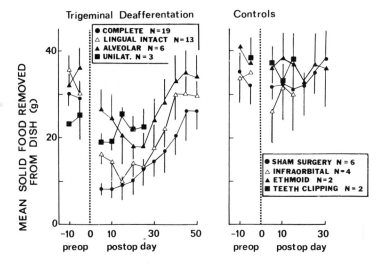

FIG. 23. Responsiveness to food as reflected in the amount of solid food removed from the dish. (From Jacquin and Zeigler, 1983.)

Miller (1981) has also found that although alveolar subjects typically ate all three solid foods within 10 days postoperatively, they remained hypophagic for more than a month beyond that point.

As this analysis indicates, trigeminal orosensory deafferentation produces a complex mixture of consummatory impairments and responsiveness deficits whose recovery tends to parallel that of food intake. To dissociate the contribution of the two types of deficits to the reduced intake of the deafferented subjects requires experimental analyses involving direct measures of responsiveness to food (and water). These experiments are described in detail in Section VIII.

VII. Trigeminal Orosensation and Ingestive Reflexes

Although the jaw-opening reflex of mammals has been extensively studied by physiologists, there is little agreement about its functional significance. It has sometimes been viewed as a protective response to excessive mechanical stimulation of intraoral structures during biting and chewing. Alternatively, it has been suggested that the reflex contributes to the reciprocal operation of the opener and closer muscles in masticatory rhythms (reviews in Dubner et al., 1978; Luschei and Goldberg, 1981). However, as has been pointed out by Lund et al. (1982), reflex

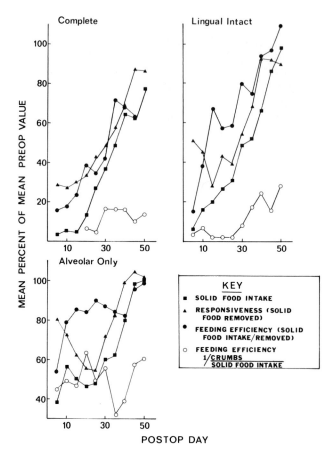

FIG. 24.   Relations among efficiency, responsiveness, and food intake measures in three deafferented groups. Data are plotted as a percentage of preoperative values. Sample sizes as in Fig. 17, 22, and 23. (From Jacquin and Zeigler, 1983.)

responses to low-intensity tactile stimulation of orofacial regions are likely to have a different function than those elicited by high-intensity (noxious) stimuli.

The jaw-opening reflex to low-intensity perioral stimulation of the fetus or infant is the earliest reflex to develop in the head region of mammals (Humphrey, 1970). It has been presumed to facilitate grasping of the nipple during suckling, a hypothesis that was confirmed by Hofer *et al.* (1981). These workers showed that section of the infraorbital nerve supplying the snout disrupted the initiation and maintenance of grasping, mouthing, and licking of the nipple in rat pups. Analogous effects of infraorbital nerve section on jaw opening during retrieving in adult (lactating) rats have been reported by Kenyon *et al.* (1983).

Such observations are quite consistent with our finding that trigeminal orosensory deafferentation produces deficits in the sensorimotor control of ingestive behavior (Jacquin and Zeigler, 1983; Miller, 1981). These deficits were manifested in a decreased probability of mouth opening and tongue protrusion (protraction) to *perioral* stimuli, although vigorous oromotor activity could be elicited by *intraoral* (cotton swab, food, water) or *extraoral* (tail pinch, paw pinch) stimuli.

While approach and orientation to a food pellet or sipper tube is normal in these animals, mouth opening fails to occur when contact is made with the pellet, nor does tongue protrusion take place on contact with the sipper tube. The deficit is not easily explicable, since the motor systems for the tongue and jaw were intact in these animals, as were jaw proprioception, vision, and olfaction.

These observations suggested two hypotheses.

1. The sensorimotor deficits of the deafferented rat reflect interruption of the afferent limb of a trigeminally mediated jaw-opening reflex.

2. The perioral inputs eliciting this reflex also play a critical role in the functional organization of ingestive behavior in the *normal* adult rat. (This hypothesis is consistent with the observation that tactile stimulation of the perioral region always precedes jaw opening during normal eating and drinking; see Section III).

These hypotheses were tested in physiological and neurobehavioral experiments designed (1) to identify orofacial regions eliciting jaw-opening reflexes to mechanical stimulation and (2) to examine the effects on jaw opening and tongue protrusion of deafferenting these regions.

In the first experiment, jaw-opening reflexes were elicited by mechanical and electrical stimulation of orofacial regions in anesthetized rats. The reflex was recorded from the central stump of the mylohyoid nerve, which innervates jaw-opening muscles. A psychophysical scaling procedure was used to determine tactile thresholds (grams) for elicitation of the electrophysiologically defined reflex during stimulation with calibrated Von Frey hairs. Reflex latencies were defined using electrical stimulation of sites previously shown to elicit the reflex in response to mechanical stimulation.

Figure 25 illustrates the type of multiunit activity evoked in the mylohyoid nerve by suprathreshold stimulation of a variety of body sites. The reflex discharge typically had multiple peaks, reflecting stimulation of

RHINARIUM   IPSI UPPER LIP   CONTRA UPPER LIP

UPPER ROSTRAL GUMS   IPSI FACIAL PAD   CONTRA FACIAL PAD

IPSI CHEEK PAD   CONTRA CHEEK PAD   PALATE

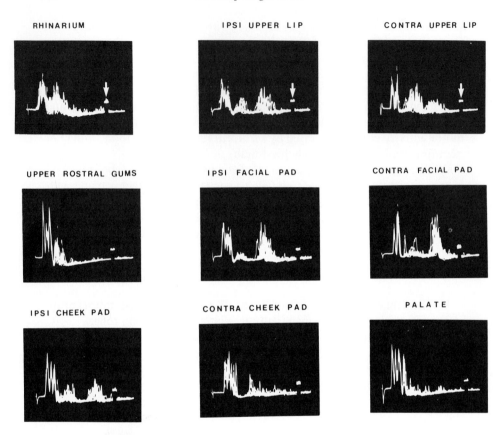

Fɪɢ. 25.   Multiunit (jaw-opening reflex) activity evoked in the mylohyoid nerve by supra-threshold electrical stimulation (10-mA stimulus, calibration = 2 msec, 50μV) at a variety of orofacial sites. (From Zeigler *et al.*, 1984.)

multiple afferent fiber types, multiple afferent pathways to the jaw open-ers, and motoneuron recruitment.

Reflex latencies to electrical stimulation of the orofacial region ranged from 5 to 15 msec, with the shortest latencies (5–9 msec) obtained from intraoral structures and the upper lip. Reflex activity could also be elicited at low levels of stimulus intensity by mechanical stimulation, with the most effective sites clustering about the region of the upper lip and supe-rior portions of the oral cavity (Fig. 26). For this region, mechanical displacement of less than 1 g was often sufficient to elicit the reflex in these anesthetized preparations.

These observations demonstrate that trigeminal inputs from the pe-rioral region have access (at relatively short latencies) to reflex mecha-

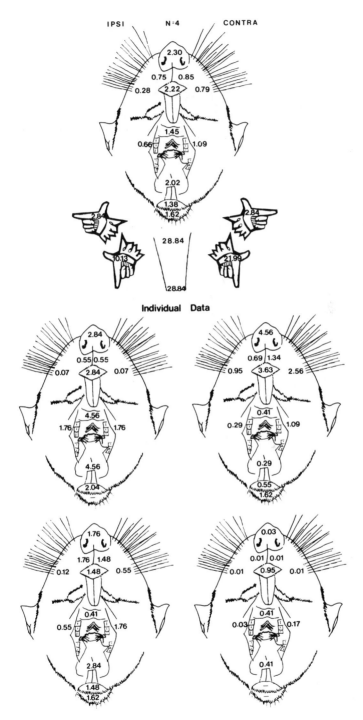

FIG. 26. Tactile thresholds (in grams) of jaw-opening reflex activity to mechanical stimulation (Von Frey hair) at various body sites. Data for four individual animals and summary diagram showing group means. (From Zeigler et al., 1984.)

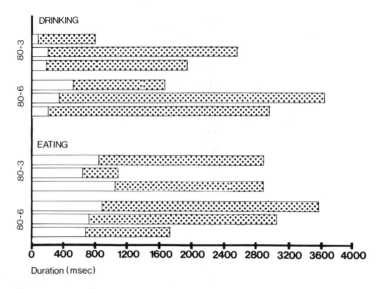

FIG. 27.   Duration of components of ingestive behavior sequences in deafferented rats. Note the prolonged duration of perioral contact (dotted bars) and the absence of the mouth-opening and tongue-protrusion phases. Open bars, approach. (From Zeigler, *et al.,* 1984.)

nisms of jaw opening in the rat and that reflex thresholds in these regions are quite low. While they support the hypothesis that perioral inputs are *sufficient* to elicit jaw-opening reflexes in the anesthetized preparation, they do not demonstrate that such inputs are *necessary* for its elicitation during normal ingestive behavior. The second experiment was designed to test this hypothesis as well as to provide systematic data on the effects of orosensory deafferentation on jaw opening and tongue protrusion during eating and drinking.

Preoperatively, ingestive behavior was videotaped using the apparatus described in Section III. Jaw opening and tongue protrusion were measured using scales whose modal points were derived from samples of individual eating and drinking acts. For each subject, the mean of its set of preoperative scale values was assigned a percentile score of 100% to permit comparisons with its postoperative values. Subjects then sustained various types and degrees of trigeminal deafferentation, and their ingestive behavior was monitored for periods of up to 2 months postoperatively.

Figure 27 illustrates the temporal relations among the components of ingestive behavior sequences in representative rats subjected to a complete trigeminal orosensory deafferentation, sparing the lingual nerves. It should be compared with Fig. 2, which presents comparable data for these subjects.

Deafferentation produced significant changes in both eating and drinking movement patterns. First, while the approach phase of the behaviors appeared unaffected in form or duration, the contact phase was markedly prolonged. Second, the jaw-opening and tongue protrusion phases were absent. Subjects approached the sipper tube or pellet with normal postures and maintained appropriate orientations; their initial mode of contact with the food or water source appeared unchanged. However, even after prolonged contact with the pellet, the jaw did not open and the tongue did not protrude to bridge the gap between the end of the sipper tube and the inside of the mouth.

Under these circumstances, the animals behaved as if they were "fixed" in the contact phase, continually rubbing the snout against the pellet or sipper tube but eventually aborting the ingestive sequence. In some cases, ingestion was accomplished by forcing the pellet or sipper tube through the lips and into the oral cavity, but this tactic was seen only after the least extensive deafferentations.

One consequence of these sensorimotor deficits was a reduction in the probability of successive bites at the pellet, that is, in the ratio of bites to contacts. Preoperatively, these ratios ranged from 0.56 to 1.00 (perfect efficiency). During the first postoperative month they ranged from 0.00 (complete absence of bites) to 0.21. The deficit in tongue protrusion was reflected primarily in the distribution of drinking bout durations. Normal rats tend to ingest water from a sipper tube in sustained bouts, whose duration varies with the degree of thirst (Stellar and Hill, 1952). Trigeminal deafferentation produced a major shift in this distribution. Preoperatively, bout durations were fairly evenly distributed, with short bouts (<20 sec) accounting for only about 30% of the total. During the first postoperative month, short bouts made up almost 85% of the total, reflecting a reduction in the probability of sustained drinking.

The magnitude and persistence of the deficits in jaw opening and tongue protrusion varied with the extent and location of the trigeminal denervations. The slightest and most transient effects were seen after section of the three maxillary branches (exclusive of the infraorbital nerve). These subjects were eating the drinking normally within the first postoperative week. Infraorbital nerve section produced a more disruptive but still quite transient effect (Fig. 28A). Larger and more persistent deficits were seen after mandibular (inferior alveolar) sections (Fig. 28B). In the immediate postoperative period these subjects showed a partial jaw opening that was insufficient to allow a full bite but did permit some nibbling at the food pellet. The most substantial deficits were produced by a combination of

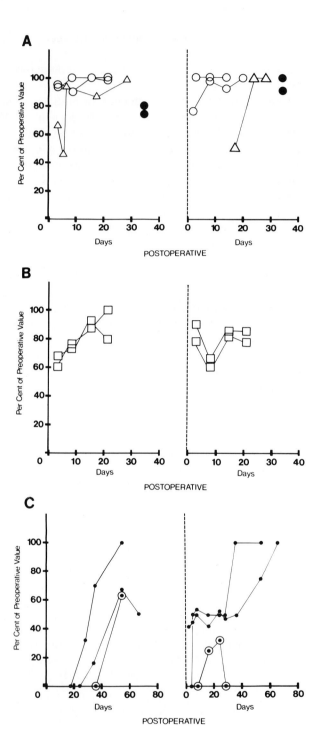

mandibular and maxillary denervations (Fig. 28C), which disrupted eating and drinking for periods of more than a month.

It is important to note that these preparations will show jaw opening and tongue protrusion to extraoral or intraoral stimuli, an observation consistent with the fact that the motor systems for the tongue and jaw are intact. Thus, while their denervation is a sensory one, its effects are sensorimotor. The magnitude of the deficit is proportional to the total number of sensory nerves sectioned, and there does not appear to be a specific "trigger zone" that is critical for eliciting jaw opening or tongue protrusion. The locus of the denervation appears to be of some significance, since the greatest deficits were seen after denervation of *perioral* rather than intraoral areas.

Our observations of eating and drinking in normal animals (Section III) indicated that prolonged contact of perioral areas always preceded jaw opening and tongue protrusion. Inputs from these areas were shown to have access to reflex mechanisms of jaw opening. That removal of these inputs by trigeminal deafferentation disrupts jaw opening is consistent with these observations.

That this procedure also disrupted tongue protraction is also consistent with the existence of a significant trigeminal orosensory contribution to the control of tongue reflexes. Modulation of reflex activity in tongue protractor (genioglossus) muscles or motoneurons can be produced by jaw rotation or by inferior alveolar nerve stimulation (Lowe, 1981). Thus the reduction in tongue protrusion could reflect either an indirect effect of reduced jaw-opening activity or a direct effect of trigeminal deafferentation on cutaneous sensory fields.

The reduction in jaw opening and tongue protrusion in the deafferented rat is particularly striking when we consider that its visual, olfactory, and oral proprioceptive afferent systems are intact as are the efferent systems controlling vibrissae, jaw, and tongue movements. Conversely, disruptions of olfaction (LaRue and LeMagnen, 1972), taste (Jacquin, 1983; Pfaffmann, 1952), and jaw proprioception (Daunton, 1977) do not impair jaw opening and tongue protrusion. We conclude, therefore, that trigemi-

---

FIG. 28.   Effects of trigeminal orosensory deafferentation on jaw opening and tongue protrusion during eating and drinking. Data are plotted as a percentage of their preoperative values. For (A–C), left-hand graph reflects jaw opening, right-hand graph reflects tongue protrusion. (A) (○) Maxillary sections (exclusive of the infraorbital nerve). Data for a subject with an infraorbital section (△) are presented for comparison. (●) Effect of adding mandibular sections to the two maxillary subjects. (B) Effects of mandibular sections (lingual nerve intact). Conventions as in (A). (C) Effects of complete (◉; maxillary plus mandibular) denervation. (●) Lingual intact. Conventions as in (A) and (B). (From Zeigler *et al.,* 1984.)

nal orosensory inputs are *necessary* for the elicitation of jaw and tongue movements during ingestive behavior in the *normal* hungry or thirsty rat.

VIII. Denervation Effects on Responsiveness to Food: Dissociation of Sensorimotor and Motivational Deficits

As indicated in the preceding sections, interpretation of the reduced intake of the deafferented rat is complicated by the presence of impairments in the sensorimotor control of the consummatory response. Not only are the oromotor reflexes of these subjects depressed (Section VII), there is also an obvious interaction between the magnitude of the intake deficit and the sensory properties of the diet. Given these findings, it is possible that the reduced intake of the deafferented rat is a secondary consequence of denervation effects on sensorimotor rather than motivational processes.

In considering this hypothesis, it may be useful to distinguish between the two types of intake deficits: absence of intake (aphagia, adipsia) and reduction of intake (hypophagia, hypodipsia). Absence of intake might simply reflect an inability to manipulate a food object or water source orally rather than a decrease in hunger or thirst. In such cases, subjects might be expected to continue to exhibit appetitive and ingestive behaviors and even to show compensatory increases in such behavior similar to those seen when animals are placed on an "extinction" schedule. However, in the absence of the primary reinforcement provided by the intake, these instrumental behaviors would be expected to decrease. Such an "extinction" hypothesis would predict that responsiveness to a food or water source would be high in the immediate postoperative period, declining thereafter. Alternatively, motivational deficits should be reflected in reduced levels of responsiveness to food or water sources in the immediate postoperative period.

Sensorimotor impairments could also account for the reduction in intake of water or of specific diets if the ingestive effort required were excessive. An *effort* hypothesis would predict a considerable increase in the amount of time spent feeding accompanied by a reduction in the amount of food or water per unit ingestive time. In the absence of compensatory increases in responsiveness, sensorimotor deficits could lead to a persistent hypophagia or hypodipsia.

Such dissociations of motivational and sensorimotor deficits cannot be achieved solely by analyses involving intake measures but require parallel measurements of intake and responsiveness. The first such data were

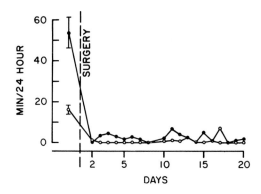

Fig. 29. Time spent feeding (●) and drinking (○) of a typical animal subjected to extensive trigeminal orosensory deafferentation. Preoperative data are indicated by the mean ± 1 SD of 7 days preceding surgery. (From Miller, 1981.)

provided by Miller (1981), who monitored the time spent eating and drinking in deafferented rats using feedometers and drinkometers. As Fig. 29 indicates, there was a dramatic reduction in such activity.

These observations were confirmed and extended in subsequent studies in which the eating and drinking behavior of deafferented subjects were compared with that of oromotor controls, subjected to section of the efferents to the tongue (XII motor) and jaw (V motor) muscles.

A. Effects on Drinking

To assess responsiveness to water in deafferented rats, we used a standard drinkometer circuit modified so that discrete licking movements and contacts with the sipper tube were monitored separately. This permitted us to record not only the frequency of licking behavior but also the amount of time spent in contact with the tube. As in our other studies, we compared the effects of trigeminal orosensory deafferentation with those produced in oromotor controls by section of efferents to the jaw (V motor) and tongue (XII motor).

Table IV compares preoperative and postoperative data on water intake for all treatment groups, while Fig. 30 illustrates denervation effects on intake and drinking efficiency for a representative subject in each group. An efficiency index was obtained by calculating the ratio of sipper contact time to water intake. The lower the ratio, the more efficient the drinking behavior. Both oromotor subjects showed a marked reduction in drinking efficiency, reflecting their increased contact time per milliliter of

TABLE IV
WATER INTAKE AFTER OROSENSORY OR OROMOTOR DENERVATION

| Surgical group | Intake (ml)[a] | |
and rat number	Preoperative	Postoperative
Orosensory V (complete)		
77-12	296	5
77-33	231	0
78-15	329	5
Orosensory V (lingual intact)		
78-13	251	16
78-16	273	68
78-17	360	12
Oromotor XII (hypoglossal)		
78-14	245	22
78-53	175	57
78-55	365	152
Oromotor V (trigeminal)		
78-9	403	110
78-10	336	36
78-11	271	18

[a] Data are for a 10-day period preceding and following denervation.

water intake. (Intake values for oromotor controls in Table IV were inflated by excessive spillage.) In contrast, no efficiency ratio could be calculated for the orosensory subject because the rat showed no water intake during the first 10 postoperative days. Moreover, while preoperative contact times for this subject ranged from 10 to 20 min of drinking per day, postoperatively, less than 1 min/day was spent in contact with the sipper tube.

These differences in responsiveness are obvious in Figs. 31 and 32, which provide direct measures of contact time for the orosensory and oromotor subjects. Subjects in the oromotor group (Fig. 32), although they obtained little or no water, showed an immediate (probably compensatory) increase in contact, continuing to respond vigorously for serveral days postoperatively and then showing signs of extinction. In contrast, the deafferented subjects (Fig. 31) showed an immediate postoperative reduction in responsiveness to the water source, followed by a rather abrupt recovery of drinking several weeks later (Jacquin and Zeigler, 1983).

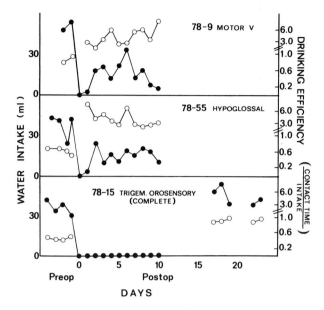

Fig. 30. Intake (●) and drinking efficiency (○) in three representative subjects with either oromotor or orosensory sections. A reduction in drinking efficiency is indicated by an increase in the contact time/intake ratio. There was considerable spillage in the oromotor groups, so that the intake values shown may be inflated. (From Jacquin and Zeigler, 1983.)

B. Effects on Eating

Eating was monitored using a video camera and tape recorder adapted for day and night viewing, and observations were carried out in a Plexiglas fish tank (10 gallons) to provide maximum visibility. Food and water were presented in fixed locations on the floor of the tank, and both solid (chow pellets) and semiliquid (cereal, mash) diets were used. On observation days, subjects were placed in the tank at 5:00 PM with the lights on. The lights were turned off at 10:30 PM and remained off until 30 min before the removal of the animal at 9:00 AM. Videotapes for each observation session were analyzed to provide data on the initiation, duration, and termination of ingestive behaviors directed at each of the diets. In addition to the deafferented (trigeminal orosensory) subjects, and the two oromotor groups (V, XII), data were also obtained from a sham/extinction control group. These subjects were presented with the same diets as the other treatment groups. However, the diets were presented in glass containers sealed with wire mesh caps. This provided the visual and olfactory

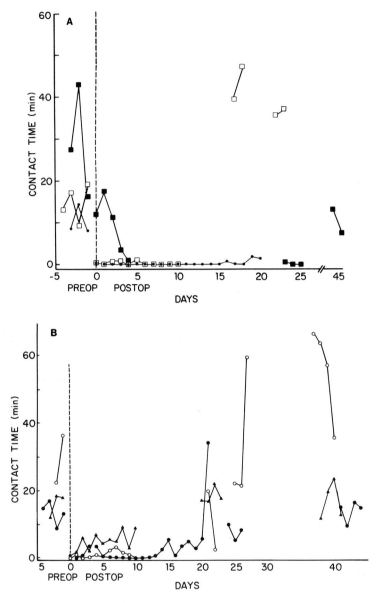

FIG. 31. (A) Effects of complete trigeminal orosensory deafferentation on time spent in contact with the sipper tube in three rats. (●) Rat sacrificed on day 21 without recovering drinking. (B) Effects of trigeminal orosensory deafferentation sparing the lingual nerves on sipper contact time in three rats. Note that in all cases the return to normal levels of responsiveness is abrupt. (From Jacquin and Zeigler, 1983.)

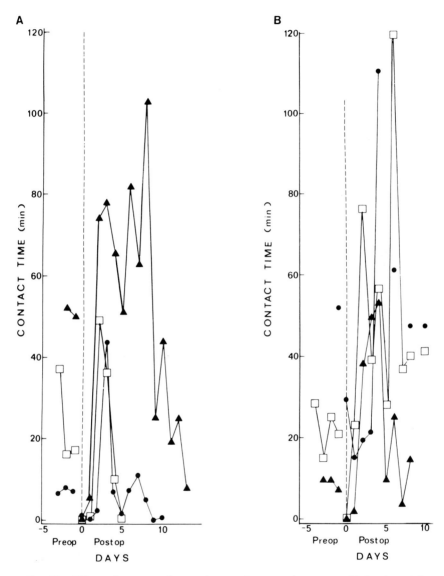

FIG. 32.   Effects of oromotor denervations on time spent in contact with the sipper tube. (A) Trigeminal motor sections; (B) hypoglossal sections. The three trigeminal motor subjects could move their tongues but could not open their mouths. The three hypoglossal subjects could open their mouths but could not move their tongues. (From Jacquin and Zeigler, 1983.)

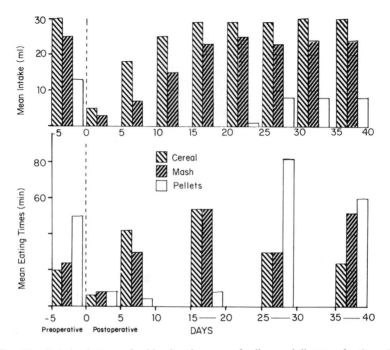

FIG. 33.   Relation between food intake, time spent feeding, and diet type for three deafferented subjects. (Olazabal *et al.,* unpublished data.)

cues associated with the diets but prevented intake. The focus of the data
analysis was on the first postoperative week.

Figure 33 presents data on food intake and feeding activity for each diet
type obtained from a group of three deafferented subjects. During the
immediate postoperative period (days 1–10) there was a marked reduction
in both daily food intake and time spent feeding. While there were individual variations in the persistence of this responsiveness deficit, the general
trend was evident in all subjects. Recovery of intake was paralleled by
increases in feeding activity. Moreover, deafferentation affected not only
the level but also the direction of feeding activity. Preoperatively, all
three diets were eaten in substantial amounts daily. After deafferentation,
there was little or no consumption of solid food (pellets) for several
weeks. A reduction in feeding efficiency was evident in the changed relation between feeding time and food consumption, and there was an obvious interaction between feeding efficiency and diet type. Preoperatively,
cereal was the diet consumed in greatest quantities, followed by mash and
then pellets. However, consumption times for the three diets were re-

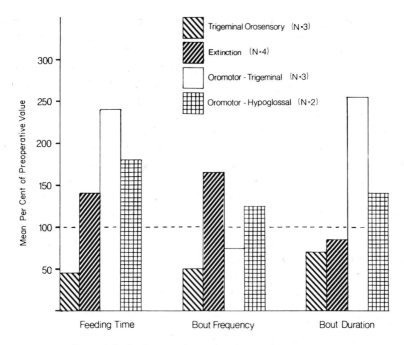

FIG. 34. Feeding activity in the experimental and control groups during the first postoperative weeks. Data are plotted as a percentage of preoperative values. (Olazabal *et al.*, unpublished data.)

versed, presumably reflecting their relative ease of ingestion. Postoperatively, these relationships were maintained, although unit consumption times for each of the diets increased so that two or three times as much feeding activity was emitted for each gram of food ingested. The return toward preoperative levels of intake was gradual and was paralleled by increasing levels of feeding activity for a specific diet. Recovery of feeding efficiency was evident in a gradual reduction of unit feeding times toward preoperative levels.

Figure 34 compares feeding activity for all four treatment groups during the first postoperative week. The reduced intake of the deafferented (orosensory) group reflects a reduction in both frequency and duration of feeding bouts. Because of their excessive spillage, intake data were not plotted for the oromotor controls. However, despite the fact that they obtained little or no food during the postoperative period, feeding activity in these animals remained above preoperative levels for most of this period. This increased feeding activity was mediated by different parameters in the two groups. The hypoglossal subjects increased both frequency and duration somewhat, while the increase in the trigeminal motor group was due primarily to a dramatic increase in bout duration. Subjects in the sham/extinction control group, of course, obtained no food at all during the 6-day observation period. Nevertheless, their total feeding activity remained above preoperative levels, an effect mediated primarily by increased bout frequency.

These experiments confirmed the fact that trigeminal orosensory deafferentation produces a mixture of sensorimotor and motivational deficits. Moreover, they demonstrated that the reduced food and water intake of the deafferented subjects is due to a genuine reduction in hunger and thirst. The most convincing evidence in support of this conclusion is the fact that the disruption and recovery of intake in deafferented subjects is accompanied by parallel variations in the level of eating and drinking activity. Abolition of water intake is accompanied by the absence or drastic reduction in contact with the water source. Its abrupt recovery is paralleled by an equally abrupt return toward preoperative levels of contact time. Similarly, the abolition and gradual recovery of solid food intake in the deafferented rat was not due simply to an inability to ingest this specific diet. It reflected the reduction and gradual recovery of feeding activity directed specifically at solid food.

It is clear from the data of the oromotor controls that severe disruptions in the sensorimotor control of eating and drinking are quite compatible with high and maintained levels of responsiveness to food and water. These subjects were almost completely unable to ingest food and water but spent much time in contact with the food and water sources. This was also true of the extinction controls, which maintained high levels of activity directed at food although they experienced neither the oropharyngeal nor the postingestive consequences of intake.

Neither an "extinction" nor an "effort" hypothesis will account for the abolition or reduction of intake in the deafferented subjects. Indeed, these terms more appropriately describe the behavior of the controls, who respond to their sensorimotor impairments first with increased effort and then with gradually decreasing responsiveness (see especially Fig. 32). Thus, the reduced intake of the oromotor and orosensory preparations reflects the operation of two quite different processes. The oromotor animal stops eating and drinking because it cannot ingest the food and water. The orosensory animal seems to be uninterested in food and water.

The effects on hunger and thirst produced by trigeminal orosensory deafferentation are reminiscent of the effects on lever pressing for food or water in an intragastric–operant paradigm when subjects are shifted from oral to intragastric reinforcement (Kissileff, 1973; Snowdon, 1969). This similarity is not surprising, since the intragastric procedure constitutes a partial, reversible deafferentation of the oral region.

C. Effects on General Activity

It is now well established that food-deprived rats will show increases in several types of general activity measures, which are presumed to express an increased responsiveness to external stimuli (Bolles, 1975). We have carried out several experiments to determine whether similar effects on general activity are seen in deafferented subjects.

In the first of these studies, Miller (1981) examined the relations among feeding, exploration, and resting activity during a 10-min period following the daily replenishing of food and water in the home cage. Preoperatively, subjects divided the period about equally between eating, grooming/exploring, and resting. Postoperatively, there was a significant increase in the time spent resting, which was greatest in the most extensively deafferented group (Fig. 35).

Comparable results were found in a study of grooming and rearing in deafferented rats. The behavioral analysis was based on videotaped observations, made during a 5-day period preoperatively and postoperatively (see Section VIII,B). Grooming and rearing frequencies were scored during the first hour after introduction to the observation chamber (lights on) and the first hour following light offset. As Fig. 36 shows, both types of activity are profoundly depressed in deafferented rats by comparison with sham surgical/extinction controls.

In a final experiment, activity in a running wheel was examined before and after trigeminal orosensory deafferentation and compared with the performance of a variety of control subjects (infraorbital, gustatory, hypoglossal, sham surgical). The data for two trigeminal orosensory subjects are presented in Fig. 37A, which shows body weight and total number of revolutions plotted in 10-day blocks. Following a period of baseline (free-feeding) measurement, subjects were totally food deprived for 10 days, brought back to free-feeding weight, and then deafferented. Preoperatively, the rats almost *quadrupled* their wheel-running activity during the period of food deprivation and weight loss. Postoperatively, activity remained well below free-feeding levels for more than a month, even though during most of that time the rats were considerably below free-feeding body weights. Figure 37B presents data on wheel-running activity for the control subjects during the first 20 postoperative days, plotted as a percentage of preoperative activity levels. While all control subjects

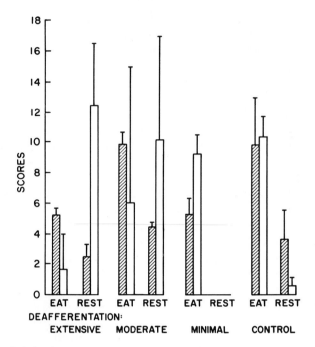

FIG. 35.   Relation between time spent eating and resting in individual experimental and control subjects during the 10-min period following the daily replenishing of the food dish. Scores are the number of 30-sec intervals within which the behavior was exhibited. Mean ± 1 SD of the last five preoperative (hatched bars) and first five postoperative days (open bars). "Eating" by the extensively deafferented animals consisted only of feeding attempts. (From Miller, 1981.)

showed some reduction in activity during the first 10 days postoperatively, all but the infraorbitals recovered preoperative levels within 20 days.

These observations make it clear that trigeminal orosensory deafferentation, in addition to its effects on responsiveness to food and water, also reduces responsiveness to other environmental stimuli that normally elicit increased levels of activity in hungry rats. Similar effects were not seen after gustatory or hypoglossal nerve section. They were evident in rats with section of the infraorbital nerve, which innervates not only the vibrissae but the upper lip and snout.

It is difficult to account for these more generalized effects of trigeminal deafferentation. Given the substantial trigeminal input into the brain stem reticular formation (Darian-Smith, 1973), it is tempting to account for such findings in terms of nonspecific activating effects (Zeigler, 1975, 1977). Until more is known about the *specific* controls of such behavior as

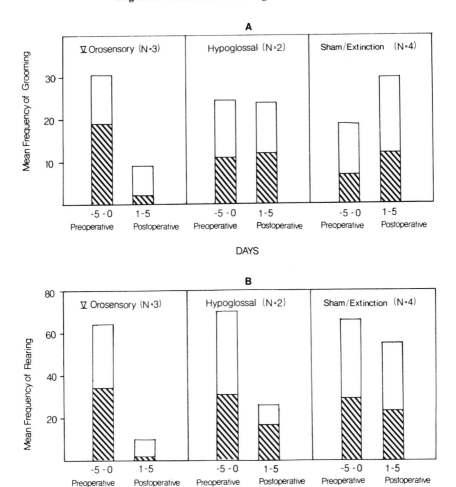

FIG. 36. Grooming (A) and rearing (B) in experimental and control (hypoglossal, sham/extinction) subjects. Open bars, day; hatched bars, night. (Olazabal *et al.,* unpublished data.)

rearing, grooming, and wheel running, this temptation should probably be avoided (Bolles, 1975). Alternatively, the reduced responsiveness of these animals to environmental stimuli may reflect a central neurochemical depletion. The latter hypothesis certainly deserves an empirical test. At the moment, however, the mechanisms mediating the more general effects of trigeminal deafferentation remain completely obscure.

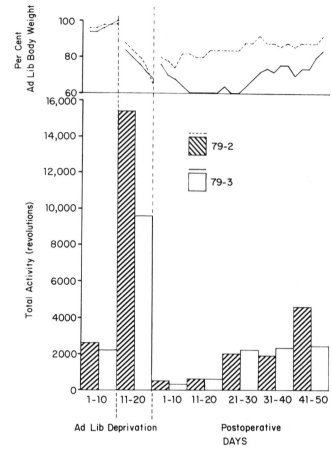

A

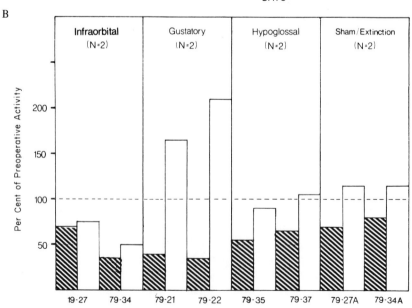

B

IX. Trigeminal Orosensation and Feeding Behavior Patterns

The ingestive behavior of an animal is a joint function of the frequency and duration of its feeding bouts. Thus, the reduced food intake of deafferented rats could reflect effects on motivational processes controlling the initiation of eating (bout frequency) or its persistence once initiated (bout duration). To resolve this issue, Miller (1981) examined the feeding patterns of deafferented rats using feedometers to measure consummatory behavior. (See Section XI for comparable data using an instrumental response measure.)

To minimize the incidental effects of deafferentation on the condition of the mouth and oromotor behavior, Miller used subjects with nerve sections restricted to the mandibular sensory branches innervating the ventral portion of the oral cavity and the anterior two-thirds of the tongue (inferior alveolar and lingual branches). Such preparations are aphagic for only 1 or 2 days, but they show a significant reduction in food intake and body weight by comparison with surgical controls and remain hypophagic for at least 4 weeks postoperatively (Fig. 38). They are thus excellent candidates for analysis of the changes in feeding parameters mediating their reduced intake.

Both control and experimental subjects showed a reduction in eating efficiency (as measured by ingestion rate) that recovered gradually so that they did not differ significantly during the third and fourth postoperative weeks (Fig. 39, top). Given their reduced feeding efficiency, the achievement of normal intake levels required a compensatory increase in feeding bout duration. Such compensation was evident in the control subjects by the second postoperative week. However, while an increase in bout durations was seen in the trigeminal subjects, it was insufficient to achieve full compensation (Fig. 39, bottom). Indeed, as feeding efficiency increased in the last 2 weeks, the deafferented subjects *decreased* the total time spent feeding, even though body weight was still below that of the control group.

Figure 40 illustrates the feeding patterns of a typical deafferented subject during the first 2 postoperative weeks. The most obvious effect is a reduction in meal frequency and a moderate increase in meal size (grams per meal). Note that on postoperative day 12, when body weight is still

---

FIG. 37.   (A) Effects of deprivation and trigeminal orosensory deafferentation on wheel-running activity. Subjects had reacquired their free-feeding weights before deafferentation. (B) Wheel-running activity in the control subjects. Data are plotted as a percentage of preoperative values. Hatched bars, days 1–10; open bars, days 11–20. (Olazabal *et al.*, unpublished data.)

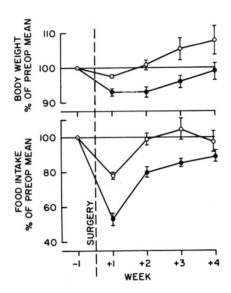

FIG. 38.   Mean body weight (upper panel) and mean food intake (lower panel; ±1 SE in both panels) of deafferented (●, $N = 9$) and control (○, $N = 5$) groups in consecutive postoperative weeks, expressed as percentage of the mean of the last preoperative week. (From Miller, 1981.)

only at 90% of free-feeding levels, there is an actual reduction in bout duration (time spent feeding).

Group data are presented in Fig. 41. The control group (Fig. 41A), after a slight reduction in meal frequencies, returned to and subsequently maintained preoperative levels. Deafferented subjects (Fig. 41B) showed a sustained reduction in meal frequency over the 4 postoperative weeks, while simultaneously increasing bout duration. However, the increase in meal size was insufficient to compensate for the reduction in meal frequency, so that food intake (and body weight) remained below preoperative levels throughout the observation period.

These data indicate that the hypophagia and decreased level of weight regulation seen after trigeminal deafferentation are the results, primarily, of a failure to *initiate* feeding bouts at the preoperative rate. Once the rat initiated a feeding bout, it could compensate for its reduced efficiency by increasing bout durations to levels exceeding preoperative values. However, even though full compensation required only a modest increase in the daily amount of feeding activity (from 87.4 to 103 min), compensation was incomplete.

This observation suggests that consummatory deficits play little or no

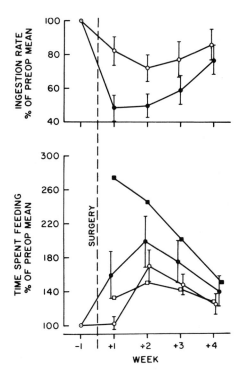

FIG. 39.   Mean ingestion rate (grams per minute; upper panel) and mean feeding time (lower panel; ±1 SE in both panels) of control (○, $N = 5$) and deafferented (●, $N = 9$) groups in consecutive postoperative weeks. The lower panel also presents the theoretical values of feeding duration (□, control; ■, deafferented) that would provide full compensation for postoperatively reduced ingestive rate. (From Miller, 1981.)

role in the *long-term* deficits in intake and weight regulation shown by the deafferented rat. Such deficits should be most disruptive of the rat's ability to maintain ingestive behavior for prolonged periods because of the combination of increased effort required of these animals and the decreased reinforcement that they obtained. Thus, as Miller points out, "the parameter that was most affected by deafferentation, meal initiation, is the one least related to the deficits of the consummatory response" (1981, p. 266).

Very similar deficits have been seen using an instrumental measure of hunger to study feeding patterns in the rat (Section XI), and decreases in the frequency of meal initiation also mediate the reduced intake and body weight of the deafferented pigeon (Miller *et al.*, 1978). This finding is of some theoretical interest. Most formulations of intake control distinguish

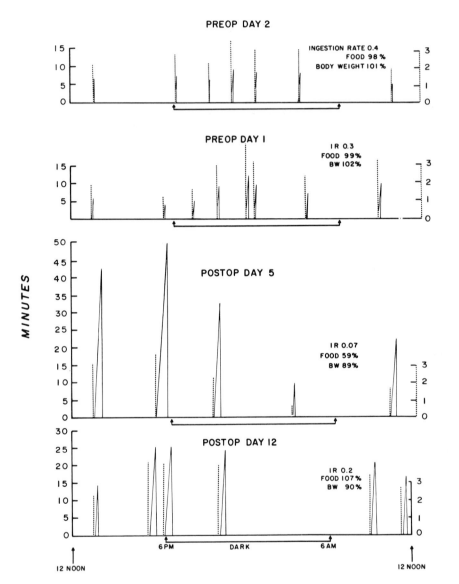

FIG. 40. Feeding patterns of an individual rat before and after trigeminal orosensory deafferentation. Note that both meal durations (solid lines) and grams of food eaten (dotted lines) are shown. (M. G. Miller, unpublished data.)

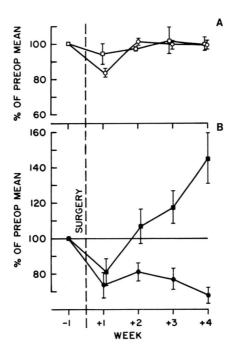

FIG. 41. Mean meal size (□, ■, in grams per meal) and mean meal frequency (○, ●, ±1 SE for both parameters) of control group (A) and deafferented group (B). (From Miller, 1981.)

between sensory factors, which are thought to be associated with short-term control processes, and metabolic factors, which are thought to mediate long-term control (Le Magnen, 1971; Panskepp, 1973). Such formulations are largely based on studies of orosensation that have focused on gustatory inputs. Miller's findings suggest a critical contribution of trigeminal orosensation to the long-term control of food intake.

X. Effects of Deafferentation on Dietary Self-Selection

Traditionally, psychologists have studied the control of food intake by presenting the subject with a single, nutritionally complete diet. For an omnivorous species like the rat this represents a highly artificial feeding situation. Under natural conditions, the rat selects from a variety of food sources with different nutritional compositions, organizing its feeding patterns so as to meet both its caloric and nutritional needs. The normal feeding behavior of the rat thus involves two distinct tasks: (1) the ingestion of foods that are potentially useful sources of specific nutrients (and the avoidance of potentially harmful substances, such as poisons) and (2) the selection of a nutritionally balanced diet from two or more foods of different nutrient composition.

The first of these tasks, *food selection*, is a qualitative one (i.e., what food to eat); the second task, *dietary self-selection*, is a quantitative one (i.e., how much to eat of a specific food). Its mastery will be reflected in the maintenance of the same growth rate as displayed when the different nutrient components are combined into one nutritionally complete diet. The distinction between the two tasks is made here for analytical purposes, since the rat must accomplish both if it is to achieve normal growth and maintain body weight.

Most of our understanding of food selection involves experimental paradigms in which feeding directed at a specific food source is associated with its postingestional consequences, positive (Booth, 1981; Simpson and Booth, 1973; Zahorik, 1977) or negative (Garcia *et al.*, 1966; Revusky, 1967; Zahorik *et al.*, 1974). In either case, it is assumed that selection (or aversion) is mediated by a conditioning process, involving the association of a food-related conditioning stimulus with a specific set of postingestional consequences.

Dietary self-selection faces the rat with a more complex problem, since it involves quantitative rather than qualitative behavioral adjustments. Nevertheless, it has been repeatedly demonstrated that rats will select the proper balance of the three major macronutrients (protein, fat, and carbohydrates) from an array of foods with mixed macronutrient content or from a selection of relatively pure macronutrient fractions (Overmann, 1976; Richter *et al.*, 1938).

While carbohydrates and fats (the two macronutrients involved in energy balance) are largely interchangeable, protein (amino acid) requirements are much more dependent on appropriate protein intake. A variety of studies have provided evidence for the specific control of protein intake. Given a choice of two diets differing mainly in protein concentration, rats will select a constant portion of their total daily intake in the form of protein, even when the protein concentration of the two diets is varied (Musten *et al.*, 1974). In response to dilution of the protein diet, rats increase intake from that diet (Schoenfeld and Hamilton, 1976; Rozin, 1968), while in response to intragastric supplementation of protein, they selectively reduce oral protein intake (Miller and Teates, 1984). When the energy requirements of rats are increased by placing them in a cold environment (Leshner *et al.*, 1971) or by providing a running wheel (Collier *et al.*, 1969a), they selectively increase carbohydrate intake. Thus it appears that the rat possesses mechanisms of dietary self-selection that control feeding behavior so as to maintain a stable protein intake while meeting additional energy requirements by increasing carbohydrate intake.

The nature of these dietary self-selection mechanisms is not understood. There is some evidence that the metabolites that mediate protein selection are the amino acids (Fernstrom and Faller, 1978; Wurtman and Wurtmann, 1977), since the tryptophan: neutral amino acid ratio of blood serum correlates significantly with protein intake (Anderson, 1979; Ashley and Anderson, 1975; Li and Anderson, 1982). However, even if we could establish unambiguously that specific metabolic parameters are invariably correlated with the control of protein intake, the mechanisms of control would remain unknown. The critical question to be answered is a neurobehavioral one; that is, how are metabolic conditions translated into compensatory behavioral choices from among the available diets.

An obvious starting point for neurobehavioral analysis is the nature of the sensory cues involved in dietary self-selection. Since the behavior has a substantial quantitative component, it seems reasonable to assume that sensory systems known to be significantly involved in other types of quantitative intake control should also play a role in dietary self-selection. In view of the past emphasis on the chemical senses (olfaction and taste) in the control of the rat's feeding behavior, it is surprising to note that the contribution of taste and smell to the quantitative control of food intake in the rat is relatively minor in contrast to that of oral somatosensation (Jacquin, 1983; Jacquin and Zeigler, 1983; LaRue and LeMagnen, 1972; Miller, 1981; Pfaffmann, 1952; Richter, 1956). Miller has therefore initiated a series of studies designed to assess the contribution of trigeminal orosensation to dietary self-selection.

In all these experiments, the subjects were allowed to choose between a high-protein diet and a protein-free carbohydrate diet. The two diets were isocaloric and contained equal and sufficient amounts of fat, minerals, and vitamins, while a control diet contained the same components as both selection diets combined. Texturally, the diets were a slightly oily, dry mash; the high-protein diet was somewhat coarse, the carbohydrate diet was smooth, and the control diet had an intermediate consistency. Trigeminal orosensation was manipulated by the use of a moderate deafferentation procedure that minimized disruptive effects on consummatory responses but produced significant effects on intake. (For further details on methods and diet composition, see Miller, 1984.)

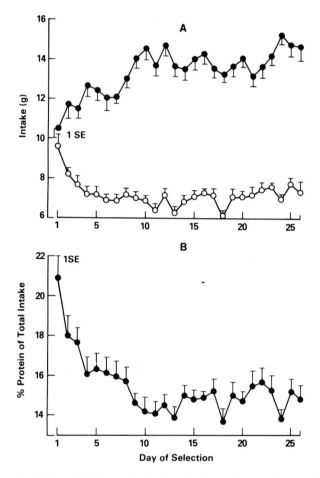

FIG. 42. Acquisition of dietary self-selection in the rat. Intake of normal (naive) rats beginning at the first day of exposure to two diets of different compositions. (A) Daily intake from the high-protein and protein-free carbohydrate diets. (B) The resulting ratio of protein/total intake. (Each data point represents the group mean ±1 SE: N = 13. ○, High-protein diet; ●, protein-free carbohydrate diet.) (From Miller and Teates, 1985.)

A. ACQUISITION OF DIETARY SELF-SELECTION

Underlying all these studies was the hypothesis that the continuous adjustment of the rat's feeding patterns to fluctuations in its metabolic condition depends on a learning process. To test this hypothesis, the acquisition of dietary self-selection was studied in a group of experimentally naive rats. As Fig. 42A indicates, subjects showed no significant differential selection from the two diets during the first 24 hr of exposure.

While individual animals chose varying percentages of their total intake from the high-protein diet, the group mean (20.9%; SE 1.1) was close to the random level of 22% (Fig. 42B). Over subsequent days, beginning as early as day 2, subjects began to show differential intake of the two diets, and by about the end of the first week subjects were maintaining a stable ratio of protein to total intake.

To examine the contribution of oral somatosensation to the acquisition of this adjustment process, the same observations were carried out in trigeminally deafferented rats. As the group data of Fig. 43A indicate, the deafferented rats did not show the gradual development of stable intake of both diets characteristic of normal subjects. However, the selection behavior of individual animals was by no means random (Fig. 43B). They showed consistent, albeit idiosyncratic, patterns of protein intake over several days, but might cover the entire range of permissible protein intake (0–44%) during the period of these observations. It is clear from these data that the ability to maintain a stable protein intake requires a period of experience with dietary self-selection and that trigeminal orosensation plays a critical role in the *acquisition* of that ability in naive rats (Miller and Teates, 1985).

B. EFFECTS OF DEAFFERENTATION ON THE MAINTENANCE OF DIETARY SELF-SELECTION

In a second study, Miller (1984) examined deafferentation effects on the *retention* of previously acquired self-selection behavior in experienced subjects. One group of rats (selection group) selected their total intake from the two selection diets. Their behavior and body weight were compared with that of a nonselection group presented with a single, complete diet consisting of the same nutrient components. The two groups had similar total food intakes and grew at the same rate. The selection group showed gradual acquisition of intake control, ingesting a stable proportion of their daily intake (mean 12.6%; SE 0.6) in the form of protein. At this point half of each of the two groups (selection, nonselection) underwent trigeminal deafferentation, while the other half sustained a surgical control procedure.

Both experimental groups showed the characteristic reduction of food intake (hypophagia) and body weight loss expected after deafferentation. However, the use of the selection paradigm revealed that the hypophagia of deafferented subjects did not involve equal reductions in the intake of both dietary fractions. As Fig. 44 illustrates, intake of the high-protein diet in deafferented subjects was severely depressed during the first postoperative week, increased gradually over subsequent weeks, and tended

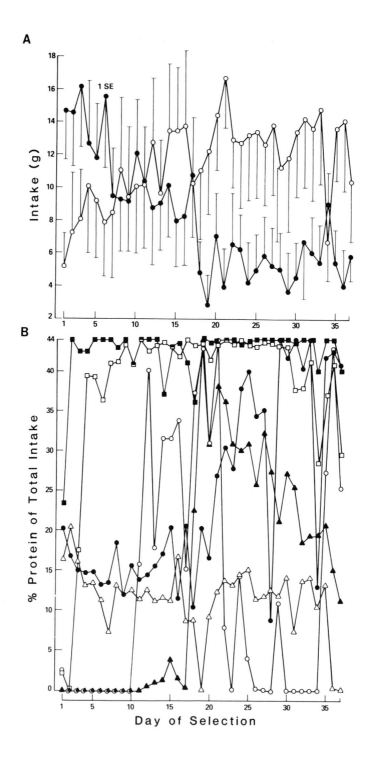

A

B

Day of Selection

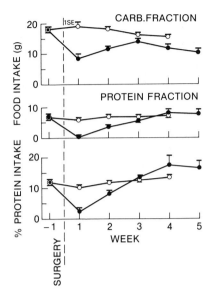

FIG. 44.   Effects of trigeminal deafferentation on previously acquired dietary self-selection behavior. Deafferentation group (●), $N = 12$. Surgical control group (○), $N = 11$. (From Miller, 1984.)

to fluctuate at or slightly above preoperative levels thereafter. In contrast, intake of the carbohydrate diet remained reduced throughout the 7-week period of postoperative observation.

The precise nature of these effects is more readily apparent in the data of individual animals, since trigeminal deafferentation is typically followed by an increase in the individual variability of self-selection behavior. Preoperatively, dietary self-selection behavior was both consistent and effective (as judged by the rate of growth), and control surgery produced only a minor and transient disruption (Fig. 45).

All the deafferented subjects showed the initial reduction in the level of protein intake, but thereafter they adopted idiosyncratic intake strategies that, although they remained fairly consistent, showed greater day-to-day variation and were quite ineffective in maintaining the rate of growth. One such strategy involved equal intakes from the two diets (Fig. 46); another

---

FIG. 43.   Effects of trigeminal orosensory deafferentation on the acquisition of dietary self-selection. (A) Daily intake from the high-protein (○) and protein-free carbohydrate (●) diets. (B) Selection behavior of individual animals as reflected in the resulting ratio of protein/total intake ($N = 6$). (From Miller and Teates, 1985.)

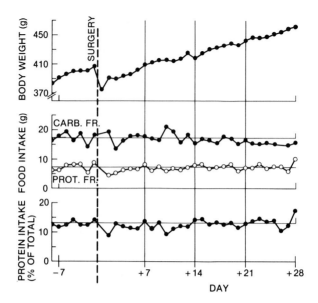

FIG. 45.   Effects of control surgery on dietary self-selection in an individual rat. (From Miller, 1984.)

involved extreme preferences for either the protein or the carbohydrate diet (Fig. 47).

Despite the severity of these disruptions, the rats were clearly not insensitive to their nutritional requirements. With few exceptions, they recovered (and even exceeded) preoperative intake levels of protein (the nutrient that is not metabolically interchangeable with carbohydrates or fat). Even subjects that ate primarily from the carbohydrate diet interspersed periods of high protein intake. However, while most of the rats avoided protein deficiency they did so by overeating from the high-protein diet rather than by adjusting the relative proportions of the two diets.

The deafferented rat has not lost the ability to discriminate grossly (qualitatively) between the two diets, that is, to show food selection behavior. Trigeminal orosensory deafferentation appears to have disrupted the ability to make the fine (quantitative) adjustments of intake on a day-to-day basis that are characteristic of normal rats.

C. DEAFFERENTATION EFFECTS ON THE CONTROL OF PROTEIN INTAKE

Long-term observations of deafferented rats indicated that, over a 2- to 3-month period of free feeding, 50% of the animals recovered nearly

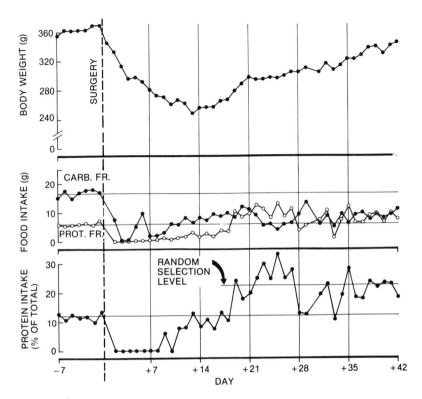

FIG. 46. Equal intake of two selection diets in an individual, deafferented rat. Note that intake of both diets is depressed during the immediate postoperative period and that recovery of body weight is delayed and incomplete. (From Miller, 1984.)

normal protein intake ratios. To assess their ability to adjust dietary self-selection to metabolic requirements, Miller exposed these "recovered" animals to several types of metabolic stress: food deprivation and intragastric (ig) loading of nutrients (protein, carbohydrates). Normal and surgical control subjects typically respond to such metabolic challenges with appropriate compensatory adjustments of intake (Miller and Teates, unpublished data; Picquard et al., 1978; Rozin, 1968; Schutz and Pilgrim, 1954). In deafferented rats such adjustments were lacking, delayed, or incomplete (Miller and Teates, 1984).

In response to 4 days of total food deprivation, for example, surgical controls showed (at refeeding) an immediate and appropriate compensatory increase in food intake that was due entirely to increased intake from the high-protein diet, while intake from the protein-free carbohydrate diet was unchanged (Fig. 48, left). Over the next few days, protein intake

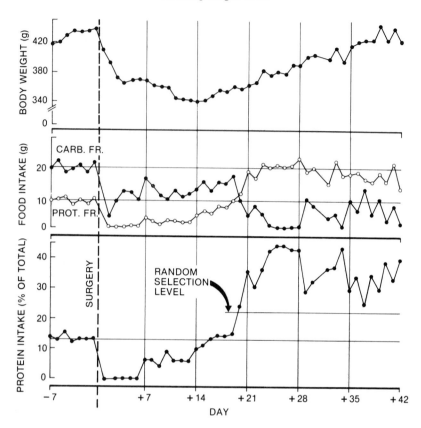

FIG. 47. Extreme preference for protein in an individual, deafferented rat following the initial depression of intake. (M. G. Miller, unpublished data.)

gradually returned to baseline levels as body weight was regained. In contrast, deafferented rats showed no such immediate adjustment of dietary selection, either of caloric or of specific nutrient intake. They required several days to produce an increase in total food intake, and this increase reflected proportionate increases of intake from both diets without a change in the protein intake ratio (Fig. 48, right).

To test for compensatory dietary selection in response to nutrient supplementation, subjects received daily ig loads of protein or carbohydrate suspensions for 10 consecutive days. The surgical control group reduced intake of the protein or carbohydrate diet so as to compensate for the nutritional composition of the supplement (Fig. 49A). "Recovered" deafferented rats (Fig. 49B) compensated only for the caloric value of the ig load by reducing intake from both diets in approximately equal propor-

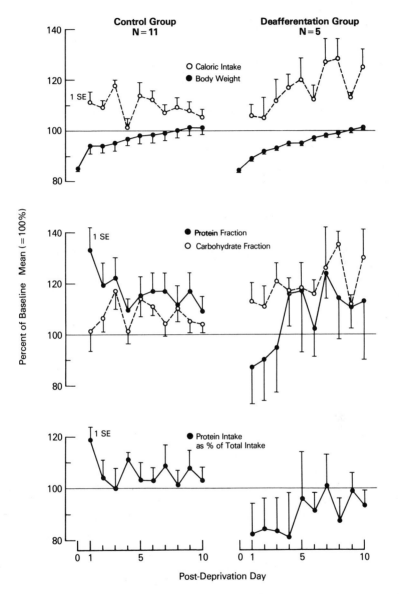

FIG. 48. Caloric intake, self-selection, and body weight during 10 consecutive days of refeeding after a 4-day period of total food deprivation. (From Miller and Teates, 1984.)

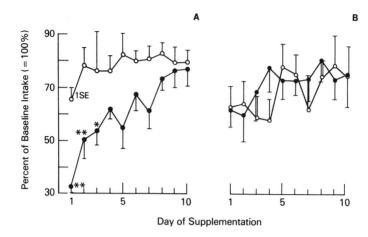

FIG. 49.   Protein (●) and carbohydrate (○) selection during 10 consecutive days of ig protein supplementation in (A) controls, $N = 8$; and (B) deafferented group, $N = 9$. Data points are group means (± 1 SE) expressed as a percentage of the baseline mean (= 100%) from the 5-day period preceding supplementation; *, $p < 0.01$; **, $p < 0.005$. (From Miller and Teates, 1984.)

tions, irrespective of the nutritional composition of the dietary load. Even in the control rats, compensation was not perfect (100%) and was more specific after protein than after carbohydrate intubation. Nevertheless, in comparing the protein intake ratios of control and deafferented subjects (Fig. 50), the differential effect of supplementation in the two groups is obvious. Thus, deafferented rats that have recovered normal protein intake ratios under free-feeding conditions are seen to remain deficient in their regulation of both caloric and protein intake in the face of food deprivation and ig nutrient supplementation.

The fact that deafferented rats can recover normal protein intake ratios under free-feeding conditions but cannot adjust dietary selection to large metabolic changes suggests that other mechanisms come into play in recovery. Recovery in the free-feeding situation could be based on other feeding-related sensory factors, such as taste and smell, which have been found to be effective in establishing preferences for protein (Booth, 1981; Booth and Simpson, 1971). If recovery is based on preference conditioning with the remaining sensory cues simply replacing the trigeminal cues, the rats should also be able to master the selection task under varying metabolic conditions. As there is no indication of compensatory adjustment of protein selection under either deprivation or supplementation, the remaining sensory input available to the deafferented rat is apparently not as effective as trigeminal orosensation. Thus the deficiency of the deaf-

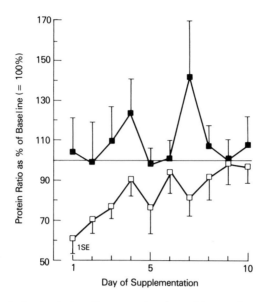

FIG. 50. Protein intake during 10 consecutive days of ig protein supplementation (■, deafferented; □, controls). Data points as in Fig. 49. (M. G. Miller, unpublished data.)

ferented subjects seems to relate specifically to the ability to adjust selection to fluctuations in metabolic conditions.

To account for her findings, Miller suggests that protein intake in the recovered trigeminal rat could be more under the control of postingestional factors (e.g., stomach extension, postabsorptional factors) that by their very nature can only act with delay after ingestion. Postingestional factors would not afford fine tuning of selection behavior comparable to that possible with orosensory inputs that are linked closely to feeding behavior.

This hypothesis is consistent with the major experimental findings. After deprivation, the deafferented rat responds with delay and only to the larger caloric insult, not the smaller protein depletion. Similarly, caloric adjustment after dietary supplementation occurs only after several days, and no nutritional composition is observed that would require a more finely tuned response. In contrast, all compensatory nutrient selection of control rats is a fast response, being most pronounced on the first day of refeeding or supplementary feeding. Protein compensation in the controls has essentially waned at the time when caloric compensation appears in the deafferented rats (about 4 to 5 days later). Again, the major defect appears to concern the immediate adjustment of intake selection to metabolic fluctuations.

The time course of the response by the deafferented rat is certainly congruent with the action of postabsorptional factors, which by their nature can act only after a considerable postingestive delay. By contrast, trigeminal orosensory inputs occur in close temporal association with food intake and provide a potential source of signals that could mediate the relatively rapid and fine adjustment of selection patterns to metabolic fluctuations. The implications of these observations for mechanisms of incentive and reinforcement are discussed at length in Section XIV.

XI. Trigeminal Denervation and Operant Behavior

We may conceive of hunger and thirst as being mediated by physiological mechanisms that control a hierarchy of response systems from reflexes to motivated behavior. It has been suggested (Teitelbaum, 1966, 1967) that the position of a specific behavior along this conceptual continuum is determined by the "fixity" of the link between stimulus and response. Thus, the elementary ingestive reflexes are assumed to lie at the base of the hierarchy, while at its apex are found an almost infinite variety of instrumental behaviors associatively linked to food and water.

In our earliest studies of the "trigeminal syndrome" we focused primarily on measures at the "respondent" end of this conceptual continuum: reflexes, movement patterns, and consummatory sequences. In the present section we review studies of deafferentation effects on "operant" measures of hunger and thirst.

A. EFFECTS OF DENERVATION ON AN INSTRUMENTAL INGESTIVE RESPONSE

As a starting point for such studies we developed an instrumental response paradigm that may be viewed as lying midway between eating and lever pressing on the conceptual continuum from respondent to operant responses. This paradigm was suggested by the fact that deafferented subjects frequently develop "scooping" as an alternative mode of ingesting mash in the home cage. Subjects were therefore trained, preoperatively, to obtain their total daily food intake by extending one paw into a food magazine attached to the front of the home cage (Fig. 51) and scooping up the mash. Ingestion was accomplished either by licking mash from the paw or inserting the paw into the mouth. Scooping was monitored by a drinkometer circuit in the food magazine. Because it involves paw reaching reinforced by food, this paradigm may reflect the operation of both respondent and operant processes.

FIG. 51. Feedometer used to measure "scooping" behavior patterns. The device made oral access to the mash impossible; thus, paw extension, grasping, and paw retraction were required for food intake.

Figure 52 contrasts the performance of trigeminal orosensory and oromotor (hypoglossal) subjects on this paw-reaching task. Preoperatively, both subjects show a daily pattern of scooping bouts that approximates the feeding patterns of normal rats. Their postoperative behavior is markedly different. The hypoglossal subject is unable to ingest food (the intake data largely reflect its excessive spillage) and loses weight over the next 2 weeks. It responds to this weight loss by dramatically increasing the duration of its scooping bouts, until, by the end of the second week, it is spending most of its time trying to eat. The orosensory subject, in contrast, reduces both the frequency and duration of its scooping bouts in the immediate postoperative period, even though it too is losing weight. There was no sign of an "extinction" process. Instead, as weight loss continued, there was a (compensatory?) increase in the duration of scooping bouts sufficient to restore body weight to about 85% of its free-feeding value. However, instead of continuing to generate the slight increases in bout duration required to move toward preoperative weight levels, the orosensory subject decreased scooping to a level that produced a reduction in body weight. Thus, even when allowed unlimited access to a palatable food by a paradigm not directly involving oral responses, orosensory subjects showed the same reduced level of responsiveness, intake, and weight regulation as was reflected in their consummatory behavior (See Section IX).

We next carried out a series of three experiments employing operant (lever-pressing) behavior to assess the integrity of the rat's hunger and

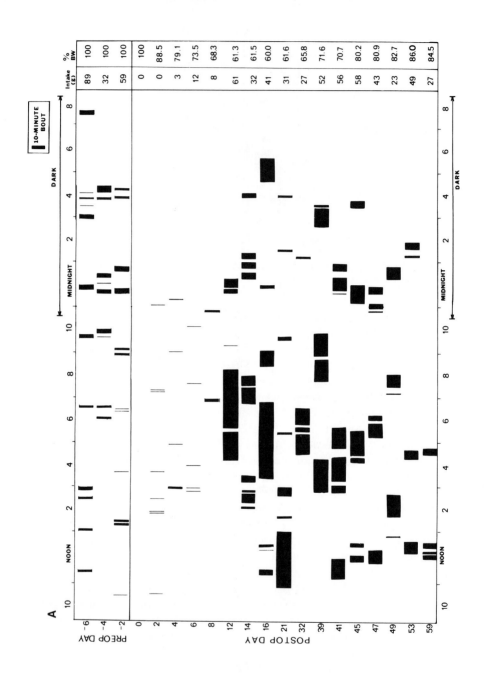

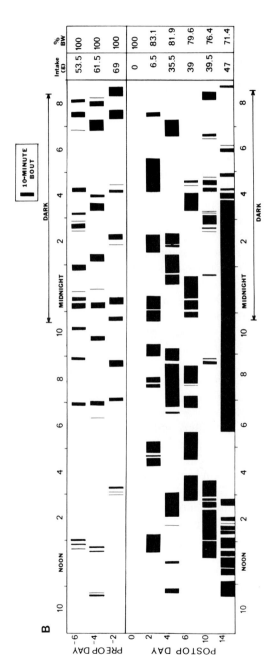

Fig. 52. Feeding behavior patterns ("scooping") following orosensory (trigeminal) and oromotor (hypoglossal) denervation. (A) Effects of complete orosensory deafferentation. (B) Effects of section of the ascending ramus of the hypoglossal nerve. Although the procedure produces a profound oromotor impairment, responsiveness to food is maintained. Compare with the pattern shown by the deafferented rat (A). (From Jacquin and Zeigler, 1982.)

thirst systems after trigeminal denervation. In the first two experiments, water and food, respectively, were used as reinforcers. In the third, we used electrical stimulation of the brain to provide comparative data from a reinforcement system that does not involve the ingestion of food and water. In all three experiments we compared the effects of trigeminal orosensory denervation with those produced by interruption of efferents to oromotor structures (Jacquin *et al.*, 1982a; Jacquin and Zeigler, 1984).

Both the food- and water-reinforced subjects were trained preoperatively on a variable-interval (1-min) schedule, and training was carried out in daily 30-min sessions until subjects met a performance criterion. Observations were carried out in a standard operant chamber that had been modified to permit monitoring of lever presses, reinforcements, entrances into the magazine, and contacts with the reinforcement dipper. Reinforcement (mash, water) was delivered for 5 sec, and the total amount of food or water ingested was noted after each session. After meeting the performance criterion, subjects underwent one of a number of types of bilateral deafferentations or motor nerve sections. Sham control surgery involved bilateral exposure of the entire operative area. Preoperatively, subjects were maintained on deprivation schedules that maintained them at between 80 and 85% of their free-feeding weights. To minimize the confounding effects of postoperative variations in home cage intake, subjects in the water-reinforced group were totally water deprived throughout the 7-day postoperative test period (except for water obtained in the test chamber), while food-reinforced subjects were offered mash in amounts calculated to maintain them at 85% of their free-feeding weights.

Denervated subjects were active and alert and showed no obvious impairments of posture or locomotion. However, they exhibited the characteristic oromotor deficits described in Section VI. In the deafferented subjects, there was an obvious reduction in the probability of jaw opening and tongue protrusion to perioral contact with a food or water source. Subjects with section of the trigeminal motor root had their mandible fixed in its resting position, while the hypoglossal animals could not move the tongue. *Food or water intake in the test situation was reduced or completely abolished in most subjects*, a fact that complicated interpretation of the results (but see Section XI,E).

In addition to these sensorimotor deficits, experimental subjects showed a profound decrease in responsiveness in the test situation. They were frequently found asleep in the chamber at the end of a test session, despite the fact they were on a total water deprivation schedule (experiment B) or were being tested at between 65 and 85% of their free-feeding weights (experiment C).

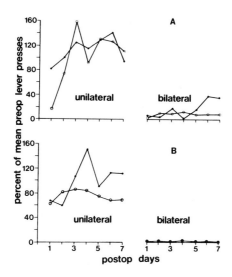

FIG. 53. Effects of unilateral and then bilateral "complete" V orosensory deafferentation (A) or V motor root section (B) on water-reinforced lever pressing. Data are presented as a percentage of the mean of the last seven preoperative sessions for two representative rats in each group. (From Jacquin and Zeigler, 1984.)

B. EFFECTS OF DENERVATION ON OPERANT BEHAVIOR REINFORCED WITH WATER

Denervation effects on water-reinforced lever pressing are illustrated in Fig. 53. Unilateral trigeminal denervations produced only a transient reduction in lever pressing. Section of the remaining innervation was followed by severe and persistent reductions evident within the very first postoperative session.

Comparison with the sham controls indicated that the denervation procedure also produced significant reductions in lever pressing, magazine approaches, and dipper contacts. These effects were greatest in the trigeminal sensory and motor groups but were evident in the hypoglossal subjects as well.

To assess the nature of these deficits in more detail, we compared the behavior of representative individual subjects during preoperative and postoperative sessions (Fig. 54). The cumulative records provide data primarily on response rate and its intrasession distribution. The event recorder data illustrate the temporal relations among various elements of the behavioral sequence: lever pressing, reinforcement, magazine approach, and dipper contact (licking).

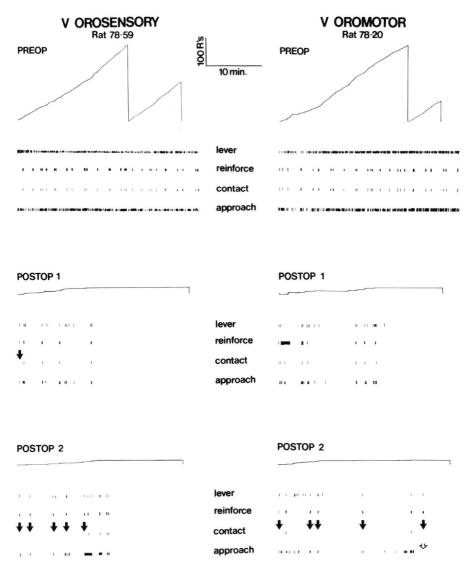

FIG. 54. Cumulative and event records illustrating water-reinforced lever-pressing rate and operant sequencing, respectively, for the last preoperative and first two postoperative sessions in a respresentative rat from each treatment group. A typical operant sequence consists of a lever press, reinforcement, magazine approach, and dipper contact. Note the occasionally aborted sequence where delivery of reinforcement is not followied by dipper contact (solid arrows) or where reinforcement is not followed by magazine approach (open arrow). (From Jacquin and Zeigler, 1984.)

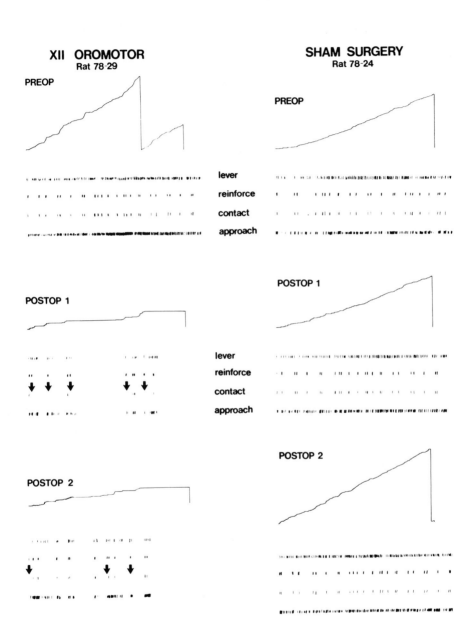

XII OROMOTOR
Rat 78-29

PREOP

lever
reinforce
contact
approach

POSTOP 1

lever
reinforce
contact
approach

POSTOP 2

SHAM SURGERY
Rat 78-24

PREOP

POSTOP 1

POSTOP 2

The cumulative record of the sham-operated control shows a slight increase in rate at the start of the first postoperative session, with a return to preoperative levels by its end. The denervated subjects never approached their preoperative rates and showed extremely low levels of lever pressing even during the first few minutes of the first postoperative session. Moreover, there was a marked decrease in the probability of approaches to the water magazine even after a reinforcement was delivered (arrows in Fig. 54). This effect is evident even when the decrease in reinforcements delivered is taken into account. Preoperatively, the subjects whose data are shown in Fig. 54 exhibited a ratio of magazine approaches to reinforcement of 22, 24, and 20, respectively. In the first postoperative session, the corresponding ratios were 4.8, 7.4, and 3.3. There were frequent instances of magazine approaches without dipper contact subsequent to delivery of reinforcement. These observations, together with the reduced lever pressing of the experimental subjects, suggests that the denervation procedures produced a genuine reduction in "thirst."

C. Effects on Food-Reinforced Operant Behavior

The data of the water-reinforced subjects suggested that the reduction in operant behavior seen after trigeminal denervation reflects a motivational deficit. However, as noted with respect to intake deficits (Section VI), two alternative possibilities must be considered. First, in view of their consummatory deficits, the reduced lever pressing of the denervated animals could be an indirect consequence of the increased effort required to obtain reinforcement. Alternatively, given the abolition of water intake in these animals, the reduction in operant behavior may simply reflect its extinction. We attempted to assess these possibilities in a second experiment by including "effort" and "extinction" control groups. For the extinction controls the food magazine was empty during testing but mash was placed behind the front panel to provide normal olfactory stimuli. For the effort controls, the dipper was adjusted so that its surface remained sufficiently below the aperture of the food magazine that very little mash could be obtained even with considerable effort. Both control groups sustained a sham operative procedure before retesting. In addition to the lever-pressing subjects, two rats were trained to obtain food in the test chamber by reaching a paw through the hole in the food magazine and bringing mash up to the mouth.

Figure 55 compares the effects on food-reinforced lever pressing of unilateral and bilateral trigeminal denervations. After unilateral denervation, subjects continued to emit substantial numbers of responses. As in

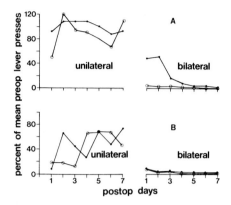

Fɪɢ. 55. Effects of unilateral and then bilateral "complete" V orosensory deafferentation (A) or V motor root section (B) on food-reinforced lever pressing. Conventions as in Fig. 53. (From Jacquin and Zeigler, 1984.)

the water-reinforced subjects, extending the denervation to the contralateral side produced a severe and persistent reduction in the responses of both trigeminal and orosensory and oromotor groups.

Figure 56 summarizes data on all four of the measures recorded in the test situation over the 7-day postoperative period. The trigeminal orosensory group is subdivided into "ingestion" versus "noningestion" subgroups, since three subjects showed significant food intake in the test situation. No intake was seen in the hypoglossal and trigeminal oromotor groups. Examination of these data suggests that the presence or absence of significant ingestion in the test situation does not predict the magnitude of the deficit in operant behavior produced by denervation.

This conclusion is borne out by several observations. First, there was no significant difference between the level of postoperative lever pressing in the ingestion and noningestion groups. Second, the ingestion group made significantly ($p < 0.05$) fewer responses than the effort control group, even though there was no difference in their intake in the test situation. Third, the trigeminal oromotor group made significantly ($p < 0.05$) fewer lever-pressing responses than the hypoglossal group, although *neither* group was ingesting food.

All trigeminally denervated subjects made significantly fewer lever presses than the effort controls, while three of the four orosensory (noningestion) and all of the trigeminal oromotor subjects performed below the extinction controls. Most important, examination of the detailed individual records demonstrates marked differences in the behavior of the extinction controls and of the experimental subjects (Fig. 57).

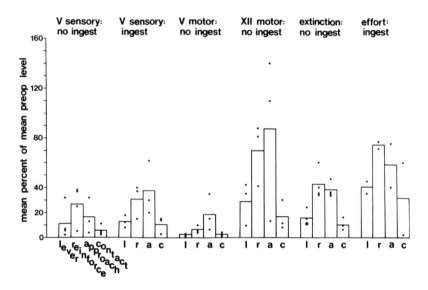

FIG. 56. Denervation effects on lever pressing, reinforcement, approach, and contact in subjects of the various treatment groups. The V orosensory subjects were divided (post hoc) into food-ingesting and noningesting groups. (From Jacquin and Zeigler, 1984.)

In the very first postoperative session the extinction control animal began pressing at a rate close to its preoperative level and then showed a typical extinction curve. Some spontaneous recovery was evident at the start of the second session, but there were no responses in the latter half of that session. In contrast, the trigeminal (orosensory, oromotor) subjects showed extremely low response rates in the first postoperative session and no signs of spontaneous recovery subsequently. The hypoglossal subject, although showing a decreased response rate, continued to emit a substantial number of responses throughout both sessions. A reduced responsiveness to reinforcement is also evident in the two trigeminal groups, as is apparent in the ratio of magazine approaches to reinforcements. While there was little change in the extinction control subject (9.1 versus 8.4) and an increase in the hypoglossal subject (6.5 versus 10.8), both trigeminal subjects showed significant decreases from their preoperative ratios (V sensory, 9.1 versus 4.2; V motor, 6.4 versus 2.5). As in the water-reinforced subjects, there were multiple instances of disrupted sequences (e.g., lever pressing without magazine approaches, magazine approaches without dipper contacts: arrows in Fig. 57).

In several subjects, testing was continued for periods of a month or more postoperatively, and the data for one such animal are presented in Fig. 58 to illustrate the relations among lever presses, magazine approaches, food intake, and body weight. Following bilateral trigeminal orosensory deafferentation, lever pressing and magazine approaches dropped to about 30 and 50% of their respective properative values for several sessions and then dropped still further, remaining, for the most part, at or close to zero levels for almost a month. Then there was an abrupt and dramatic increase in both instrumental behaviors and intake, and over the next 10 days all three measures approached preoperative levels. This sudden, coupled return of lever pressing and intake was typical of subjects tested over extended periods. However, the effect was transient and lever pressing was rarely maintained at preoperative levels for prolonged periods.

Figure 59 illustrates the effects of trigeminal orosensory and oromotor denervations on "scooping" behavior reinforced with food. In both cases bilateral denervation immediately reduced the number of scooping responses almost to zero levels, an effect that persisted until sacrifice in the trigeminal motor animal (Fig. 59B), and for almost 6 weeks in the orosensory subject (Fig. 59A). Throughout this period the orosensory subject ingested little or no food in the test chamber and was quite inactive, often falling asleep within 5 to 15 min of the start of the test session. Both food intake and scooping behavior resumed abruptly on day 33 and remained at preoperative levels until the subject was sacrificed a week later.

D. TRIGEMINAL DENERVATION AND INTRACRANIAL SELF-STIMULATION

In the final experiment of this series we examined the effects of denervation on operant, lever-pressing responses whose acquisition and maintenance were mediated by a reinforcement system (brain stimulation) that does not involve ingestion.

In addition to its methodological significance, this experiment was also of theoretical interest. Accounts of intracranial self-stimulation (ICSS) and stimulus-bound feeding have often assumed an identity or at least a considerable degree of overlap in central neural processes mediating these phenomena and those underlying hunger and thirst (Hoebel, 1975; Hoebel and Teitelbaum, 1962; Margules and Olds, 1962). Moreover, it has frequently been hypothesized that ICSS involves the selective facilitation of sensorimotor mechanisms controlling species-typical response patterns such as biting, chewing, and licking (Glickman and Schiff, 1967; Van der Kooy and Phillips, 1977). If hunger, thirst, and self-stimulation do indeed

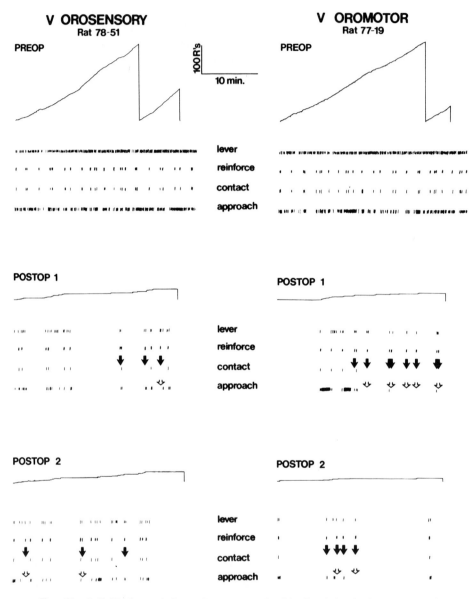

Fig. 57. Individual cumulative and event records of feeding behavior by representative individual subjects in various treatment groups. Conventions as in Fig. 54. (From Jacquin and Zeigler, 1984.)

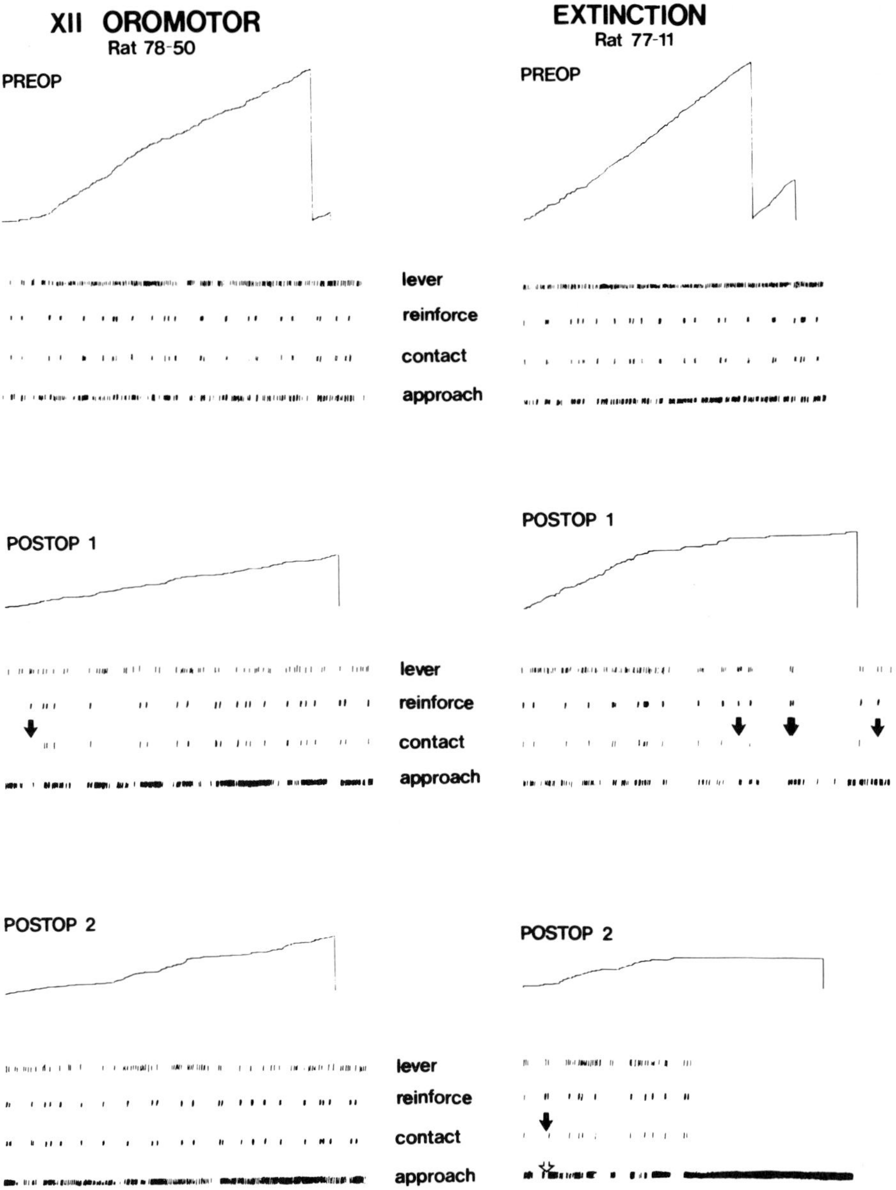

XII OROMOTOR
Rat 78-50

PREOP

lever

reinforce

contact

approach

POSTOP 1

lever

reinforce

contact

approach

POSTOP 2

lever

reinforce

contact

approach

EXTINCTION
Rat 77-11

PREOP

lever

reinforce

contact

approach

POSTOP 1

lever

reinforce

contact

approach

POSTOP 2

lever

reinforce

contact

approach

161

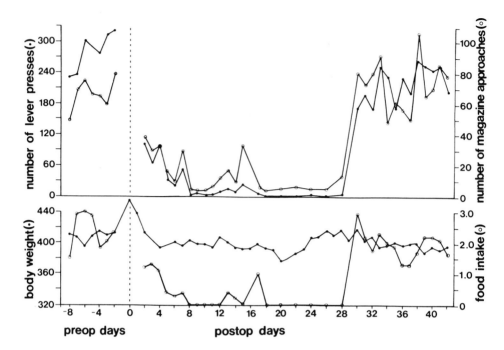

FIG. 58.   Long-term effects of bilateral V orosensory deafferentation, sparing the lingual nerve, on daily lever pressing, magazine approach, food intake, and body weight. (From Jacquin and Zeigler, 1984.)

share the same underlying neural mechanisms, trigeminal denervation should disrupt ICSS in much the same way that it disrupts behaviors reinforced by food or water.

Surprisingly, this was not the case. Trigeminal denervation (sensory or motor) was followed by significant *increases* in lever pressing reinforced by electrical stimulation of the brain (ESB). As Fig. 60 indicates, the increase in response rates was evident within the very first session and was seen in both unilaterally and bilaterally denervated subjects. The finding is even more striking because it occured in subjects showing the reduced intake typical of denervated rats and often requiring supplementary intubation to maintain body weight and prevent inanition. In Fig. 60 body weight is plotted on the same graph as ICSS to show that there is no obvious relation between response rates and weight changes. In both of the two-stage preparations illustrated, unilateral denervation had little effect on body weight, yet it was nevertheless followed by an increase in ICSS. The addition of a second stage produced a significant reduction in weight but no significant increase in ICSS.

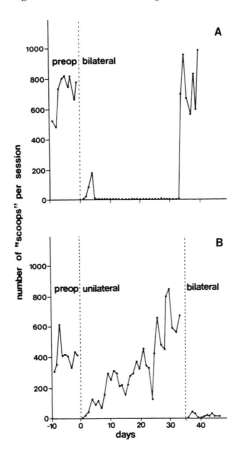

FIG. 59. Effects of (A) V orosensory or (B) V motor root section on food reinforced paw-reaching "scooping" through an aperture in the food magazine. (From Jacquin and Zeigler, 1984.)

It is important to note that many of the electrodes in this study supported both self-stimulation and stimulus-bound feeding. In this respect they are comparable to the brain regions from which the original observations on the relation between hunger and ICSS were made. Our findings are not readily reconciled with theoretical accounts of ICSS that view the phenomenon as involving the same neural circuits as do hunger and thirst or as reflecting the selective facilitation of species-typical consummatory responses. However, within the present context, the most important conclusion to be drawn from these findings is that the deficits in operant behaviors seen after trigeminal denervation are specific to behaviors acquired and maintained by food or water reinforcers.

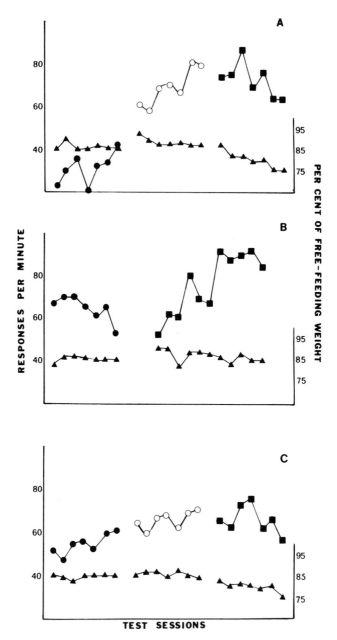

FIG. 60. Relation between intracranial self-stimulation (●, preoperative; ○, unilateral; ■, bilateral) and body weight (▲) in three denervated rats. In each case the data are for one of the pairs of bilaterally implanted electrodes. Rats (B) and (C) were deafferented, while (A) sustained V motor root section. Rat (B) underwent bilateral denervation in a single stage. (From Jacquin *et al.*, 1982a.)

E. Conclusions—Denervation Effects on Operant Behaviors: Sensorimotor or Motivational Deficits

The experiments reported in this section were designed to test the hypothesis that trigeminal denervation disrupts motivational systems mediating hunger and thirst in the rat. We therefore examined denervation effects on the performance of a food- or water-reinforced operant response sequence to assess the integrity of these systems. Our results demonstrate unambiguously that, for both types of reinforcement, interruption of trigeminal inputs from and efferents to the oral region severely disrupts performance of an operant task (lever pressing) *whose execution does not require a trigeminally mediated response.*

These results raise the same interpretative problems we dealt with earlier in considering deafferentation effects on intake. Are the deficits secondary to the sensorimotor disruptions produced by deafferentation (e.g., reduced intake, increased effort, surgical debilitation), or do they reflect a motivational deficit that is, a reduction in hunger or thirst?

While the data of the sham-operated and "effort" controls militates against an explanation in terms of debilitation or increased effort, interpretation of these results is complicated by the fact that the denervation procedure also impaired eating and drinking behaviors and reduced or abolished the intake of reinforcers in the test situation. It might be argued, therefore, that the reduced lever-pressing performance of the denervated rats was simply an *extinction* process. However, several lines of evidence are inconsistent with such an interpretation.

1. Examination of individual cumulative records during the first few postoperative sessions shows that the disruption of operant responding is abrupt. Subjects make very few responses at the very start of the first session.

2. When compared with extinction controls, experimental subjects do not show either the characteristic pattern of intrasession response decay or spontaneous recovery.

3. Their general performance suggests a lack of responsiveness to the reinforcer, since they often fail to approach the magazine after generating a reinforcement.

4. An equally significant reduction in lever pressing was seen in both ingesting and noningesting trigeminal orosensory subjects.

We therefore conclude that the reduced lever pressing of the denervated subjects cannot be accounted for solely by extinction.

Moreover, the fact that denervation does not reduce lever pressing

reinforced by brain stimulation suggests that trigeminal orosensory deafferentation does disrupt motivational processes (i.e., hunger and thirst).

This conclusion is supported by observations of the general behavior of
the denervated subjects. They seem indifferent to the reinforcements they
did generate and usually failed to respond to reinforcements delivered by
the experimenter. Because of this lack of responsiveness, retraining was
never successful. When lever pressing reappeared spontaneously after an
extended period of continued testing, it tended to parallel the return of
responsiveness to food. Such lever pressing as did occur in some subjects
tended to be unstable, even though they were often observed to ingest
substantial amounts of the reinforcer. Comparable disruptions were seen
in the performance of a scooping response that involved a topography
similar to that used in eating. Both orosensory and oromotor animals
showed an immediate and profound reduction in *scooping* after denervation, even though capable of ingesting reinforcers. Perhaps the most striking consequence of denervation was its effect on the general behavior of
subjects in the test situation. Denervated subjects are best described as
"indifferent" to the lever. They often made a few desultory presses and
then settled down to bouts of grooming, exploration, resting, or sleeping
in a manner reminiscent of satiated animals. These observations are consistent with our studies of activity patterns in denervated animals (Section
VIII).

Thus, the experiments described in this section strongly support the
general hypothesis that trigeminal denervation, in addition to its effects
on the *sensorimotor* control of ingestive behavior, also disrupts motivational mechanisms mediating hunger and thirst in the rat. More specifically, trigeminal denervation appears to reduce the *incentive* value of food
and water as reinforcers of instrumental behavior.

One additional aspect of these findings deserves brief comment. The
disruptive effects of trigeminal *orosensory* denervation is not surprising,
since it is congruent with our previous finding that deafferented subjects
show reduced responsiveness to water in the home cage (Jacquin and
Zeigler, 1983). However, the disruptive effects of *oromotor* denervation
were unexpected. Previous studies of home cage behavior in subjects
with section of the trigeminal motor root or hypoglossal nerve (Section
VIII) indicated that, while unable to ingest food or water, they were
highly responsive to the food or water source in the immediate postoperative period (Jacquin and Zeigler, 1983; Jacquin and Enfiejian, 1982).

The fact that oromotor denervations disrupt operant but not consummatory responses to water suggests that the acquisition and maintenance
of food- or water-reinforced operants involves causal mechanisms that

must differ in some critical respect from those mediating consummatory responses to a food or water source. A hypothesis with respect to the nature of these mechanisms, their vulnerability to both orosensory and oromotor denervations, and their relation to the incentive properties of food and water will be presented in Section XIV.

XII. A Note on Recovery of Function

If property maintained during the initial postoperative period, even extensively deafferented rats show a considerable recovery of ingestive behavior, intake, and body weight. As Goldberger (1980) has pointed out, the recovery of behavioral function after damage to neural pathways may reflect one or more of the following processes: (1) substitution of a new behavior with the same function, (2) regeneration of the neural system originally mediating the behavior, and (3) mediation of the original behavior by a neural system not originally involved in its control. While we have not explored the recovery problem very extensively, such data as are available suggest that all three of these processes may be involved in the recovery seen after trigeminal orosensory deafferentation.

A. Behavioral Substitution

A role for a behavioral substitution process is suggested by the development of a variety of idiosyncratic, alternative strategies for eating and drinking (e.g., ''scooping,'' ''shoveling,'' postural adjustments to the sipper tube), which are described in Section VI.

B. Neural Regeneration

The regeneration of peripheral nerves after damage is a well-established phenomenon (e.g., Jewett and McCarroll, 1980). Anatomical (Fried, 1982) and physiological (Robinson, 1981; Waite and Cragg, 1982) studies have described the structural and functional changes that occur during regeneration in the mammalian trigeminal nerve. To examine the possible contribution of regeneration, we resectioned trigeminal orosensory nerves in trigeminal subjects who had recovered normal levels of intake and body weight. The resectioning procedure produced a significant reduction in intake and body weight (Jacquin and Zeigler, 1983, Fig. 18), as well as a reinstatement of the entire syndrome of sensorimotor-reflex deficits. These findings suggest that the resectioned nerves must have been contributing significantly to the recovered ingestive behavior of these animals.

C. Mediation by a Different Neural System

It is now well established that section of cutaneous nerves, in addition to removing input from peripheral regions, produces complex changes in the activity of neurons at several levels of the somatosensory system, from brain stem to cortex, including reorganization of the somatotopic projections (e.g., Devor and Wall, 1978; Durham and Woolsey, 1978; Merzenich *et al.*, 1983; Rhodes *et al.*, 1983). Much of the research from which this generalization derives is based on studies of neural reorganization within the trigeminal (vibrissal) system of rodents.

These studies have shown that, following disruption of the afferent nerve supply to the vibrissae by infraorbital nerve section, the regions normally supplied by these (maxillary) afferents are occupied by processes responsive to inputs from other divisions of the trigeminal system (e.g., mandibular). It is thus possible that the recovery of ingestive behavior seen after deafferentation (sparing the infraorbital nerve) is mediated by a complementary process of reorganization involving changes in the central distribution of infraorbital fibers.

To test this hypothesis, we studied the effects of sectioning either infraorbital or gustatory nerves in "recovered" trigeminal subjects, comparing these preparations with normal rats that had received either infraorbital (Fig. 61A) or gustatory sections alone (Fig. 61B). The effects (on intake and body weight) of bilateral section of gustatory nerves in recovered trigeminal subjects did not differ from that seen in normal rats sustaining only gustatory deafferentation (Fig. 61B). However, adding bilateral infraorbital nerve sections to recovered trigeminals produced effects markedly greater than those seen after bilateral infraorbital sections in previously normal rats (Fig. 61A).

These data suggest that some aspects of recovery in the trigeminal orosensory subjects are mediated by a contribution from infraorbital afferents spared in the original nerve sections. Stimulation of infraorbital receptive fields has been shown to elicit jaw-opening reflexes in the rat (Zeigler *et al.*, 1984). Whether the infraorbital contribution to recovery reflects the use of such preexisting connections between infraorbital fields and jaw motoneurons or the innervation of mandibular regions by infraorbital fibers is not known. However, the present data suggest that the rat's orosensorimotor system would be a very useful model for the study of CNS recovery processes.

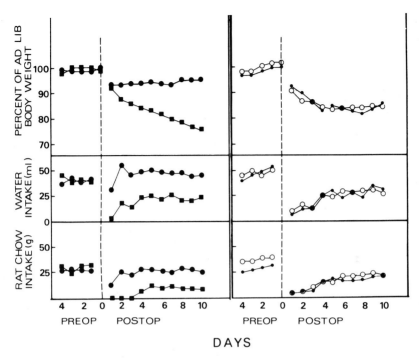

Fɪɢ. 61. (A) Effects on intake and body weight of adding a bilateral section of the infraorbital nerve in "recovered" trigeminal orosensory animals (■, *N* = 3). The effects of an infraorbital section in normal rats are presented for comparison (●, *N* = 4). (B) Effects on intake and body weight of adding bilateral gustatory sections in "recovered" trigeminal orosensory subjects (●, *N* = 2). The effects of a similar gustatory procedure in three normal rats is also shown (○). (From Jacquin and Zeigler, 1983.)

XIII. Trigeminal Orosensation: Contributions to the Control of Ingestive Behavior

Interruption of trigeminal orosensory inputs by deafferentation produces an array of morphological and behavioral effects related to the condition of the mouth, the sequential organization and temporal patterning of consumatory behavior, the quantitative control of intake and dietary self-selection, the regulation of body weight, and the maintenence of food- or water-reinforced operant behavior. An analysis of each of these effects has enabled us to infer the nature of the processes disrupted by deafferentation and has helped clarify the contribution of trigeminal orosensation to each of these processes.

A. Condition of the Mouth

In normal rats, the incisors grow continually but are kept at a constant length by the gnawing and grinding behavior (bruxism) characteristic of this species. The effectiveness of this control also depends on the precision with which the upper and lower incisors are maintained in apposition. The removal of trigeminal orosensory input reduces both the frequency of bruxism and, presumably, the accuracy of apposition. Malocclusions are common and are partially responsible for the incisor overgrowth as well as for the palate, tongue, and lip abrasions of the trigeminal animal. The more extensive tongue damage (e.g., biting of the tip) is probably the result of the removal of input from the tongue and has been reported to occur after nerve sections restricted to the lingual branch of the trigeminal nerve (Mendelson and Zec, 1972). In the absence of such inputs, the normal coordination of tongue location and biting movements is disrupted. Insofar as it contributes to the structural integrity of the oral apparatus, trigeminal orosensation may be said to have a *trophic* function.

B. Organization of the Consumatory Response Sequence

The deafferented rat is capable of biting, licking, and swallowing in response to *intraoral* tactile and gustatory stimuli. Biting can also be elicited by *extraoral* stimuli. However, trigeminal orosensory deafferentation decreases the probability with which such responses can be elicited by the *perioral* stimuli that normally evoke them. Tactile stimulation of the perioral region, whether with food, a cotton swab, or a drinking tube, while it does not elicit aversive reactions, evokes few attempts to bite or lick. Such bites as are emitted are often disoriented and lacking in vigor. Thus, trigeminal deafferentation, while it spares the elementary movement patterns comprising consumatory behavior, appears to have disrupted sensorimotor mechanisms controlling jaw opening and tongue protraction.

C. Responsiveness to Food and Water

Orosensory inputs have been shown to elicit, maintain, reinforce, and terminate consumatory behavior in the rat. While the orosensory inputs involved are likely to be mediated by both the gustatory and trigeminal systems, our studies represent the first attempts to identify the extent of the motivational contribution of trigeminal orosensation.

These studies demonstrate that trigeminal orosensory deafferentation

produces significant and persistent reductions in responsiveness to food
and water. During the immediate postoperative period, the rat emits relatively few eating or drinking bouts, and such bouts as are initiated tend
not to be sustained. Analysis of feeding patterns indicates a reduction in
the level of feeding activity, and reduced intake is found even with a
response measure requiring paw extension rather than mouth opening to
initiate the ingestive sequence. Moreover, trigeminal orosensory deafferentation abolishes or significantly reduces performance of a food- or water-reinforced lever-pressing response as well as approaches to the food
magazine. Thus, the abolition or reduction of trigeminal orosensory inputs, even with olfaction and taste left intact, decreases the frequency
with which ingestive behavior is initiated and the persistence with which
it is maintained. Chemosensory inputs alone are insufficient to maintain
operant or consumatory behavior at normal levels, even with highly
palatable diets. The diversity of response measures from which these
observations were drawn strengthens the conclusion that trigeminal orosensation makes a critical contribution to the motivational, as well as to
the sensorimotor control of intake in the rat.

D. QUANTITATIVE CONTROL OF FOOD INTAKE: DIETARY SELF-SELECTION

The disruption in ingestive behavior seen after trigeminal orosensory
deafferentation also involves interference with the long-term mechanisms
of quantitative intake control. Miller's studies of dietary self-selection
have shown that the deafferented rat is deficient in the regulation of both
caloric and protein intake. The deficit is evident in an inability to acquire
self-selection behavior patterns that will maintain normal protein: total
intake ratios, to retain such patterns once acquired, or to defend them
against metabolic challenges (depletion, supplementation). While the rat
remains sensitive to its nutritional state and can distinguish between different diets, its self-selection behavior is highly variable and idiosyncratic, and may fluctuate over a large range of protein: total intake ratios.
Trigeminal orosensation appears to play an essential role in mediating the
rat's ability to adjust its feeding behavior patterns promptly and precisely
to their metabolic consequences.

E. REGULATION OF BODY WEIGHT

In comparison with normal animals, the deafferented rat regulates its
body weight at a significantly lower level for prolonged periods. Similar
effects on weight regulation have been reported after damage to brain

structures implicated in the control of intake (e.g., Keesey, 1973), and the concept of "set point" has often been invoked to account for such effects. Since the set-point mechanism is generally equated with a central neural process, its use to account for the effects of a peripheral manipulation such as deafferentation would be inappropriate. Moreover, as Wirtshafter and Davis (1977) have argued, the set-point concept is superfluous, since many of the same data may be accounted for more parsimoniously in terms of the relation between orosensory factors and their direct effects on food intake. Just as the use of highly palatable foods can, by increasing intake, increase the level at which weight is regulated (Kratz and Levitsky, 1979; Peck, 1978), so the reduction in orosensory input produced by deafferentation should generate a lower level of long-term weight regulation. Such a formulation is certainly compatible with the observation that reduced orosensory input, whether produced by deafferentation or self-infusion procedures, significantly decreases the level of weight regulation in the rat.

F. Trigeminal Deafferentation Effects in Pigeon and Rat

Despite marked differences in orofacial morphology, trigeminal distribution, and consumatory behavior patterns, there are striking similarities in deafferentation effects on ingestive behavior in the pigeon and the rat.

1. Both species exhibit periods of aphagia whose duration is a function of the extent of the deafferentation. (The fact that deafferentation does not disrupt drinking in the pigeon appears to reflect a genuine species difference in the organization of neural mechanisms underlying thirst.)

2. In both species, the magnitude of the feeding behavior deficit varies with the sensory properties of the diet.

3. On deafferentation both the rat and the pigeon regulate their weight at a reduced level, and that level is similar in the two species.

4. In both, the reduction in intake is due primarily to a decrease in the frequency of meal *initiation*.

5. Trigeminal deafferentation disrupts the somatosensory control of the consummatory response in both species, producing deficits in grasping and food transport. Although these impairments reduce the efficiency of feeding, they are neither necessary nor sufficient to account for the long-term reduction of intake.

Thus, in both the pigeon and the rat trigeminal orosensory deafferentation produces a combination of consummatory impairments and reduced responsiveness to food. The similarity of deafferentation effects in two species differing greatly in their peripheral and central organizations suggests a high degree of generality in the contribution of trigeminal orosensation to the neural control of vertebrate ingestive behavior.

G. TRIGEMINAL OROSENSATION AND TASTE: A FUNCTIONAL COMPARISON

The findings reviewed in this article suggest that in focusing so exclusively on the role of gustatory factors, physiological psychologists have seriously underestimated the contribution of trigeminal orosensation to the control of ingestive behavior in the rat. That contribution is threefold: trophic, sensorimotor, and motivational. The trophic role of trigeminal orosensation in the regulation of tooth length has been known for some time (Addison and Appleton, 1887), as has its role in the sensorimotor control of ingestive behavior. However, the extent and diversity of the motivational deficits produced by trigeminal orosensation is both unexpected and remarkable, given the relatively restricted extent of the denervations and the fact that they involve a peripheral sensory structure.

Comparisons of the effect of trigeminal and gustatory deafferentation on food intake indicate that the contribution of trigeminal orosensation to the motivational control of ingestive behavior differs in magnitude from that of taste. Even when diets of equivalent palatability and ease of oral manipulation were used (e.g., mash and pablum), the reduction of trigeminal orosensory input produced significantly greater decreases in food intake and in the level at which weight was regulated than were seen after gustatory deafferentation (see Fig. 16, 17, and 18).

Similarly, while trigeminal deafferentation produced a massive disruption of dietary self-selection behavior (Section X), rats subjected to gustatory deafferentation recover stable self-selection patterns and defend them against metabolic challenges (M. G. Miller, unpublished data).

Differences in the magnitude of the deficits produced by trigeminal and gustatory deafferentation may reflect, to some degree, gross disparities in the extent and projection of the cranial nerve structures devoted to the two modalities in the rat. However, there is at least one specific difference between the two modalities that may have important functional implications for their role in the control of food intake.

Both trigeminal and taste stimuli can provide *qualitative* information about the sensory properties of the diet that makes possible its identification and can serve as conditioning stimuli for acceptance or rejection of specific food items. However, in contrast to taste (or smell), trigeminal orosensation has the unique property that it also is generated as *move-*

ment-produced sensory feedback during feeding activity. It is thus ideally suited to serve as a *quantitative* stimulus correlate of specifc amounts and types of feeding activity directed to particular food items. The implications of this fact for understanding the contribution of trigeminal orosensation are discussed in the next section.

XIV. From Movements to Motives: Implications for the Study of Motivation

A. TRIGEMINAL REFLEXES AND INGESTIVE BEHAVIOR IN THE RAT

It has frequently been suggested that the motivational control of behavior involves the modulation of peripheral sensorimotor (*reflex*) mechanisms by *central motive states* (Lashley, 1938; Flynn *et al.*, 1971; Gallistel, 1980). Within such a conceptual framework, ingestive behavior may be viewed as a series of response sequences, each of which is composed of an array of distinct movement patterns. The integration of these component movement patterns into an ingestive sequence involves both peripheral stimulus–response linkages (reflexes) at transitional junctures and central (motivational) processes that modulate the effectiveness of these linkages (e.g., Hinde, 1972, Chapter 25).

Early support for this hypothesis was provided by the studies of Flynn and colleagues on the neural control of aggressive behavior in the cat (Flynn *et al.*, 1971). Using electrical stimulation of the brain to elicit "aggression," they found that variations in the intensity of central stimulation produced variations in the extent of a perioral "sensorimotor field" that triggered biting reflexes in response to peripheral stimuli. Trigeminal deafferentation of this region was found to abolish the biting response (MacDonnell and Flynn, 1966). Subsequently, these observations were extended to other brain structures and to chemical as well as electrical stimulation (e.g., Block *et al.*, 1980; Goldstein and Siegel, 1981; Huston *et al.*, 1980). Rather similar interactions between central stimulation and perioral inputs have been reported during experiments in which lateral hypothalamus (LH) stimulation was used to elicit stimulus-bound feeding in the rat (Smith, 1972), and trigeminal deafferentation has been found to abolish the jaw-opening response in stimulus-bound feeders (Jacquin *et al.*, 1982; unpublished observations). Moreover, electrical stimulation of the LH region has been shown to produce impressive modulatory effects on jaw-opening reflexes in both the anesthetized and unanesthetized cat (Landgren and Olsson, 1980).

Flynn's work also provided compelling evidence for the utility of analyzing "very fundamental reflexive reaction patterns—some of the basic building blocks of complex behavior" (Schallert, DeRyck and Teitelbaum, 1980). Our studies of deafferentation effects on jaw opening (Section VII) were designed to determine whether such "basic building blocks" are involved in the construction of ingestive behavior patterns in the rat.

The results of these studies may be summarized briefly:

1. Prolonged contact of perioral areas with a food or water source always precedes mouth opening and tongue protrusion.

2. Stimulation (electrical, mechanical) of these perioral areas in anesthetized animals elicits jaw-opening reflexes.

3. Trigeminal deafferentation of these areas abolishes or significantly reduces mouth opening and tongue protrusion during eating and drinking.

Taken as a group these findings support the hypothesis that the sensorimotor deficits of deafferented rats reflect a disruption of the afferent limb of trigeminally mediated oromotor reflexes. They further suggest that *motivational processes operate through trigeminal reflex mechanisms to generate consumatory behavior in hungry and thirsty animals.*

Eating and drinking in the rat consists of sequences of behavioral units elicited by specific classes of stimuli and relatively fixed in their form, with each such response unit providing stimuli that link it to the next response. Stimulus–response chains of this type have been shown to mediate consumatory behavior in both the catfish (Atema, 1971) and the pigeon (Zeigler et al, 1980). In both these species, the orosensory stimuli eliciting and guiding specific components of the ingestive sequence have been identified by behavioral experiments. Removal of these stimuli by deafferentation procedures abolished specific ingestive components (e.g., mouth opening–pickup in the catfish; grasping–mandibulation in the pigeon), leaving other portions of the ingestive sequence intact.

Applying a similar analysis to the ingestive behaviors of the rat, we would conclude that appetitive behaviors are elicited by distal (olfactory, visual) stimuli, with proximal orosensory stimuli (somatosensory, gustatory) triggering consumatory (mouth opening, biting and licking) and incorporative (transport, swallowing) behaviors successively. Responses to *intraoral* (gustatory) stimuli have been extensively analyzed in rats and human infants (Grill and Norgren, 1978; Nowlis, 1977) and interpreted within a reflex framework. Such responses presumably represent the last phase of the ingestive sequence. The present data suggest that the penultimate phase involves reflexes triggered by *perioral* (trigeminal) stimuli.

The fact that deafferentation abolishes the jaw-opening component of eating indicates that trigeminal orosensory input is a *necessary* condition for the response. However, the fact that such input has a low probability of eliciting jaw opening in the nondeprived rat indicates that it is not a *sufficient* condition.

Observations such as these tend to support the view that the motivational control of behavior involves the modulation of reflex responses to peripheral inputs by descending influences from a variety of brain regions (see Section IV; Gallistel, 1980). Such modulatory effects has been shown to play a role in the neural control of locomotion, mastication, and sexual behavior (Grillner, 1982; Lund, 1976; Pfaff, 1980). Our findings suggest that similar mechanisms may mediate the control of eating and drinking in the rat.

B. TRIGEMINAL OROSENSATION, INCENTIVE, AND REINFORCEMENT

The relationship between trigeminal afference and "central motive states" appears to be a reciprocal one. That is, not only do central factors modulate the effectiveness of trigeminal sensorimotor pathways, but trigeminal afference appears to facilitate the responsiveness of motivational systems. In the absence of normal trigeminal orosensory inputs, responsiveness to food and water is profoundly depressed and weight is regulated at a significantly lower level. Perhaps the most convincing demonstration of the "motivational" contribution of trigeminal afference comes from studies of deafferentation effects on operant conditioning (Section XI).

The presence of an "arbitrary" operant response has often been used as the hallmark of "voluntary motivated behavior" (Teitelbaum, 1966), and the use of food- and water-reinforced operants as indices of motivation (e.g., hunger and thirst) remains widespread (but see Teitelbaum, 1977). Thus, the profound disruptions in such behaviors produced by trigeminal denervations (sensory and motor) provides additional support for the conclusion that trigeminal orosensation makes a significant contribution to motivational mechanisms mediating hunger and thirst in the rat.

The utility of this conclusion would be increased if we could specify the nature of the motivational mechanisms involved and explain how denervation of trigeminal orosensory and oromotor structures could disrupt performance of an operant (bar-pressing) response that is not itself trigeminally mediated. Answering these questions requires a satisfactory account of the motivational processes involved in the acquisition and maintenance of instrumental behaviors in normal rats and their relation to the stimulus properties of the reinforcer.

In grappling with this problem, learning theorists have invoked the concepts of *incentive* and *reinforcement* to account, respectively, for the role of stimuli in eliciting behavior and in maintaining it once it has been initiated. Experimental studies of the problem are legion (e.g., Crespi, 1944; Estes, 1948; Zeaman, 1949) and have demonstrated that orosensory stimuli have both eliciting and reinforcing properties. While many of the data come from studies involving taste (e.g, Guttman, 1953), somatosensations (cold, touch) have also been shown to elicit and maintain operant behavior (Hulse and Suter, 1970; Mendelson and Chillag, 1970). What remains problematic is the nature of the process that transforms reinforcers into incentives. How does experience (eating and drinking) that coincides with the termination of a behavior (e.g., lever pressing) come to contribute to the initiation of that behavior?

It has been suggested by a number of theorists (e.g., Hull, 1943; Seward, 1956; Spence, 1956) that incentive motivation arises through the classical conditioning of a goal response (R_g) to stimuli in the reinforcement situation. The operations for producing motivation were assumed to be identical with those producing secondary reinforcement. In order to account for the functioning of incentives in places remote from the original conditioning situation, the concept of stimulus generalization was employed. To the extent that stimuli in "start" situations are similar to those in the reinforcement situation, there is a tendency for the goal reaction (R_g) to be elicited. Since the primary reinforcer is absent, only a fractional component of R_g can occur. It is this *fractional anticipatory goal response* (r_g) and its concomitant sensory feedback that are regarded as having incentive properties. "The essence of the argument has been that certain stimuli, originally neutral with respect to motivational properties, come to have both motivating and reinforcing values by virtue of eliciting fractional components of the total goal reaction" (Osgood, 1953, p. 432).

Unfortunately, there seem to have been few systematic attempts at empirical validation of this hypotheses. In the case of behavior reinforced by food or water, such validation might take two forms. One approach would attempt to identify and monitor specific oromotor responses (e.g., licking, salivation, mouthing, chewing) that could function as putative r_g's in eliciting learned instrumental behaviors. A second technique would involve experimental manipulations designed to eliminate putative r_g's, either by preventing their occurrence or by interrupting their sensory consequences. Thus, Ellison and Konorski (1964) showed that conditioned salivation is not necessary for the initiation and maintenance of food-reinforced lever pressing.

Within this framework, the denervation procedures used in our studies could be viewed as techniques for manipulating r_g's. Orosensory deafferentation would produce its effects indirectly by abolishing or reducing somatosensory stimuli produced as feedback from oromotor (jaw, tongue) activity. Oromotor denervations would act directly to eliminate the behaviors themselves as sources of movement-produced orosensory feedback.

The significant reduction in lever pressing seen after trigeminal denervations (both sensory and motor) is congruent with an explanation in terms of mediating processes functionally equivalent to fractional anticipatory goal responses. Trigeminal denervations not only disrupt lever pressing but also abolish or reduce oromotor activity. The fact that the reduction in lever pressing is seen after *either* sensory or motor denervation suggests a commonality of causation in the two procedures. Since complete elimination of a behavior is the most effective way of removing its sensory feedback, the functional equivalence of V motor and V sensory denervations is also consistent with an r_g hypothesis. Our results suggest that trigeminal (and possibly hypoglossal) denervation produces its effects on food- and water-reinforced operants by disrupting mediating processes that may be responsible for the chaining of various components of the instrumental response sequence.

Several additional lines of evidence are consistent with this hypothesis:

1. It has been repeatedly observed that oromotor responses directed at various components of the testing environment (walls, floor, lever) are often correlated with the maintenance of operant behavior reinforced by intragastric injections of food or water (Altar and Carlisle, 1979; Holman, 1968; Kissileff, 1973; Snowdon, 1969).

2. Analogous "anticipatory" oromotor responses (lip smacking, biting, mouthing) have been reported in chimpanzees serving as subjects in "token reward" experiments (Cowles, 1938; Wolfe, 1936: cited in Osgood, 1953).

3. Developmental studies indicate that mouthing movements occur preceding food contact in rat, cat, and human neonate (Hall, 1979; Mateer, 1918: cited in Wyrwicka, 1967). Shuleikina (1978) has found, in the kitten, that chewing movements become classically conditioned to the food source and eventually occur preceding an operant response. Recording electromyograms from the masticatory muscles, she has shown that, in development, prefeeding chewing movements occur farther and farther away from the food source until they become preparatory to lever press-

ing. The potential significance of these observations merits their careful replication and extension. They suggest an ontogenetic basis for the acquisition of processes mediating incentive–reinforcer relationships.

C. Trigeminal Orosensation, Dietary Self-Selection, and the Quantitative Control of Intake

It has frequently been proposed that conditioned behaviors may function as a link between environmental and physiological factors in metabolic homeostasis (Booth, 1981; Hawkins, 1977; Miller and Dworkin, 1980). Associative processes linked to food-related stimuli could function to bridge the temporal gap between feeding responses and their postingestive consequnces, making possible the acquistion and maintenance of adaptive food selection behaviors. Miller's studies of deafferentation effects on dietary self-selection (Section X) suggest that this hypothesis may be extended from the qualitative to the quantitative control of intake.

As noted earlier, the required ingestive response in food selection behavior is a qualitative one, and either taste or smell could serve as conditioning stimuli for acceptance or rejection responses to specific food items. In dietary self-selection, on the other hand, the required behavior involved rather precise quantitative adjustments of one or more parameters of the rat's feeding pattern so as to control the total amount of a specific food ingested. While taste or smell may be important for the *identification* of appropriate food items, neither modality provides a positive correlation between specific patterns of feeding activity and specific metabolic consequences. In contrast to taste or smell, trigeminal orosensation has the unique property that, in addition to reflecting the sensory properties of the food, it is generated as *movement-produced sensory feedback* during feeding activity. It is thus ideally suited to serve as a quantitative stimulus correlate of specific amounts and types of feeding activity directed to particular food items.

Within this conceptual framework we may consider feeding behavior itself as an instrumental response. The quantitative control of intake (caloric or nutrient) would thus involve a process of instrumental conditioning in which metabolic consequnces provide the primary reinforcment for diet selection. We may assume that food-related stimuli will elicit fractional anticipatory goal responses (r_g's), and the sensory concomitants of these responses (i.e., movement-produced trigeminal sensory feedback) will gradually come to be associated with specific patterns of feeding behavior (direction, duration, frequency). Trigeminal orosensory inputs, originally unrelated to metabolic factors, but closely linked to the initiation of feeding and to feeding activity, will continue to be present later in the meal when postingestive factors come into play. In the process of conditioning, oral factors will come to acquire incentive properties, eliciting feeding patterns appropriate to the animal's metabolic requirements.

This formulation is consistent with the fact that trigeminal deafferentation impairs the rat's ability to adjust its feeding patterns promptly and accurately to their metabolic consequences, and disrupts performance on a variety of food-reinforced instrumental (operant) tasks. The generality of this formulation is further supported by the finding that the development of food selection in chicks involves an association among pecking activity, trigeminal orosensation, and the metabolic consequences of food intake (Hogan, 1977).

D. Conclusions

A persistent problem with the concept of the *fractional anticipatory goal response* has been the inability of its proponents to identify r_g with any concrete and measurable event, physiological or behavioral. Our findings have tentatively identified a class of (oral) behaviors that might function as mediating responses in the acquisition of consummatory or operant response patterns. These observations suggest that the trigeminal afference produced as feedback from such responses constitutes a sensory correlate of incentive and reinforcement processes.

XV. Mouth, Brain, and Appetite: Approaches to the Analysis of Neural Mechanisms

A. On the History of the Mouth in Physiological Psychology: A Case Study in Sensorimotor Neglect

The authors of a recent report on the consummatory behavior of decorticate and LH-lesioned rats prefaced their paper with the following statement: "There have been few studies on how brain damaged rats use their mouth and tongue to ingest food, even though such measures would seem essential to the analysis of feeding impairments" (Whishaw and Kolb, 1983). This paradoxical state of affairs reflects a continuing preoccupation among physiological psychologists with "motivational" processes at the expense of studies of sensorimotor mechanisms, which were viewed as conceptually less significant (see, e.g., Zeigler, 1976, 1983).

There are a number of reasons for this preoccupation, not the least of which is the fact that much of the earlier work on hunger and thirst was carried out within the framework of the peripheralist–centralist controversy with its emphasis on dichotomous formulations. Thus, in discussing the results of the early intragastric, self-infusion (functional deafferentation) studies, emphasis was placed on the fact that subjects did regulate, rather than the fact that (like our deafferented rats) they did so at lower than normal levels. As a result, these studies are often interpreted as minimizing the peripheral (sensory) contribution to the control of hunger and thirst (Epstein, 1967).

Perhaps the most significant factor, however, was the impact made by studies of hypothalamic lesions, which produced deficits in hunger and thirst far more disruptive than had been hitherto demonstrated by any peripheral manipulation. Despite Teitelbaum's insightful and persistent characterization of his LH lesion studies as procedures for the "analysis and resynthesis" of "motivated" *behavior* (e.g., Teitelbaum, 1982; Reddick and Hobbs, 1983) the majority of physiological psychologists persisted in viewing this paradigm as a procedure for the identification of *specific neural systems* mediating hunger and thirst. Taken together, the self-infusion studies and the analysis of hypothalamic lesions contributed to the dichotomizing of "sensorimotor" and "motivational" mechanisms. Moreover, this explicit dichotomy was paralleled by the implicit assumption that the two types of mechanisms would prove to be embodied in distinctly different neural structures, with peripheral structures mediating "sensorimotor" processes and central structures controlling "motivation."

Our studies of trigeminal function in the pigeon and rat do not support this assumption. While it is possible to classify deficits as either sensorimotor or motivational by appropriate behavioral techniques, peripheral sensory denervation produces *both* types of deficits. Moreover, even a cursory review of lesion studies involving central (putatively "nonsensory") structures in rats indicates that the "motivational" deficits in food and water intake reported in these studies are accompanied by impairments in the sensorimotor control of eating and drinking (Braun, 1975; Box and Mogenson, 1975; Evered and Mogenson, 1976; Kolb and Nonneman, 1975; Kolb *et al.*, 1977; Levine *et al.*, 1971; Marshall *et al.*, 1974; Parker and Feldman, 1967; Stricker and Zigmond, 1976; Whishaw *et al.*, 1981; Whishaw and Kolb; 1983; Wolf and DiCara, 1974; Wyrwicka *et al.*, 1975).

In reviewing these studies one is struck, first of all, by a remarkable commonality in the nature of the deficits reported. In all cases, swallowing is intact and animals will usually make lapping or chewing movements when objects are placed in the mouth (Reddick and Hobbs, 1983). On the

other hand, tongue protrusion and licking to perioral stimuli are frequently impaired. Failure to consume dry laboratory chow pellets is a
common finding, as are deficits in the consummatory response sequences
involved in grasping and orally manipulating this type of food. Disruptions in drinking behavior are frequently reported, with particular difficulties in drinking from Richter tubes. Finally, a number of investigators
have described the development of alternative forms of the "normal"
(species-typical) consummatory response. Rats have been reported to
assume "bizarre" postures while drinking, and normal eating responses
may be replaced by paw-licking of the mash of "cornering" the pellet and
gnawing it awkwardly. The resemblance of these observations to our
description of eating and drinking in the trigeminally deafferented animal
is apparent.

Similarly, when we compare the "trigeminal syndrome" in the rat with
the effects on ingestive behavior produced by lesions of the lateral hypothalamus, they are strikingly similar, both qualitatively and quantitatively. Both the LH and the trigeminal syndromes include aphagia, adipsia, "finickiness," food spillage, a lower level of weight regulation, and
recovery along a gradient of palatability. There are also some qualitative
similarities between LH effects on ingestion and those seen after gustatory deafferentation (Jacquin, 1983).

It is therefore of interest that lesions of central orosensory structures
also produce a complex mixture of sensorimotor and motivational deficits
(e.g., Emmers, 1977; Oakley, 1965; Ziegler and Karten, 1974; see also
Fig. 62). One implication of this finding is that some, as yet undefined,
portion of the deficits in hunger and thirst seen after LH lesions reflects
incidental damage to central structures mediating the orosensory control
of ingestive behavior. Given the proximity of ascending trigeminal
(Smith, 1973) and gustatory (Norgren, 1976) pathways to the LH region,
this hypothesis is a plausible one. It deserves further exploration, not
because of what it might tell us about the LH syndrome, but because it
might help clarify the contributions of central *orosensorimotor* mechanisms. The analysis of such mechanisms as they operate at successive
levels of the neuraxis is a fundamental requirement for understanding the
neural control of hunger and thirst.

B. FROM CENTERS TO CIRCUITS

It is clear from our findings and those of others (e.g., Grill, 1980, and
this volume; Novin and VanderWeele, 1977) that the time has come to
reconsider our preoccupation with hypothalamic mechanisms. We have
paid a high price for this "hypothalamocentrism," expending a vastly

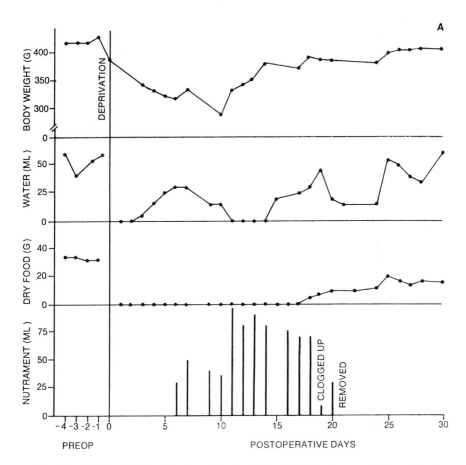

FIG. 62. Effects of bilateral lesions of central trigeminal structures on intake and body weight in the rat. (A) Effects of a bilateral lesion of the trigeminal lemniscus at the level of the interpeduncular nucleus. The rat, a male, did not respond to the food pellets until the fourth postoperative day. From day 5 to day 14 there was considerable gnawing at food but no measurable intake until day 18. From day 18 to day 30, daily spillage averaged 60% of the ration given. (B) (See p. 184.) Effects of a bilateral lesion of VBm. This male rat made no responses to either food or water until the thirteenth postoperative day. Spillage over the next 2 weeks averaged about 65% of the ration presented. Both rats were "finicky" in the sense that they ingested large quantities of a chocolate-flavored liquid diet during periods when intake of food or water was absent or reduced below preoperative levels. (From Zeigler and Karten, 1974.)

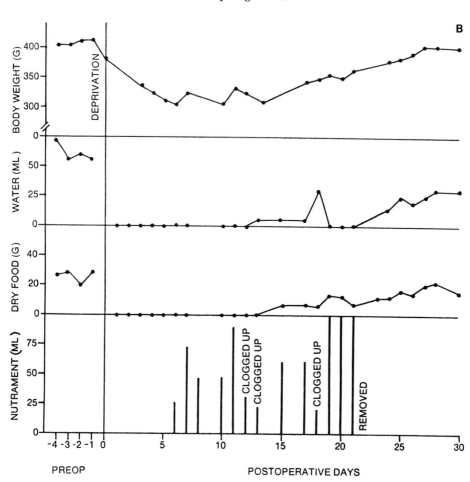

F_IG. 62B.   (See legend on p. 183.)

disproportionate percentage of our intellectual and material resources on a handful of methodological paradigms applied to the study of a single brain region. In fact, what began as a search for the neural basis of hunger and thirst gradually became transformed into a search for the neural basis of the LH syndrome. In the process, "motivation" tended to become a sort of Cartesian ghost in the neural machinery, without any links to either the sensory or motor control of ingestive behavior.

Advances in the development of anatomical tracing techniques (Jones and Hartman, 1978) have made it possible to take sensory and motor

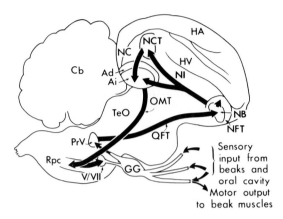

FIG. 63. A trigeminal sensorimotor circuit in the pigeon. The afferent pathway includes the Gasserian ganglion (GG), the quintofrontal tract (QFT), and the nucleus basalis (NB). Intratelencephalic components include the fronto-archistriate tract; the neostriatum frontale, pars trigeminale (NFT); the neostriatum caudale, pars trigeminale (NCT); and the archistriatum. Efferent components include the occipitomesencephalic tract (OMT) projecting upon the lateral (parvocellular) reticular formation (Rpc), which projects in turn upon motor neurons of the jaw opener and closer muscles (V/VII). All structures in the circuit have been implicated in the control of feeding, pecking, and grasping behaviors. (From Wild *et al.,* 1984.)

systems as starting points for the delineation of functionally significant neural circuits. Utilizing such procedures and starting from a sensorimotor analysis of the lordosis reflex, Pfaff (1980) has made considerable progress in defining neural circuits for the motivational control of sexual behavior in the female rat. In our laboratory, we have taken the sensorimotor control of the consummatory response (pecking, grasping) as a starting point for the analysis of neural circuits mediating feeding behavior in the pigeon (Wild *et al.,* 1984, 1985) (Fig. 63).

Our review of brain lesion studies of ingestive behavior indicates that there is likely to be a considerable overlap in the CNS structures mediating the control of "motivated" behavior and the sensorimotor systems involved in the generation of consummatory responses. Moreover, our own findings indicate a role for jaw reflex mechanisms in the rat's ingestive behavior that may parallel the role of the lordosis reflex in its sexual behavior. We suggest, therefore, that the analysis of CNS pathways mediating the sensorimotor control of jaw movement may be a productive starting point for research on the "motivational" control of hunger and thirst in the rat.

C. CONCLUSIONS: FROM MOVEMENTS TO MOTIVES

Although motivation and movement share a common etymology, physiological psychologists have tended to treat them as both separate and unequal: separate, in the sense that movements and their control were viewed as means, that is, mechanisms; unequal, in the sense that just as means are subordinate to ends, mechanisms are subordinate to goals. Given the flexibility that is the hallmark of goal-directed (motivated) behavior and the presumed rigidity of the neural mechanisms underlying movement, it is not surprising that most psychologists placed goals at the top of their intellectual hierarchy and movement at its bottom. The study of motivation in psychology became the search for brain structures mediating central motive states (drive), leaving the study of sensorimotor mechanisms to the physiologist. Yet goals are ultimately achieved by the initiation, direction, and termination of behaviors, and behavior, after all, consists entirely of movements and postural adjustments. So somehow, the twain (movements and motives) must meet. Our studies suggest that, in the case of ingestive behavior, one such meeting place is likely to be the trigeminal sensorimotor system.

References

Addison, W. H. F., and Appleton, J. L. (1887). The structure and growth of the incisor teeth of the albino rat. *Journal of Morphology* **1,** 43–95.

Adolph, E. F. (1947). Urges to eat and drink in rats. *American Journal of Physiology* **151,** 110–125.

Altar, A., and Carlisle, H. J. (1979). Intragastric drinking in the rat: Evidence for role of oropharyngeal stimulation. *Physiology and Behavior* **22,** 1221–1225.

Anderson, G. H. (1979). Control of protein and energy intake: Role of plasma amino acids and brain neurotransmitter. *Canadian Journal of Physiology and Pharmacology* **57,** 1043–1057.

Arends, J. J. A., and Dubbeldam, J. L. (1982). Exteroceptive and proprioceptive afferents of the trigeminal and facial motor nuclei in the Mallard (*Anas platyrhynchos L.*). *Journal of Comparative Neurology* **209,** 313–329.

Armstrong, S., Coleman, G., and Singer, G. (1980). Food and water deprivation: changes in rat feeding, drinking activity and body weight. *Neuroscience and Biobehavioral Reviews* **4,** 377–402.

Ashley, D. V. M., and Anderson, G. H. (1975). Correlation between the plasma tryptophan to neutral amino acid ratio and protein intake in the self-selecting weanling rat. *Journal of Nutrition* **105,** 1412–1421.

Atema, J. (1971). Structures and functions of the sense of taste in the catfish (*Ictalurus natalis*). *Brain, Behavior and Evolution* **4,** 273–294.

Berkhoudt, H., Klein, B. G., and Zeigler, H. P. (1982). Afferents to the trigeminal and facial motor nuclei in Pigeon (*Columba livia L.*): Central connections of jaw motoneurons. *Journal of Comparative Neurology* **209,** 301–312.

Block, C. J., Siegel, A., and Edinger, H. (1980). Effects of amygdaloid stimulation upon trigeminal sensory fields of the lip that are established during hypothalamically-elicited quiet biting attack in the cat. *Brain Research* **197**, 39–55.

Bolles, R. C. (1961). The interaction of hunger and thirst in the rat. *Journal of Comparative and Physiological Psychology* **54**, 580–584.

Bolles, R. C. (1975). "Theory of Motivation," 2nd. Ed. Harper, New York.

Bonvallet, M., and Gary-Bobo, E. (1975). Amygdala and masseteric reflex. II. Mechanism of the diphasic modifications of the reflex elicited from the "defense reaction area." Role of the spinal trigeminal nucleus (pars oralis). *Electroencephalogry and Clinical Neurophysiology* **39**, 341–352.

Booth, D. A. (1981). The physiology of appetite. *British Medical Bulletin* **37**, 135–140.

Booth, D. A., and Simpson, P. C. (1971). Food preferences acquired by association with variations in amino acid nutrition. *Quarterly Journal of Experimental Psychology* **23**, 135–145.

Box, B. M., and Mogenson, G. J. (1975). Alterations in ingestive behaviors after bilateral lesions of the amygdala in the rat. *Physiology and Behavior* **15**, 679–688.

Braun, J. J. (1975). The neocortex and feeding in the rat. *Journal of Comparative and Physiological Psychology* **89**, 506–522.

Brenowitz, G. (1980). Control of food handling by cutaneous receptor input in squirrels. *Brain, Behavior and Evolution* **17**, 478–490.

Burgess, P. R., and Perl, E. R. (1973). Cutaneous mechanoreceptors and nociceptors. *In* "Handbook of Sensory Physiology, Vol. 2, Somatosensory System" (A. Iggo, ed.), pp. 29–78. Springer-Verlag, Berlin and New York.

Chalupa, L. M., and Rhoades, R. W. (1977). Responses of visual, somatosensory and auditory neurones in the golden hamster's superior colliculus. *Journal of Physiology (London)* **270**, 195–226.

Chase, M. H., McGinty, D. J., and Sterman, M. B. (1968). Cyclic variations in the amplitude of a brainstem reflex during sleep and wakefullness. *Experientia* **24**, 47–48.

Collier, G. (1969). Body weight loss as a measure of motivation in hunger and thirst. *Annals of the New York Academy of Sciences* **157**, 594–609.

Collier, G., Leshner, A. I., and Squibb, R. L. (1969a). Dietary self-selection in active and non-active rats. *Physiology and Behavior* **4**, 79–82.

Collier, G., Leshner, A. I., and Squibb, R. L. (1969b). Self-selection of natural and purified protein. *Physiology and Behavior* **4**, 83–86.

Cowles, J. T. (1938). Food tokens as incentives for learning by chimpanzees. *Comparative Psychological Monographs* **14**, 1–96.

Crespi, L. P. (1944). Amount of reinforcement and level of performance. *Psychological Review* **51**, 341–357.

Darian-Smith, I. (1973). The trigeminal system. *In* "Handbook of Sensory Physiology, Somatosensory Systems" (A. Iggo, ed.), Vol. 2, pp. 1271–1273. Springer-Verlag, Berlin and New York.

Daunton, N. G. (1977). Sensory components of bite-force response in the rat. *Journal of Comparative and Physiological Psychology* **91**, 203–220.

Dellow, P. G., and Lund, J. P. (1971). Evidence for central timing of rhythmical mastication. *Journal of Physiology (London)* **215**, 1–13.

Dethier, V. G. (1976). "The Hungry Fly: A Physiological Study of the Behavior Associated with Feeding." Harvard Univ. Press, Cambridge, Massachusetts.

Devor, M., and Wall, P. D. (1978). Reorganization of spinal cord sensory map after peripheral nerve injury. *Nature (London)* **276**, 75–76.

Drager, U. C., and Hubel, D. H. (1975). Responses to visual stimulation and relationship between visual, auditory and somatosensory inputs in mouse superior colliculus. *Journal of Neurophysiology* **38**, 690–713.

Dubner, R., Sessle, B. J., and Storey, A. T. (1978). "The Neural Basis of Oral and Facial Function." Plenum, New York.

Durham, D., and Woolsey, T. A. (1978). Acute whisker removal reduces neuronal activity in barrels of mouse Sm I cortex. *Journal of Comparative Neurology* **178**, 629–644.

Ellison, D. G., and Konorski, J. (1964). Separation of the salivary and motor responses in instrumental conditioning. *Science* **146**, 1071–1072.

Emmers, R. (1965). Organization of the first and second somasthetic regions (SI and SII) in the rat thalamus. *Journal of Comparative Neurology* **124**, 215–228.

Emmers, R. (1977). Tonic control of water intake via the thalamic taste nucleus. *Annals of the New York Academy of Sciences* **200**, 124–138.

Epstein, A. N. (1967). Oropharyngeal factors in feeding and drinking. *In* "Handbook of Physiology, Section 6: Alimentary Canal, Volume 1: Control of Food and Water Intake" (C. E. Code, ed.). Amer. Physiol. Soc., Washington, D. C.

Epstein, A. N., and Teitelbaum, P. (1962). Regulation of food intake in the absence of taste, smell and other oropharyngeal sensations. *Journal of Comparative and Physiological Psychology* **55**, 753–759.

Estes, W. K. (1948). Discrimination conditioning. II. Effects of a Pavlovian conditioned stimulus upon a subsequently established operant response. *Journal of Experimental Psychology* **38**, 173–177.

Evered, M. D., and Mogenson, G. J. (1976). Regulatory and secondary water intake in rats with lesions of the zona incerta. *American Journal of Physiology* **230**, 1049–1057.

Fernstrom, J. D., and Faller, D. V. (1978). Neutral amino acids in the brain: Changes in response to food ingestion. *Journal of Neurochemistry* **30**, 1531–1538.

Flynn. J. P., Edwards, S. B., and Bandler, R. J. (1971). Changes in sensory and motor systems during centrally elicited attack. *Behavioral Science* **16**, 1–19.

Fried, K. (1982). Development, degeneration and regeneration of nerve fibres in the feline inferior alveolar nerve nerve and mandibular incisor pulps. *Acta Physiologica Scandinavica, Supplement* **504**, 1–28.

Gallistel, C. R. (1980). "The Organization of Action: A New Synthesis." Erlbaum, Hillsdale, New Jersey.

Garcia, J., Ervin, F. R., and Koelling, R. A. (1966). Learning with prolonged delay of reinforcement. *Psychonomic Science* **5**, 121–122.

Gary-Bobo, E., and Bonvallet, M. (1975). Amygdala and masseteric reflex I. Facilitation, inhibition and diphasic modifications of the reflex, induced by localized amygdaloid stimulation. *Electroencephalography and Clinical Neurophysiology* **39**, 329–339.

Glickman, S. E., and Schiff, B. B. (1967). A biological theory of reinforcement. *Psychological Review* **74**, 81–109.

Goldberger, M. E. (1980). Motor recovery after lesions. *Trends in Neurosciences* **3**, 288–291.

Goldstein, J. L., and Siegel, J. (1981). Stimulation of ventral tegmental area and nucleus accumbens reduces receptive fields for hypothalamic biting reflex in cats. *Experimental Neurology* **72**, 239–246.

Greene, E. C. (1968). "Anatomy of the Rat." Hafner, New York.

Gregg, J. M., and Dixon, A. D. (1973). Somatotopic organization of the trigeminal ganglion in the rat. *Archives of Oral Biology* **18**, 487–498.

Grill, H. J. (1980). Production and regulation of ingestive consummatory behavior in the chronic decerebrate rat. *Brain Research Bulletin* **5** (Suppl. 4), 79–87.

Grill, H., and Norgren, R. (1978). The taste reactivity test I. Mimetic responses to gustatory stimuli in neurologically normally rats. *Brain Research* **143**, 263–279.

Grillner, S. (1982). Control of locomotion in bipeds, tetrapods and fish. *In* "Handbook of Physiology: Motor Control" (V. Brooks, ed.), Vol. II, pp. 1179–1236. Amer. Physiol. Soc., Bethesda, Maryland.

Guttman, N. (1953). Operant conditioning, extinction and period reinforcement in relation to concentration of sucrose used as a reinforcing agent. *Journal of Experimental Psychology* **46**, 213–224.

Hall, W. G. (1979). Feeding and behavioral activation in infant rats. *Science* **205**, 206–209.

Halpern, B. (1977). Functional anatomy of the tongue and mouth of mammals. *In* "Drinking Behavior: Oral Stimulation, Reinforcement and Preference" (J. A. W. M. Weijnen and J. Mendelson, eds.). Plenum, New York.

Hawkins, R. C. (1977). Learning to initiate and terminate meals: theoretical, clinical and developmental aspects. *In* "Learning Mechanisms in Food Selection" (L. M. Barker, M. R. Best, and M. Domjan, eds.), pp. 201–224. Baylor Univ. Press, Waco, Texas.

Hiiemae, K. M., and Ardran, G. M. (1968). A cinefluorographic study of mandibular movement during feeding in the rat. *Journal of Zoology* (*London*) **154**, 139–154.

Hinde, R. A. (1972). "Animal Behavior: A synthesis of ethology and comparative psychology." McGraw-Hill, New York.

Hobson, J. A., and Scheibel, A. B. (1980). The brainstem core: Sensorimotor integration and behavioral state control. *Neurosciences Research Program Bulletin* **18**, 3–173.

Hoebel, B. G. (1975). Brain reward and aversion systems in the control of feeding and sexual behavior. *In* "Nebraska Symposium on Motivation" (J. K. Cole and T. B. Sonderegger, eds.), pp. 49–112. Univ. of Nebraska Press, Lincoln, Nebraska.

Hoebel, B. G., and Teitelbaum, P. (1962). Hypothalamic control of feeding and self-stimulation. *Science* **135**, 375–377.

Hofer, M. A., Fisher, A., and Shair, H. (1981). Effects of infraorbital nerve section on survival, growth and suckling behaviors of developing rats. *Journal of Comparative and Physiological Psychology* **95**, 123–133.

Hogan, J. A. (1977). The ontogeny of food preferences in chicks and other animals. *In* "Learning Mechanisms in Food Selection" (L. M. Barker, M. R. Best, and M. Domjan, eds.), pp. 71–97. Baylor Univ. Press, Waco, Texas.

Holman, G. (1969). Intragastric reinforcement effect. *Journal of Comparative and Physiological Psychology* **69**, 432–441.

Holstege, G., Kuypers, H. G. J. M., and Dekker, J. J. (1977). The organization of the bulbar fiber connections to the trigeminal, facial and hypoglossal motor nuclei. II. An autoradiographic tracing study in the cat. *Brain* **100**, 265–286.

Huerta, M., Frankfurter, A. J., and Harting, J. K. (1981). The trigemino- collicular projection in the cat: Patch-like endings within the intermediate grey. *Brain Research* **211**, 1–13.

Hull, C. L. (1943). "Principles of Behavior." Appleton, New York.

Hulse, S. H., and Suter, S. (1968). One-drop licking in rats. *Journal of Comparative and Physiological Psychology* **66**, 536–539.

Hulse, S. H., and Suter, S. (1970). Emitted and elicited behavior: An analysis of some learning mechanisms associated with fluid intake in rats. *Learning and Motivation* **1**, 304–325.

Humphrey, T. (1970). Reflex activity in the oral and facial area of the human fetus. *In* "Second Symposium on Oral Sensation and Perception" (W. F. Bosna, ed.), pp. 195–223. Thomas, Springfield, Illinois.

Huston, J. P., Nef, B. Papadopolous, G., and Welzl, H. (1980). Activation and lateralization of sensorimotor fields for perioral biting reflex by intranigral GABA agonist and systemic apomorphine in the rat. *Brain Research Bulletin* **5,** 745–749.

Jacquin, M. F. (1980). Peripheral orosensory mechanisms: Contributions to the neural control of ingestive behavior in the rat. Unpublished doctoral dissertation, City University of New York.

Jacquin, M. F. (1983). Gustation and ingestive behavior in the rat. *Behavioral Neuroscience* **97,** 98–109.

Jacquin, M. F., and Enfiejian, H. (1982). Trigeminal mediation of an oromotor fractional anticipatory goal response. *In* "The Neural Basis of Feeding and Reward" (B. G. Hoebel and D. Movin, eds.), pp. 85–96. Haer Institute, Brunswick, Maine.

Jacquin, M. F., and Zeigler, H. P. (1982). Trigeminal orosensory deafferentation disrupts feeding and drinking mechanisms in the rat. *Brain Research* **238,** 198–204.

Jacquin, M. F., and Zeigler, H. P. (1983). Trigeminal orosensation and ingestive behavior in the rat. *Behavioral Neuroscience* **97,** 62–97.

Jacquin, M. F., and Zeigler, H. P. (1984). Trigeminal denervation and operant behavior in the rat. *Behavioral Neuroscience* **98,** 1004–1022.

Jacquin, M. F., Harris, R., and Zeigler, H. P. (1982a). Dissociation of hunger and self-stimulation by trigeminal deafferentation in the rat. *Brain Research* **244,** 53–58.

Jacquin, M. F., Semba, K., Rhoades, R. W., and Egger, M. D. (1982b). Trigeminal primary afferents project bilaterally to dorsal horn and ipsilaterally to cerebellum, reticular formation and cuneate, solitary, supratrigeminal and vagal nuclei. *Brain Research* **246,** 285–291.

Jacquin, M. F., Rhodes, R. W., Enfiejian, H., and Egger, M. D. (1983a). Organization and morphology of masticatory neurons in the rat: A retrograde HRP study. *Journal of Comparative Neurology* **218,** 239–256.

Jacquin, M. F., Semba, K., Egger, M. D., and Rhoades, R. W. (1983b). Organization of HRP-labelled trigeminal mandibular primary afferent neurons in the rat. *Journal of Comparative Neurology* **215,** 397–420.

Jerge, C. R. (1963). The function of the nucleus supratrigeminalis. *Journal of Neurophysiology* **26,** 393–402.

Jewett, D. L., and McCarroll, H. R. (1980). "Nerve Repair and Regeneration: Its Clinical and Experimental Basis." Mosby, St. Louis, Missouri.

Jones, E. G., and Hartman, B. K. (1978). Recent advances in neuroanatomical methodology. *Annual Review of Neuroscience* **1,** 215–296.

Kassel, J. (1980). Superior colliculus projections to tactile areas of rat cerebellar hemispheres. *Brain Research* **202,** 291–305.

Keesey, R. E. (1973). Weight regulation and the lateral hypothalamic syndrome. *In* "Neurosciences Research Program Bulletin, Vol. 11: Neural Control of Motivated Behavior" (E. Stellar and J. Corbit, eds.), pp. 342–353. MIT. Press, Cambridge, Massachusetts.

Kenyon, P., Cronin, P., and Keeble, S. (1983). Role of the infraorbital nerve in retrieving behavior in lactating rats. *Behavioral Neuroscience* **97,** 255–269.

Kidokoro, Y., Kubota, K., Shuto, S., and Sumino, R. (1968). Reflex organization of cat masticatory muscles. *Journal of Neurophysiology* **31,** 695–708.

Killackey, H. P., and Erzurumlu, R. (1981). Trigeminal projections to the superior colliculus of the rat. *Journal of Comparative Neurology* **201,** 221–242.

Kissileff, H. R. (1973). Non homeostatic controls of drinking. *In* "The Neuropsychology of Thirst: New Findings and Advances in Concepts" (A. N. Epstein, H. R. Kissileff, and E. Stellar, eds.), pp. 163–198. Holt, New York.

Kolb, B., and Nonneman, A. J. (1975). Prefrontal cortex and the regulation of food intake in the rat. *Journal of Comparative and Physiological Psychology* **88**, 806–81.

Kolb, B., Whishaw, I. Q., and Schallert, T. (1977). Aphagia, behavior sequencing and body weight set point following frontal orbital lesions in the rat. *Physiology and Behavior* **19**, 91–103.

Kratz, C. M., and Levitsky, D. A. (1978). Post-ingestive effects of quinine on intake of nutritive and non-nutritive substances. *Physiology and Behavior* **21**, 851–854.

Kratz, C. M., and Levitsky, D. A. (1979). Dietary obesity: Differential effects with self-selection and composite diet feeding techniques. *Physiology and Behavior* **22**, 245–249.

Landgren, S., and Olsson, K. A. (1980). The effect of electrical stimulation in the hypothalamus on the monosynaptic jaw-closing and disynaptic jaw-opening reflexes in the cat. *Experimental Brain Research* **39**, 389–400.

LaRue, C. G., and LeMagnen, J. (1972). The olfactory control of meal patterns in rats. *Physiology and Behavior* **9**, 817–821.

Lashley, K. S. (1938). The experimental analysis of instinctive behavior. *Psychological Review* **45**, 445–471.

LeMagnen, J. (1971). Advances in studies on the physiological control and regulation of intake. *In* "Progress in Physiological Psychology" (E. Stellar and J. M. Sprague, eds.), Vol. 4. Academic Press, New York.

Leshner, A. I., Collier, G., and Squibb, R. L. (1971). Dietary self-selection at cold temperatures. *Physiology and Behavior* **6**, 1–3.

Levine, M. S., Ferguson, N., Kreinick, C. J., Gustafson, J. W., and Schwartzbaum, J. S. (1971). Sensorimotor dysfunctions and aphagia and adipsia following pallidal lesions in rats. *Journal of Comparative and Physiological Psychology* **77**, 282–293.

Li, E. T. S., and Anderson, H. (1982). Self-selected meal composition, circadian rhythms and meal responses in plasma and brain tryptophan and 5-hydroxytryptophane in rats. *Journal of Nutrition* **112**, 2001–2010.

Lidsky, T. I., Robinson, J. H., Denaro, F. J., and Weinhold, P. M. (1978). Trigeminal influences on entopeduncular units. *Brain Research* **141**, 227–234.

Lowe, A. A. (1981). The neural regulation of tongue movements. *Progress in Neurobiology* **15**, 295–344.

Lund, J. P. (1976). Evidence for a central neural pattern generator regulating the chewing cycle. *In* "Mastication" (D. J. Anderson and B. Matthews, eds.), pp. 204–212. Wright, Bristol.

Lund, J. P., Appenteng, K., and Sequin, J. J. (1982). Analogies and common features in the speech and masticatory control systems. *In* "Speech Motor Control" (S. Grillner, ed.), Vol. 36, pp. 231–245. Wenner-Gren Center International Symposium Series; Pergamon, Oxford.

Luschei, E. S., and Goldberg, L. J. (1981). Neural mechanisms of mandibular control: mastication and voluntary biting. *In* "Handbook of Physiology: Motor Control" (V. Brooks, ed.), Vol. II, pp. 1237–1274. Amer. Physiol. Soc., Bethesda, Maryland.

MacDonnell, M., and Flynn, J. F. (1966). Sensory control of hypothalamic attack *Animal Behaviour* **14**, 399–405.

MacIntosh, S. R. (1975). Observations on the structure and innervation of the rat snout. *Journal of Anatomy* **119**, 537–546.

Marfurt, C. F. (1981). The somatotopic organization of the cat trigeminal ganglion as determined by the horseradish peroxidase technique. *Anatomical Record* **201**, 105–118.

Margules, D. L., and Olds, J. (1962). Identical "feeding" and "rewarding" systems in the lateral hypothalamus of the rat. *Science* **135**, 374–375.

Marowitz, L. A., and Halpern, B. (1973). The effects of environmental constraints upon licking patterns. *Physiology and Behavior* **11**, 259–263.

Marshall, J. F., Richardson, J. S., and Teitelbaum, P. (1974). Nigrostriatal bundle damage and the lateral hypothalamic syndrome. *Journal of Comparative and Physiological Psychology* **87**, 808–830.

Mazza, J. P., and Dixon, A. D. (1972). A histological study of chromatolytic cell groups in the trigeminal ganglion of the rat. *Archives of Oral Biology* **17**, 377–387.

Mendelson, J. (1977). Air licking and cold licking in rodents. *In* "Drinking Behavior: Oral Stimulation, Reinforcement and Preference" (J. A. W. M. Weijnen and J. Mendelson, eds.), pp. 157–197. Plenum, New York.

Mendelson, J., and Chillag, D. (1970). Tongue cooling: A new reward for thirsty rodents. *Science* **170**, 1418–1421.

Mendelson, J., and Zec, R. (1972). Effects of lingual denervation and desalivation on airlicking in the rat. *Physiology and Behavior* **8**, 711–714.

Merzenich, M. M., Kaas, J. H., Wall, J. T., Sur, M., Nelson, R. J., and Felleman, D. J. (1983). Progression of changes following median nerve section in the cortical representation of the hand in areas 3B and 1 in adult owl and squirrel monkeys. *Neuroscience* **10**, 639–665.

Miller, M. G. (1981). Trigeminal deafferentation and ingestive behavior in rats. *Journal of Comparative and Physiological Psychology* **95**, 252–269.

Miller, M. G. (1984). Oral somatosensory factors and dietary self-selection in rats. *Behavioral Neuroscience* **98**, 416–423.

Miller, M. G., and Teates, J. F. (1984). Oral somatosensory factors in dietary self-selection after food deprivation and supplementation. *Behavioral Neuroscience* **98**, 424–434.

Miller, M. G. and Teates, J. F. (1985). Acquisition of dietary self-selection in rats with normal and impaired oral sensation. *Physiology and Behavior* **34**.

Miller, M. G., Zeigler, H. P., and Miller, A. E. (1978). Trigeminal deafferentation and feeding behavior patterns in the pigeon (*Columba livia*). *Journal of Comparative Physiology and Psychology* **6**, 1025–1040.

Miller, N. E., and Dworkin, B. R. (1980). Different ways in which learning is involved in homeostasis. *In* "Neural Mechanisms of Goal-directed Behavior and Learning" (R. F. Thompson, L. H. Hicks, and V. B. Shvyrkov, eds.), pp. 57–73. Academic Press, New York.

Mizuno, N., Nakamura, Y., and Iwahori, N. (1974). Central afferent fibers to trigeminal motor system. *Bulletin of the Tokyo Medical and Dental University* **21**, 19–21.

Mizuno, N., Konishi, A., and Sato, M. (1975). Localization of masticatory nmotoneurons in the cat and rat by means of retrograde transport of horseradish peroxidase. *Journal of Comparative Neurology* **164**, 105–116.

Mizuno, N., Nomura, S., Ich, K., Nakamura, Y., and Konishi, A. (1978). Commisural interneurons for masticatory motoneurons: a light and electron microscope study using the horseradish peroxidase tracer technique. *Experimental Neurology* **59**, 254–262.

Musten, B., Peace, D., and Anderson, G. H. (1974). Food intake regulation in the weanling rat: self-selection of protein and energy. *Journal of Nutrition* **104**, 563–572.

Nakamura, Y. (1980). Brainstem neuronal mechanisms controlling the trigeminal motoneuron activity. *In* "Spinal and Supraspinal Mechanisms of Voluntary Motor Control and Locomotion. Progress in Clinical Neurophysiology" (J. E. Desmedt, ed.), Vol. 8, pp. 181–202. Karger, Basel.

Nakamura, Y., Takatori, M., Kubo, Y., Nozaki, S., and Enomoto, S. (1979). Masticatory rhythm formation—facts and a hypothesis. *In* "Integrative Control Functions of the

Brain'' (M. Ito, N. Tsukahara, K. Kubota, and K. Yagi, eds.), Vol. II, pp. 321–331. Kodansha Scientific, Tokyo.

Nakamura, Y., Hiraba, K., Enomoto, S., and Sahara, Y. (1982). Bulbar reticular unit activity during food ingestion in the cat. *Brain Research* **253**, 312–316.

Nicolaidis, S., and Rowland, N. (1977). Intravenous self-feeding: Long-term regulation of energy balance in rats. *Science* **195**, 589–591.

Nord, S. G. (1967). Somatotopic organization in the spinal trigeminal nucleus, the dorsal column nuclei and related structures in the rat. *Journal of Comparative Neurology* **130**, 343–356.

Nord, S. G. (1968). Receptor field characteristics of single cells in the rat trigeminal complex. *Experimental Neurology* **21**, 236–243. 1968.

Norgren, R. (1974). Gustatory afferents to ventral forebrain. *Brain Research* **82**, 285–295.

Norgren, R. (1976). Taste pathways to hypothalamus and amygdala. *Journal of Comparative Neurology* **166**, 17–30.

Novin, D., and VanderWeele, D. A. (1977). Visceral involvement in feeding: There is more to regulation than the hypothalamus. *In* ''Progress in Psychobiology and Physiological Psychology'' (J. E. Sprague and A. N. Epstein, eds.), Vol. 7, pp. 193–241. Academic Press, New York.

Nowlis, G. H. (1977). From reflex to representation: taste elicited tongue movements in the human newborn. *In* ''Taste and Development'' (J. M. Weiffenbach, ed.), pp. 190–204. DHEW Publ. No. (NIH) 77–1068, Bethesda, Maryland.

Oakley, B. (1965). Impaired operant behavior following lesions of the thalamic taste nuclei. *Journal of Comparative and Physiological Psychology* **59**, 202–210.

Olsson, K. A., and Landgren, S. (1980). Facilitation and inhibition of jaw reflexes evoked by electrical stimulation of the cat's cerebral cortex. *Experimental Brain Research* **39**, 149–164.

Osgood, C. E. (1953). ''Method and Theory in Experimental Psychology.'' Oxford Univ. Press, London and New York.

Overmann, S. R. (1976). Dietary self-selection by animals. *Psychological Bulletin* **83**, 218–235.

Panskepp, J. (1973). Reanalysis of feeding patterns in the rat. *Journal of Comparative and Physiological Psychology* **82**, 78–94.

Parker, S. W., and Feldman, S. M. (1967). Effects of mesencephalic lesions on feeding behavior in rats. *Experimental Neurology* **17**, 313–326.

Peck, J. (1978). Rats defend different body weights depending on palatability and accessibility of their food. *Journal of Comparative and Physiological Psychology* **92**, 555–570.

Pelletier, V., Poulos, D., and Lende, R. A. (1974). Functional localization in the trigeminal root. *Journal of Neurosurgery* **40**, 504–513.

Pfaff, D. W. (1980). ''Estrogens and Brain Function: Neural Analysis of a Hormone Controlled Mammalian Reproductive Behavior.'' Springer-Verlag, Berlin and New York.

Pfaffmann, C. (1952). Taste preference and aversion following lingual denervation. *Journal of Comparative and Physiological Psychology* **45**, 393–400.

Pfaffmann, C. (1960). The pleasures of sensation. *Psychological Review* **67**, 253–268.

Pfaffmann, C., Frank, M., and Norgren, R. (1979). Neural mechanisms and behavioral aspects of taste. *Annual Review of Psychology* **30**, 283–325.

Picquard, F., Schaefer, A., and Haberey, P. (1978). Influence of fasting and protein deprivation on food self-selection in the rat. *Physiology and Behavior* **20**, 771–778.

Reddick, S. E., and Hobbs, S. H. (1983). Changes in the consummatory behavior of the rat following lesions of the trigeminal lemniscus at the level of the ventrobasal thalamus. *Neuroscience Abstracts* **57**, 8.

Revusky, S. H. (1967). Hunger level during food consumption: Effects on subsequent preferences. *Psychonomic Science* **7,** 109–110.

Rhoades, R. W., Fiore, J. M., Math, M. M., and Jacquin, M. F. (1983). Reorganization of
trigeminal primary afferents following neonatal infraorbital nerve section in hamster.
Developmental Brain Research **7,** 337–342.

Richter, C. P. (1956). Salt appetite of mammals: Its dependance on instinct and metabolism.
In "L'Instinct dans le comportement des animaux et de l'homme" (M. Autuori, ed.),
pp. 577–629. Masson, Paris.

Richter, C. P., Holt, L. E., and Barelare, B. (1938). Nutritional requirements for normal
growth and reproduction in rats studied by the self-selection method. *American Journal
of Physiology* **122,** 734–744.

Robinson, P. P. (1981). Reinervation of teeth, mucous membrane and skin following section
of the inferior alveolar nerve in the cat. *Brain Research* **220,** 241–253.

Rozin, P. (1968). Are carbohydrate and protein intakes separately regulated? *Journal of
Comparative and Physiological Psychology* **65,** 23–29.

Schallert, T., DeRyck, M., and Teitelbaum, P. (1980). Atropine stereotypy as a behavioral
trap: A movement subsystem and electroencephalographic analysis. *Journal of Comparative and Physiological Psychology* **94,** 1–24.

Schoenfeld, T. A., and Hamilton, L. W. (1976). Multiple factors in the short term behavioral
control of protein intake in rats. *Journal of Comparative and Physiological Psychology*
90, 1092–1104.

Schutz, H. G., and Pilgrim, F. J. (1954). Changes in the self-selection pattern for purified
dietary components by rats after starvation. *Journal of Comparative and Physiological
Psychology* **47,** 444–449.

Sessle, B. J. (1977). Identification of alpha and gamma trigeminal motoneurons and effects of
stimulation of amygdala, cerebellum and cerebral cortex. *Experimental Neurology* **54,**
303–322.

Seward, J. P. (1956). Drive, incentive and reinforcement. *Psychological Review* **63,** 195–
203.

Shambes, G. M., Gibson, J. M., and Welker, W. I. (1978). Fractured somatotypy in granule
cell tactile areas of rat cerebellar hemispheres revealed by micromapping. *Brain, Behavior and Evolution* **15,** 94–140.

Sherrington, C. S. (1917). Reflexes elicitable in cat from pinna, vibrissae and jaws. *Journal
of Physiology* (*London*) **51,** 404–431.

Simpson, P. C., and Booth, D. A. (1973). Olfactory conditioning by association with histi-
dine-free or balanced amino acid loads in rats. *Quarterly Journal of Experimental
Psychology* **25,** 354–359.

Smith, D. A. (1972). Increased perioral responsiveness: A possible explanation for the
switching of behavior observed during lateral hypothalamic stimulation. *Physiology and
Behavior* **8,** 617–621.

Smith, R. L. (1973). The ascending fiber projections from the principal trigeminal sensory
nucleus in the rat. *Journal of Comparative Neurology* **148,** 423–446.

Snowdon, C. T. (1969). Motivation, regulation and the control of meal patterns with oral and
intragastric feeding. *Journal of Comparative and Physiological Psychology* **69,** 91–100.

Snowdon, C. T. (1970). Gastrointestinal sensory and motor control of food intake. *Journal
of Comparative and Physiological Psychology* **71,** 68–76.

Spence, K. W. (1956). "Behavior Theory and Conditioning." Yale Univ. Press, New Ha-
ven, Connecticut.

Stellar, E., and Hill, H. (1952). The rat's rate of drinking as a function of water deprivation.
Journal of Comparative and Physiological Psychology **45,** 96–102.

Stricker, E. M., and Zigmond, M. J. (1976). Recovery of function after central catecholamine containing neurons: A neuronal model for the lateral hypothalamic syndrome. *In* "Progress in Psychobiology and Physiological Psychology" (E. Stellar and J. M. Sprague, eds.), Vol. 6. Academic Press, New York.

Teitelbaum, P. (1966). The use of operant methods in the assessment and control of motivational states. *In* "Operant Behavior: Areas of Research and Application" (W. K. Honig, ed.). Prentice-Hall, New York.

Teitelbaum, P. (1967). "Physiological Psychology." Prentice-Hall, New York.

Teitelbaum, P. (1977). Levels of integration of the operant. *In* "Handbook of Operant Behavior" (W. K. Honing and J. E. R. Staddon, eds.), pp. 7–27. Prentice-Hall, New York.

Teitelbaum, P. (1982). What is the "zero condition" for motivated behavior? *In* "The Neural Basis of Feeding and Reward" (B. G. Hoebel and D. Novin, eds.), pp. 7–23. Haer Inst., New Brunswick, Maine.

Travers, J. B., and Norgren, R. (1983). *Journal of Comparative Neurology* **220,** 280–298.

Van der Kooy, D., and Phillips, A. G. (1977). Trigeminal substrates of intracranial self-stimulation in the brainstem. *Science* **196,** 447–449.

Vincent, S. B. (1912). The function of the vibrissae in the behavior of the white rat. *Behavior Monographs, Series* **5.**

Waite, P. M. E., and Cragg, B. G. (1982). The peripheral and central changes resulting from cutting or crushing the afferent nerve supply to the whiskers. *Proceedings of the Royal Society of London, Series B* **214,** 191–211.

Weijnen, J. A. W. M., and Mendelson, J. (1977). "Drinking Behavior: Oral Stimulation, Reinforcement and Preference." Plenum, New York.

Weijs, W. A., and Dantuma, R. (1975). Electromyography and mechanics of mastication in the albino rat. *Journal of Morphology* **146,** 1–34.

Welker, C. (1971). Microelectrode delineation of fine grain somatotopic organization of SmI cerebral cortex in albino rat. *Brain Research* **26,** 254–275.

Welker, W. I. (1964). Analysis of sniffing of the albino rat. *Behaviour* **22,** 223–244.

Whishaw, I. Q., and Kolb, B. (1983). "Stick out your tongue": Tongue protrusion in neocortex and hypothalamic damaged rats. *Physiology and Behavior* **30,** 471–480.

Whishaw, I. Q., Schallert, T., and Kolb, B. (1981). An analysis of feeding and sensorimotor abilities of rats after decortication. *Journal of Comparative and Physiological Psychology* **94,** 85–103.

Wild, J. M., and Zeigler, H. P. (1980). Central representation and somatotopic organization of the jaw muscles within the facial and trigeminal nuclei in the the pigeon. *Journal of Comparative Neurology* **192,** 175–201.

Wild, J. M., Arends, J. J. A., and Zeigler, H. P. (1984). A trigeminal sensorimotor circuit for pecking, grasping and feeding in the pigeon. *Brain Research* **300,** 146–151.

Wild, J., Arends, J. J. A., and Zeigler, H. P. (1985). Telencephalic connections of the trigeminal system in the pigeon (*Columba livia*): A trigeminal sensorimotor circuit. *Journal of Comparative Neurology,* in press.

Wirtshafter, D., and Davis, J. D. (1977), Set points, settling point and the control of body weight. *Physiology and Behavior* **19,** 75–78.

Wolf, G., and DiCara, L. (1974). Impairments in sodium appetite after lesions of gustatory thalamus: Replication and extension. *Behavioral Biology* **10,** 105–112.

Wolfe, J. B. (1936). Effectiveness of token rewards for chimpanzees. *Comparative Psychological Monographs* **12,** 1–72.

Wurtman, J. J., and Wurtmann, R. J. (1977). Fenfluramine and fluexitine spare protein consumption while suppressing caloric intake by rats. *Science* **198,** 1178–1180.

Wyrwicka, W. (1967). Conditioned behavioral analysis of feeding mechanisms. *In* "Handbook of Physiology, Section 6: Alimentary Canal, Vol. 1: Control of Food and Water Intake" (C. E. Code, ed.), pp. 63–78. Amer. Physiol. Soc., Washington, D. C.

Wyrwicka, W. (1969). Sensory regulation of food intake. *Physiology and Behavior* **4**, 853–858.

Wyrwicka, W., Chase, M. A., and Clemente, C. D. (1975). The effects of lateral hypothalamic lesions on the masseteric reflex. *Anatomical Record* **181**, 514.

Young, J. Z. (1968). Influence of the mouth on the evolution of the brain. *In* "Biology of the Mouth" (P. Person, ed.). Amer. Assoc. for the Advancement of Science, Washington, D.C.

Zahorik, D. M. (1977). Associative and non-associative factors in learned food preferences. *In* "Learning Mechanisms in Food Selection" (L. M. Barker, M. R. Best, and M. Domjan, eds.), pp. 181–199. Baylor Univ. Press, Waco, Texas.

Zahorik, D. M., Maier, S. F., and Pies, R. W. (1974). Preferences for tastes paired with recovery from thiamine deficiency in rats: Appetitive conditioning or learned safety. *Journal of Comparative Physiology and Psychology* **87**, 1083–1091.

Zeaman, D. (1949). An application of SER quantification procedure. *Psychological Review* **56**, 341–350.

Zeigler, H. P. (1975). Trigeminal deafferentation and hunger in the pigeon. *Journal of Comparative and Physiological Psychology* **89**, 827–844.

Zeigler, H. P. (1976). Feeding behavior in the Pigeon. *In* "Advances in the Study of Behavior" (J. Rosenblatt, R. A. Hinde, C. Beer, and E. Shaw, eds.), Vol. 7, pp. 285–389. Academic Press, New York.

Zeigler, H. P. (1977). Trigeminal deafferentation and feeding behavior in the pigeon. Dissociation of tonic and phasic effects. *In* "Tonic Functions of Sensory Systems" (B. M. Wenzel and H. P. Zeigler, eds.), pp. 331–347. Annals of the New York Academy of Sciences.

Zeigler, H. P. (1983). The trigeminal system and ingestive behavior. *In* "Handbook of Behavioral Neurobiology: Motivation" (E. Satinoff and P. Teitelbaum, eds.), pp. 265–328. Plenum, New York.

Zeigler, H. P., and Karten, H. J. (1974). Central trigeminal structures and the lateral hypothalamic syndrome. *Science* **186**, 636–638.

Zeigler, H. P., Levitt, P., and Levine, R. R. (1980). Eating in the pigeon (*Columba livia*): Movement patterns, stereotypy and stimulus control. *Journal of Comparative and Physiological Psychology* **94**, 783–794.

Zeigler, H. P., Semba, K., and Jacquin, H. P. (1984) Trigeminal reflexes and ingestive behavior in the rat. *Behavioral Neuroscience* **98**, 1023–1038.

PROGRESS IN PSYCHOBIOLOGY AND PHYSIOLOGICAL PSYCHOLOGY, VOL. 11

The Stomach: A Conception of Its Dynamic Role in Satiety*

Paul R. McHugh and Timothy H. Moran

Department of Psychiatry and Behavioral Sciences
The Johns Hopkins University School of Medicine
Baltimore, Maryland

I. Introduction

The anatomy and physiology of the stomach illuminate its functions in feeding. The stomach is a distendable sac located at the start of the digestive tract. It has walls formed from intricate interlocking muscle bundles, and it is shaped like a hopper funneling down to a narrow portal.

* This work was supported by the National Institute of Arthritis, Metabolism, and Digestive Disease Grant AM-19302.

197

It has an extensive afferent and efferent innervation, and its lumen is lined with a secretory mucosa releasing acids and enzymes. Such a structure suits several interrelated functions.

The distendable stomach can accept a large quantity of food, facilitating the activity of feeding as an intermittent, meal-centered, rather than persistent, behavior. The combination of muscles, glands, and a restrictive portal permits the stomach to act as a grinding, pulverizing, liquifying way station in digestion that can prepare ingestants of widely varying compositions for the absorptive surfaces of the intestine. The narrow exit portal with its circumferential muscular bundle can assist in regulating the delivery of the stomach's contents to the intestine. The neural linkages to and from the central nervous system relate the stomach to the brain in a two-way traffic through which brain and gastric states coordinate feeding behavior.

Perhaps because the stomach's functions as both a reservoir and a preparatory way station for nutrients on the pathway of digestion seemed clear, physiological psychologists turned their attention from this peripheral organ to the brain in seeking the site of convergence of signals controlling food intake. However, in the last decade attention has been redirected to the periphery and to influences not only of the stomach (Deutsch *et al.*, 1978), but of the liver (Friedman and Stricker, 1976) and the intestine (Novin *et al.*, 1974) and of hormones such as insulin (Woods *et al.*, 1974), glucagon (Martin and Novin, 1977; Geary and Smith, 1982), and cholecystokinin (Gibbs *et al.*, 1973) on feeding behavior. This has resulted in an extensive body of new knowledge.

We plan to summarize here the work of our laboratory on gastric function and feeding, so as to depict the flow of conception and experiment that has run through our work. We do not plan a general review of all the emerging work relating gastrointestinal function and feeding, but what we lose in comprehensiveness we hope to repay with the sense of the "narrative line" in our research.

II. Methods

Most of the subjects in our experiments were male rhesus monkeys maintained in a standard fashion and studied by standard techniques. The monkeys weighed between 4 and 10 kg and were kept in individual cages in temperature- and light-controlled rooms. The animals were prepared with chronically indwelling silastic intragastric cannulas. The cannula was passed through the greater curvature of the stomach and to about 3 cm into the lumen, placing its end in the most dependent portion of the stomach. The free end was exteriorized through the back of the monkey and carried out of the cage through a multiflexible stainless-steel cable. This cable was held in place by being attached to a soft leather vest of our own design that fitted the torso of the monkey. The cannula, passing out of the cage through the cable, permitted the infusion of fluids into the stomach, the extraction of fluids from the stomach, and the insertion of smaller cannulas to be carried by gastric activity from the stomach down into the intestine.

Monkeys invested in this jacket were only slightly restrained by the protective cable that acted as a leash. They could move about the cage with little hindrance and were always studied in the unanesthetized state.

All of the experiments were done after animals had become accustomed to a restriction in their feeding time to 4 hr each day. From 10 AM to 2 PM the animals were either given food in a tray or permitted to work a lever for food pellets. After this time, the food was unavailable until the next day. Thus, the animals always began the experiments with an empty stomach and had fasted a comparable 20 hr. The animals quickly compensated for this time restriction and were soon eating exactly the same amount of food as animals with food available 24 hr/day. The animals slowly gained weight and took quantities of food and drink comparable to those reported in free-ranging monkeys both in the wild and in cage settings (Marriott, 1978; Hamilton *et al.,* 1976).

In the study of gastric emptying we employed a modification of the Hunt and Spurrell (1951) serial test meal method with phenol red as an indicator. This is a simple and accurate means of following the emptying of transparent liquids from the stomach. A liquid meal warmed to 37°C and containing a known concentration of phenol red, a dye that is not absorbed from the stomach, was infused into the stomach through the gastric cannula. An emptying period of some minutes permitted the stomach to pass on a portion of the inserted volume through the pylorus into the small intestine. The remnant volume in the stomach at the end of that emptying period was withdrawn through the cannula, measured, a correction made for the secretions from the stomach by assessing with colorimetry the dilution of the phenol red marker, and the amount of the original meal that passed through the pylorus during the emptying period estimated by subtracting the dye-corrected remnant volume from the volume of the original liquid meal. By varying day after day the duration of the emptying period during which a similar liquid meal was in the stomach, we could display the emptying characteristics of that meal from the stomach. We will be employing various modifications of this serial test meal method in the experiments reported here. This method is accurate and can estimate changes in volume of less than 5 ml.

III. From Central to Peripheral Studies

The path of research in our laboratory actually began with a study of hypothalamic hyperphagia in rhesus monkeys. We had adapted the Halasz and Pupp (1965) technique for making knife-cut lesions in the hypothalamus of rats to the rhesus monkey, and, with knife cuts disconnecting the ventromedial hypothalamus, produced hypothalamic hyperphagia (McHugh and Gibbs, 1972).

We thought that monkeys with knife cuts would be better subjects than ones with traditional destructive lesions for an analysis of feeding controls. The knife cuts appeared so discrete and so precisely localized and specific in their isolation of neural regions that it seemed that changes in behavioral functions such as satiety could, after knife cuts, be more confidently attributed to the loss or retention of parts of the hypothalamus. We therefore began a series of experiments in such monkeys, examining the influence of intragastric infusions of nutrient on their feeding (McHugh *et al.,* 1975a). We supplied nutrients to the animals through indwelling intragastric cannulas and observed the effect that these nutrients had on the amount of food eaten in the 4-hr meal period that followed immediately. We expected that food inserted into the stomach would have less effect on the subsequent meals in the hyperphagic animals, because we assumed that we had disconnected their "satiety center."

In fact we demonstrated in these monkeys something that others were independently discerning in rats (Panksepp, 1971; Thomas and Mayer, 1968). The basal food intake of the lesioned animals was certainly greater than that of unlesioned controls. They were hyperphagic. However, a given caloric infusion into the stomach of either the lesioned or the control animals reduced their food intake an identical amount. Thus, for every calorie infused into the stomach there was a calorie reduction in the food eaten in the subsequent 4-hr feeding period for both the lesioned and the intact animals. We could only conclude that if satiety is defined as that graded inhibition on feeding produced by food itself, then by these results normal and hyperphagic monkeys do not differ in satiety. Both sets of animals demonstrated a similar capacity for regulating feeding so as to control accurately the energy they take in meals. As there was no loss of this capacity in the hyperphagic animals, a deficit in satiety so defined could not explain their hyperphagia.

The most interesting aspect of this result to us, however, was not the results with the hyperphagic animals, but those with the controls. It seemed remarkable that rhesus monkeys would reduce their daily food intake precisely calorie for calorie in response to intragastric nutrient infusions. We had of course stumbled onto the "caloric homeostasis" of

Richter (1942) by a roundabout route. We repeated the observations and demonstrated this phenomenon again and again in normal nonhyperphagic monkeys and in the process showed that the phenomenon could be demonstrated with liquid nutrients of many different kinds—fats, carbohydrates, proteins—and even when they were presented as mixtures or in different volumes or concentrations (McHugh *et al.*, 1975b; McHugh and Moran, 1978).

In a search for some physiological mechanisms to explain this "homeostasis," we made an observation that directed our attention peripherally. We followed by X-ray studies a load of 150 cal of glucose and saw that a large part of this load was not emptied from the monkey's stomach by the end of the 4-hr feeding period. It seemed intriguing that nutrients still in the stomach and thus presumably not entered into energy metabolism could so effectively influence feeding that an accurate compensation for the energy content of this yet-to-be-absorbed nutrient occurred. Two clear questions were posed by these results. First, if feeding can display such quantitative, calorie-related compensation, can any intragastric mechanisms be found to function in quantitative specificity to calories? Second, could these mechanisms be invoked to explain any aspect of satiety such as the reduction or interruption of a meal or the prolongation of intermeal intervals?

IV. The Quantitation of Gastric Emptying

Since nutrients still in the stomach and not entered into energy metabolism were nontheless quantitatively effective in influencing feeding, we decided to seek a quantitative feature in the rate at which the stomach emptied different liquid meals.

The study of the dynamic characteristics of the stomach's management of its contents is linked to the beginnings of modern physiology itself. Beaumont, Pavlov, Cannon, and Wolff, among the fathers of physiology, all worked on the stomach. However, the textbook teaching on gastric emptying stated that the stomach emptied exponentially when filled with liquids, that its rate slowed when the contents were nutrients, high-osmolar solutions, or acids, and that fats slowed stomach emptying disproportionately. No relationship of emptying to energy was known.

Hunt and Stubbs (1975) provided a landmark observation in their review of past studies of gastric emptying. They demonstrated that nutrients of comparable caloric concentration were equally effective in slowing gastric emptying whether they were supplied in the form of carbohydrates, fats, or proteins.

This was the first observation to our knowlege of a regulative role of calories in gastric emptying. However, Hunt and Stubbs presumed that the emptying was exponential even though modified by calories, and they could not show that the slowing of gastric emptying was truly regulatory. From their data it appeared that although the slowing of gastric emptying increased as the concentration of calories increased and did so equally for calories of carbohydrate and fat, the increase in slowing was not large enough to compensate completely for an increasing caloric concentration in the meal. Such a compensatory slowing would be needed to make the flow of calories from the stomach constant with different meals. However, their suggestion that gastric emptying was in some fashion tied to the energy content of the nutrients in the stomach encouraged further studies, because any demonstration of quantitative accuracy in the function of this organ that relates to the caloric content of ingested foods might provide a mechanism for precision of preabsorptive satiety in the regulation of caloric ingestion.

Hunt and Stubbs reported on the results of past experiments in humans. We elected to study this issue at first in the rhesus monkey, employing the gastric cannulas already described for infusion and withdrawal of solutions of various concentrations and volumes (McHugh and Moran, 1979).

BIPHASIC GASTRIC EMPTYING OF NUTRIENTS

Test loads used were one of the following: physiological saline, glucose solutions in various concentrations (0.05–0.5g/ml), 0.125 g/ml casein hydrolysate solution, or a suspension of 19.5 ml of medium-chain triglyceride (MCT) oil and water. All the nutrient loads were given in the volume of 150 ml; the saline and the 0.125-g/ml glucose meal were also given in a 300-ml volume.

As shown in Fig. 1, test loads of physiological saline empty rapidly and exponentially from the monkey's stomach; increasing the volume from 150 to 300 ml increases the rate of emptying. These saline-emptying curves conform to an exponential (first-order kinetics) equation with a significant level of $p < 0.001$.

In Fig. 2, from 20 min after their infusion, glucose loads empty in a manner conforming to a straight line (zero-order kinetics) equation with a significant level of $p < 0.001$. Increasing the glucose concentration of the test loads results in a progressive slowing of gastric emptying.

A regulatory implication of this progressive slowing with increasing concentrations of glucose was revealed when the y axis of Fig. 2 was changed from load volume remaining in the stomach over time to load calories remaining. Figure 3 is the result: three parallel lines, one above

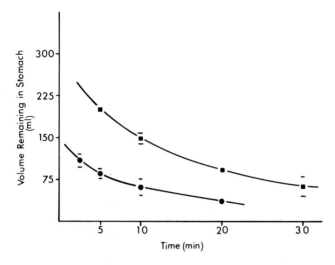

FIG. 1. Gastric emptying of 150 (●) and 300 (■) ml of physiological saline over time. Points are means ± SE. (Used with permission, McHugh and Moran, 1979.)

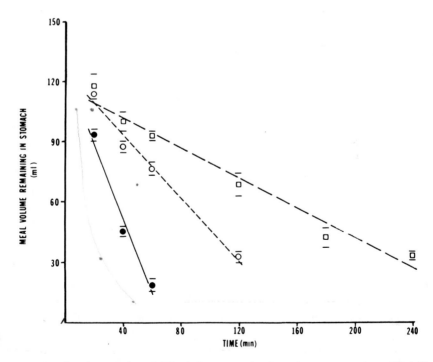

FIG. 2. Gastric emptying of 150-ml glucose meals of varying concentrations. (●) 0.05 g/ml; (○) 0.125 g/ml; (□) 0.25 g/ml. (Used with permission, McHugh and Moran, 1979.)

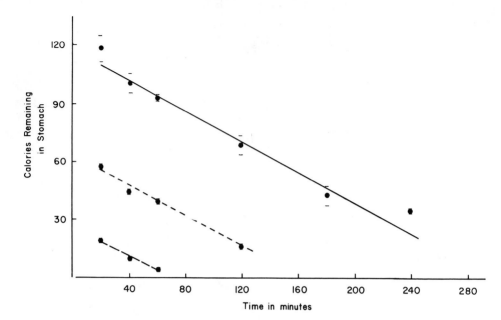

FIG. 3.   Caloric emptying of 150-ml glucose meals of varying concentrations. (– – –) 0.05 g/ml, 0.2 kcal/ml, 0.363 ± 0.024 kcal/min emptied; (- - -) 0.125 g/ml, 0.5 kcal/ml, 0.391 ± 0.020 kcal/min emptied; (——) 0.25 g/ml, 1.0 kcal/ml, 0.373 ± 0.025 kcal/min emptied. (Used with permission, McHugh and Moran, 1979).

the other. This result can be explained in the following fashion. With each increase in the concentration of the glucose load, there is an increase in the total calories infused into the stomach as reflected in the elevation of the value for calories remaining in the stomach at 20 min. However, the rate of emptying of calories from this point on, as shown by the slope of these emptying curves, is the same. A rate of gastric emptying of 0.4 kcal/min is sustained over the emptying period studied for each of the glucose loads across a range of concentrations of 0.2 to 1.0 kcal/ml. As shown in Table I, the same rates of emptying are assumed by glucose, casein hydrolysate, and MCT.

We concluded, both from these experiments and the X-ray studies, that there are two phases of gastric emptying. Immediately after filling the stomach with a liquid there is a rush of emptying into the duodenum. This rush appears to be dependent on the volume filling the stomach, as it is greater for large volumes and less for small volumes. If the liquid is physiological saline, this exponential-like function will continue until the stomach is empty. However, if the liquids are nutrients, this rapid empty-

TABLE I

GASTRIC-EMPTYING RATES OF TEST MEALS

N^a	Meal	g/ml	kcal/ml	Volume (ml)	Osmolality (mOsm/kg)	Emptying rate (ml/min)	Emptying rate (kcal/min)
25	NaCl[b]	0.009	—	150	290	4.25 ± 0.6	—
24	Glucose	0.05	0.2	150	291	1.8 ± 0.1	0.36 ± 0.02
32	Glucose	0.125	0.5	150	722	0.78 ± 0.04	0.39 ± 0.02
26	Glucose	0.25	1.0	150	1425	0.37 ± 0.03	0.37 ± 0.03
16	Casein hydrolysate	0.125	0.5	150	839	0.77 ± 0.07	0.39 ± 0.03
16	MCT	—	0.5	150	—	0.76 ± 0.05	0.38 ± 0.03
12	D-Xylose	0.125	—	150	916	0.78 ± 0.05	—
24	Fructose[b]	0.125	0.5	150	721	1.36 ± 0.14	0.68 ± 0.08

[a] N = Number of test meals from which a regression was derived.
[b] Emptying rates, though exponential, are here expressed as averaged over time.

ing phase is interrupted within minutes and gastric emptying takes on a
linear function.

We can recognize the initial rush both on the X-ray film and from the
fact that the linear regressions for nutrient loads (Fig. 2) do not extrapo-
late back to intersect the y axis at the infused volume (150 ml) but fall
below by 20 to 30 ml. It is this biphasic characteristic of gastric emptying
that obscured the accuracy of regulation for Hunt and Stubbs (1975). They
used the time to half-empty a given volume as a measure of the rate of
gastric emptying. By that method, the precision of regulation would be
obscured by the unregulated calories in the initial rush phase of emptying.

Since our studies in the monkey, we have also confirmed in humans
that physiological saline empties exponentially with a half-empty time of
approximately 8 min. There is also a similar biphasic emptying of liquid
glucose with a settling of gastric emptying to a rate of approximately 2.1
kcal/min. Changes in the concentration of glucose in the stomach are
matched by compensatory alterations in gastric emptying, so that this rate
of 2.1 kcal/min is found across a range of glucose concentrations from 0.2
to 1.0 kcal/ml in humans.

V. Feedback Control of Gastric Emptying

The linear, calorie-constant emptying pattern of liquid nutrients suggests a precise feedback control on the stomach evoked by nutrient but
not by saline. To test this possibility we sought to demonstrate that physiological amounts of postpyloric glucose could inhibit gastric emptying in
some quantitative fashion. In our first experiments we took advantage of
the initial rush that follows an infusion of glucose into the stomach
(McHugh, 1979; McHugh et al., 1982).

A. Gastric Infusions

Specifically the monkey's stomach was filled with 150 ml of a glucose
solution containing 0.25 g/ml along with the phenol red marker. This meal
was left in place for 20 min, permitting some glucose to pass through the
pylorus. After 20 min the stomach's contents were withdrawn and the
amount of glucose from the initial load passed by the stomach into the
intestine in this 20 min was measured. Then the stomach was refilled with
a test meal of 150 ml of physiological saline and phenol red. Without the
preceding glucose this load would empty rapidly, at least 45 ml in 10 min.
We defined a rate of saline emptying less than 45 ml in 10 min as evidence
of some inhibition on gastric emptying.

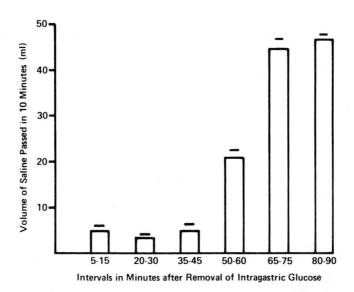

Fig. 4. Inhibition of gastric emptying of physiological saline provoked by a preceding intragastric glucose load. These results are derived from three experiments in which the same amount of glucose passed from the stomach. Inhibition of saline emptying was deemed present until the end of the 50- to 60-min interval. (Used with permission, McHugh *et al.*, 1982.)

The first saline test load (150 ml) was placed in the stomach 5 min after removing the glucose. It was left in the stomach for 10 min, removed, and the amount emptied by the stomach measured. After a 5-min interval to manage this second exchange, the stomach was again refilled with a 150-ml test load of saline and phenol red, which as before was left in place for 10 min, then withdrawn. The saline exchanges were repeated until the stomach was emptying more than 45 ml of the saline test loads in a 10-min emptying period. The time taken after the initial glucose load to reach this emptying rate for saline was a period of gastric inhibition that we could correlate with the amount of glucose that passed through the pylorus in the first 20 min of the procedure (see Fig. 4).

In 15 trials of this experiment on five monkeys the amount of glucose delivered into the intestine with the initial glucose load varied from 8 to 29 kcal (mean 18.2 ± 1.9 kcal). Subsequent duration of inhibition of saline emptying varied from 15 to 60 min (mean 33.5 ± 5 min). The results are displayed in Fig. 5, in which a regression of inhibition against glucose calories is drawn. The slope of this line, 2.34 ± 0.24 min/kcal, represented the inhibitory response of the stomach across the range of postpyloric glucose calories delivered by the stomach's action. The value of 2.34 min

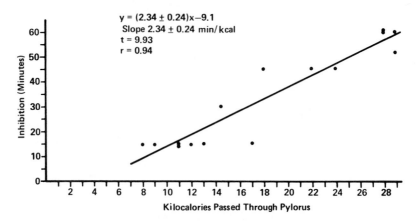

FIG. 5.   Least-squares linear regression displaying the duration of gastric inhibition following calories of glucose passed into the small intestine. (Used with permission, McHugh *et al.*, 1982.)

of inhibition per kilocalorie certainly intrigued us, because it was so close to the reciprocal (2.5 min/kcal) of the gastric-emptying rate for glucose (0.4 kcal/min).

However, this experiment had several aspects that complicated its interpretation. The 10-min emptying periods of the saline demanded long intervals that could obscure the loss of inhibition. Also, the stomach was initially filled with glucose, and the possibility of glucose receptors located in the gastric wall inhibiting subsequent gastric emptying could not be excluded.

B. INTESTINAL INFUSIONS

For the next experiment we turned to a direct infusion of glucose into the duodenum using a thin, small-bore cannula that we passed down the large gastric cannula into the monkey's stomach. The tip of this cannula was carried by the stomach's own action through the pylorus into the small intestine.

The intragastric test loads for this experiment were 100 ml of physiological saline infused through the gastric cannula and left in place for 2 min. Loads were removed and exchanged in 3 min for another 100-ml saline load. The amount of saline remaining in the stomach and the amount passed through the pylorus in 2 min could be measured as before. A saline test load before the intraduodenal glucose infusion served as a control

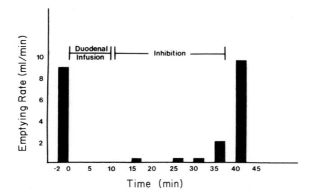

FIG. 6. Inhibition of gastric emptying of saline provoked by an intraduodenal infusion of glucose. On this occasion 15 kcal of glucose was infused over a 10-min period in a concentration of 1 kcal/ml. Emptying of 100 ml of saline in 2 min was followed by 3-min intervals until control rate returned. Here inhibition lasted for 37 min after infusion. (Used with permission, McHugh *et al.*, 1982.)

assuring that the stomach was emptying a saline load rapidly at a rate of 15 to 20 ml in 2 min.

As shown in Fig. 6, the duration of inhibition of gastric emptying produced by glucose infused into the duodenum could be displayed by repeated intragastric exchanges of 100-ml saline loads carried out until the saline load recovered to the control rate of more than 15 ml in 2 min. From the knowledge derived from the previous experiment of the quantities of glucose passed by the stomach, we could design a dose–response study using infusions into the duodenum that were varied within the same range.

As shown in Fig. 7, we carried out 27 trials of this experiment in four monkeys. The regression of gastric inhibition against calories in the intestine now had a slope of 2.46 ± 0.19 min/kcal, a slope not significantly different from the 2.34 ± 0.24 min/kcal found when glucose was delivered by the action of the stomach and even closer to a reciprocal of the gastric-emptying rate for glucose, 0.4 kcal/min.

We also demonstrated that the gastric-inhibitory effect was not simply an osmolar effect, as shown in Table II. In the same monkey, we delivered the same amount of glucose (7.5 kcal) into the duodenum on five different occasions but across almost a 10-fold range of volumes, concentrations, and osmolarity. The duration of inhibition found at this dose did not differ from the mean of 22 min by more than 3 min. There was no relationship between these small deviations from the mean and the vol-

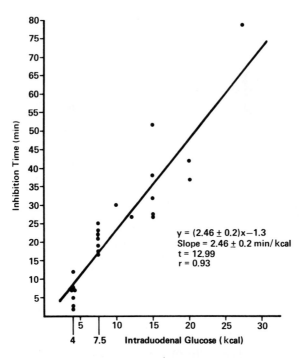

FIG. 7. Least-squares linear regression of duration of gastric inhibition after intra-duodenal infusions of glucose. (Used with permission, McHugh *et al.*, 1982.)

TABLE II
VOLUME–CONCENTRATION CONTROL[a,b]

Osmolality (mOsm/kg)	Volume (ml)	Glucose concentration (kcal/ml)	Total (kcal)	Inhibition duration (min)
2800	3.75	2.0	7.5	23
1400	7.5	1.0	7.5	25
700	15.0	0.5	7.5	22
700	15.0	0.5	7.5	19
350	30.0	0.25	7.5	21

[a] Used with permission, McHugh *et al.* (1982).
[b] Duration of gastric inhibition in the same monkey with the same intraduodenal load of glucose given in differing volumes and concentrations.

ume, concentration, or osmolarity of the duodenal load. It appeared to be the amount of glucose delivered into the intestine that determined the duration of inhibition.

C. INTERRELATIONSHIPS OF GASTRIC EMPTYING AND FEEDBACK INHIBITION

We conclude from these results that for each calorie passed into the intestine an inhibition of gastric emptying of approximately 2.5 min was eventually demonstrable. The inhibition appeared to be a near-total cessation of gastric emptying following a bolus of nutrient into the duodenum. Since the duration of inhibition (2.5 min/kcal) is the reciprocal of the glucose-emptying rate (0.4 kcal/min), the rate of gastric delivery of that nutrient into the intestine and the effects of glucose in the intestine on the stomach seem interdependent functions. These views in fact fit a simple control theory description of the regulation of gastric emptying of liquids.

Gastric emptying of nonnutrient osmotically neutral physiological saline is uninfluenced by any obvious inhibitory feedback. It has the characteristics of an "open-loop" function, emptying rapidly and exponentially, depending for its rate of emptying primarily on the volume remaining in the stomach.

When a glucose solution fills the empty stomach, there is at first a variable amount delivered unimpeded under the existing open-loop condition to the intestine, the "rush." However, this glucose evokes an inhibition, and a "closed-loop" condition is soon imposed on the system by the feedback influence derived from glucose beyond the pylorus. Since calories delivered and the duration of gastric inhibition are reciprocally interrelated functions, they will tend soon to establish and maintain a steady-state condition in which caloric delivery is a constant regardless, within limits, of perturbations in the volume or concentration of gastric contents (Fig. 8).

With essentially the same methods we have been able to demonstrate similar phenomena in gastric emptying of glucose in humans (Brener *et al.*, 1983). Again a biphasic emptying feature is seen, with an initial rush of glucose emptying under the open-loop condition followed by a closed-loop condition with a steady state due to the interrelationship of two reciprocal functions—a gastric-emptying rate of 2.13 kcal/min and a inhibition on gastric emptying of 0.46 min/kcal of duodenal glucose.

Once we appreciated that the original gastric-emptying curves derived from the serial test meal method actually represented a steady state as assumed in a closed-loop system, it became easier to explain certain characteristics of those results. For example, the emptying of the stomach

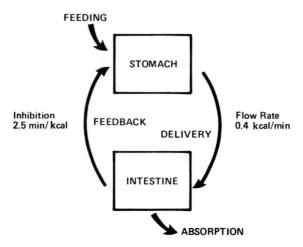

F<small>IG</small>. 8. A diagrammatic proposal of the regulatory system for control of gastric empty-ing. (Used with permission, McHugh *et al.,* 1982.)

is mostly a discontinuous, peristaltically derived gushing affair, yet the curves from our serial test meal method can give the impression, being lines of a constant slope, that the emptying of glucose through the pylorus is a constant, slow passage of liquid. The serial test meal method, how-ever, does not follow gastric emptying moment by moment. It measures rather a remnant volume of the gastric load at such intervals as 10, 20, 40, 60 min after the stomach is filled. This remnant volume of the initial glucose load decreases at each interval by a constant amount, hence the linear appearance that resulted from the display of these volumes over time.

Such a result, however, can be the outcome of the intermittent delivery of peristaltic gushes into the duodenum. Each gush delivers calories to the duodenum and produces a variable inhibition on further delivery, an inter-delivery interval. The caloric load in one gush determines the interde-livery interval to the next by extending the duration of that interval by the inhibitory constant for each calorie. Although the caloric content in indi-vidual gushes and the duration of each interval can vary, they remain tightly interrelated. Any emptying curves derived by measuring meal rem-nants in the stomach will average out the variation in the discrete peri-staltic events to display a linear function with a slope in kilocalories per minute that is the reciprocal of the interdelivery inhibition in minutes per kilocalorie.

That a steady-state closed-loop relation ties gastric delivery to postpyloric glucose can also explain the persistence of a constant caloric delivery rate for any given meal over the duration of gastric emptying even though that meal is being diluted by gastric secretions during its stay in the stomach. Dilution will affect the amount of glucose delivered to the duodenum with any given gush, but the following interdelivery interval will also change appropriately and so adjust the caloric delivery. Gushes of the intragastric glucose diluted by secretion late in the gastric-emptying time would be more frequent than the gushes of the more concentrated glucose present when the meal originally fills the stomach. This frequency change tied to caloric concentration will produce the picture of linear emptying across the whole emptying period.

Finally, we understood why test meals of different glucose concentrations settle to a constant comparable rate of caloric delivery. The interdelivery inhibition on gastric emptying varies with the postpyloric glucose load and will be longer for concentrated and shorter for dilute meals by a constant.

VI. Inhibiting Signals and Transmitters

Although these studies on both gastric emptying and intestinal control were intended primarily to display the integrative activity of the gastroduodenal system, that is, its actions and its outcomes rather than the mechanism within it that could mediate them, we have studied some of the constituent mechanisms.

A. Nutrient Signals

The first and most accessible element for investigation was the signal being carried by nutrients to the duodenum that acts to slow gastric emptying. Fats, proteins, and carbohydrates all appear to slow gastric emptying equally in proportion to their calories (Table I), yet it is difficult to see any physical characteristics all three share other than their nutrient value.

Although a relation between osmotic pressure and gastric inhibition had been demonstrated (Hunt, 1961), we have considerable evidence that osmotic pressure cannot have any simple relationship to the emptying of nutrients. Fats with no osmotic pressure slow emptying equally to carbohydrates and protein (Table I). Glucose at 0.2 kcal/ml empties more slowly than equiosmolar physiological saline (McHugh and Moran, 1979). Xylose empties gram for gram in a fashion identical to glucose (Moran and McHugh, 1981). However, as xylose is a pentose, it exerts a higher osmotic pressure per gram than glucose. Fructose, with similar osmotic pressure to glucose, empties exponentially and more rapidly. When we infused glucose into the duodenum (Table II), the duration of inhibition of gastric emptying did not vary with the volume, the concentration, or the osmolality of the duodenal load across a 10-fold range (McHugh *et al.*, 1982). It seems likely that osmotic pressure participates in but does not explain the precision of control of gastric emptying provoked by intra-duodenal nutrients. We lack a definition of the signal derived from nutrient calories acting in the duodenum.

B. HORMONAL SIGNALS

In our effort to consider other elements within the gastroduodenal system that could mediate the inhibition of gastric emptying, we did examine the inhibition provoked by the intestinal hormone cholecystokinin (CCK) (Moran and McHugh, 1982). We observed the gastric emptying of 150 ml of physiological saline during the intravenous infusion of the C-terminal octapeptide of CCK (CCK-8) across a dose range of 0.75, 1.5, and 3.0 pmol/kg/min. As mentioned earlier, saline should empty rapidly and exponentially from the stomach, but with these doses of CCK a progressive inhibition of gastric emptying of saline appeared, so that the dose of 3.0 pmol/kg/min slowed the gastric emptying of saline to a rate similar to that of nutrient solutions (Table III).

We then chose the dose of 3.0 pmol/kg/min to study the dynamics of CCK-induced gastric inhibition. We again employed a saline exchange method. We filled the stomach with 100 ml saline with phenol red, left it in place for 2 min, and then removed it, observed how much had passed out, and replaced it with another 100-ml load 3 min later. These exchanges of saline occurred before, during, and after the intravenous infusion of CCK-8. The results were striking, as shown in Fig. 9.

TABLE III
INHIBITION OF GASTRIC EMPTYING[a,b]

Intravenous O-CCK dose (pmol/kg/min)	N	Control condition (ml)	CCK condition (ml)	Inhibition (%)
0.75	8	101.4 ± 7.1	74.7 ± 2.7	23.5 ± 6.0
1.5	8	95.3 ± 5.0	47.8 ± 2.4	48.3 ± 3.5
3.0	8	98.7 ± 4.4	6.3 ± 3.1	91.5 ± 3.6

[a] Used with permission, Moran and McHugh (1982).

[b] Values are means ±SE. Gastric emptying inhibited by intravenous O-cholecystokinin (O-CCK) expressed as volume of saline emptied in 10 min after 150-ml test meal.

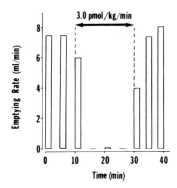

FIG. 9.   Typical example of temporal characteristics of inhibition and recovery of gastric emptying of saline that results from an intravenous infusion of *O*-cholecystokinin (*O*-CCK). (Used with permission, Moran and McHugh, 1982.)

Saline emptied rapidly before the CCK infusion, but an inhibition on its emptying was apparent immediately on beginning the hormone infusion, and by the second exchange saline emptying had essentially ceased. Also, when the hormone infusion was discontinued, there was an immediate recovery of the gastric emptying of the saline.

Thus, the onset of gastric inhibition by CCK was rapid and, at this dose and with this gastric load (100 ml), essentially complete. Its duration beyond the cessation of hormone infusion was brief. We could refer to this inhibitory effect on the stomach as a kind of "endocrine square wave" suggesting a role for CCK in the precision of gastric emptying.

Rayford *et al.* (1975), established that CCK is a hormone with a brief half-life (minutes) in circulation. We have now shown that it has no prolonged action on gastric emptying. Cholecystokinin might function to regulate gastric emptying in the following fashion. When CCK is released from the intestine by the entrance of food it will interrupt the delivery of further nutrient into the intestine by stopping gastric emptying. This will assist in one important role of the distendable stomach: the avoidance of the flooding of the intestinal and postintestinal compartments of the body with nutrients in amounts beyond the body's capacity to manage them efficiently. Yet with the absorption of the nutrients from the intestine, CCK secretion will decline, leading promptly to the further delivery of nutrients through the pylorus and further secretion of the hormone. Presumably, a kind of steady state will be established by which a sustained secretion of CCK acts, with other mechanisms, to cause a regulated supply of nutrients to pass from the stomach onto the absorptive surfaces of the intestines. Although the relationship of CCK to other inhibitory factors and the relationship of calories in the intestine to the stimulation of

CCK release is unknown, this proposal would fit CCK into digestion in a fashion that makes sense of its dynamic characteristics as a hormone of brief "half-life" and a quick on–off effect on the stomach.

VII. Gastric Distention as a Satiety Signal

With the recognition that gastric emptying of calorie-laden liquids tended to develop into a steady-state, tightly regulated function, we conceived of an integration between the functions of the stomach and the small intestine that would act in the regulation of food intake, and particularly the inhibition on food intake produced by food itself—that is, satiety. Our hypothesis stems in part from Cannon and Washburn's demonstration in 1912 that distention of the stomach is a potent satiety signal. Distention, however, could be viewed as the result of two events: the ingestion of food and the restriction of the food's passage from the stomach by the physiological inhibition of gastric emptying produced by the entry of nutrients into the small bowel.

The stomach thus may act to prevent nutrients from immediately entering the intestine. With the progression of a meal the stomach would gradually fill. The gastric distention from this filling could slow and eventually interrupt feeding, producing the intermeal interval during which a proportion of the calories in the stomach would be gradually emptied and appropriately absorbed.

Thus, gastric distention would influence satiety but as a link in a chain, the initiation of which and the regulation of which lay beyond the stomach, presumably in the duodenum and jejunum. Distention as a signal for satiety, first proposed by Cannon, would thus be the outcome of gastroduodenal coordination.

A. COMPARABLE INTESTINAL LOADS AND GASTRIC DISTENTION IN SATIETY

With this hypothesis in mind we first demonstrated that with equal and physiological amounts of nutrient in the postpyloric compartment, the state of the stomach—distended or empty—would have a powerful influence on consumption (Wirth and McHugh, 1983). We took advantage of the fact that the gastric emptying of glucose solutions is constant. Thus, we could observe circumstances in which the postpyloric nutrient signals were similar.

The monkeys in these experiments drank 0.5 kcal/ml glucose solutions containing the phenol red marker. They took this solution avidly and within 15 min had their fill as evidenced by their ceasing to consume more. We then observed how much glucose they would consume in a subsequent 15-min period after one of the following interventions carried out on different days: (1) immediate removal of the gastric contents leaving the stomach empty, (2) removal of the gastric contents but refilling of the stomach with saline, or (3) leaving the gastric contents undisturbed, that is, filled with the glucose of the first period of consumption.

The pertinent observation was that on all three occasions the same amount of glucose passed from the stomach into the intestine during the first 15-min bout of consumption. The subsequent consumption of further glucose, however, depended on the state of the stomach. If the stomach was empty, the monkey would consume two or three times as much glucose on the subsequent opportunity than when the stomach was full, either with glucose that had been drunk or with a saline load.

These results seemed to support the view that although there certainly are postpyloric satiety signals, signals derived from the state of gastric distention are more potent in determining short-term glucose consumption.

B. GASTRIC-EMPTYING RATE DISTINCTIONS IN SATIETY

A second test of our hypothesis took advantage of the distinctions in gastric emptying that are found with some different sugars (Moran and McHugh, 1981). Fructose is an interesting compound in that it empties faster than glucose from the stomach of the rhesus monkey. D-Xylose empties at the same rate as glucose (Table I) but is known to be a poor metabolic fuel once absorbed (Wyngaarden et al., 1958). If the dynamic characteristics of the filled stomach could provide visceral sensory signals that accurately provided preabsorptive estimates of the calories within the stomach, then comparing a monkey feeding after a fructose or xylose preload could be informative.

Again we employed the same method of giving 150 cal in solution into the stomach just before a 4-hr feeding period and found intriguing results as shown in Table IV. Xylose, which emptied gram for gram like glucose from the stomach, produced on the day it was given as a preload an identical reduction in food intake as did glucose. Xylose, however, is not adequately metabolized. Therefore, the reduction in the animals feeding cheated them of nutrient energy on the experimental day. They compensated for this deficit by overeating on the next day.

With fructose, although there was a suppression of chow intake as with glucose, the pattern of feeding was not the same. The early suppression of food intake in the first hour of the 4-hr feeding that is found with glucose

TABLE IV

FEEDING RESPONSES TO INTRAGASTRIC PRELOADS[a,b]

| Type | N | Chow eaten (g) | | | Reduction[c] (g) | Reduction (kcal) |
		On day 1 (control)	On day 2 (experimental)	On day 3 (control)		
Glucose	16	198 ± 17	164 ± 22	203 ± 16	36.5 ± 3.2	153 ± 13
Xylose	16	201 ± 20	163 ± 18	234 ± 19[d]	38.0 ± 6.0	160 ± 25
Fructose	16	201 ± 15	161 ± 16	191 ± 17	35.4 ± 3.2	149 ± 13

[a] Used with permission, Moran and McHugh (1981).
[b] Values are means ± SE. Preload of 150-ml volume at 0.25-g/ml concentration.
[c] For glucose and fructose, reduction is estimated by subtracting day 2 results from the mean of days 1 and 3. For xylose, reduction is estimated by subtracting day 2 only from day 1.
[d] Versus day 1 (matched pair t) $p < 0.05$.

and xylose did not occur. Suppression of feeding by fructose came later in the last 2 hr of the feeding period.

The results with xylose seemed to suggest that a particular gastric-emptying pattern can be a sufficient stimulus for the accurate preabsorptive control of food intake. The similarity of the gastric dynamics produced by xylose and glucose would seem the likely source of signals for their comparable influence on feeding on the experimental day. The overeating on the subsequent day is a confirmation that xylose is not fully metabolized and as a gastric load leads to a miscalculation of caloric homeostasis.

Our results with fructose, though, indicate that the pattern of gastric emptying characteristic of glucose and xylose is not a necessary condition for calorically accurate reduction of food intake under our conditions. Fructose produces a more rapid gastric emptying (Table I), and yet the animal compensated as accurately for fructose calories as for glucose. Therefore, the gastric-emptying signals need not resemble those of glucose for control to occur. The observation that fructose's reduction in food intake occurred later in the feeding period than that produced by glucose indicates that other satiety signals arise from postabsorptive sites yet to be identified (Rowland and Stricker, 1979).

We concluded from these experiments that a sustained gastric distention can provide signals for preabsorptive regulation of caloric ingestion but that the dynamics of distention found with glucose and xylose loads are not necessary for caloric homeostasis in feeding. This feeding regulation must be produced through several different but effectively redundant mechanisms of control. Signals derived from the dynamic characteristics of the nutrient-filled stomach provide the animal with one mechanism but not the only mechanism for short-term control of food intake.

C. DIFFERENT GASTRIC STATES AND SATIETY

These experiments repeatedly supported the concept of a gastric role in satiety, but the linkage to the dynamic aspects of gastric emptying that had been previously documented by us was only indirect. In particular, we had not as yet taken direct advantage of the distinctions between the gastric emptying of saline (rapid, exponential) and that of glucose (biphasic, with at first a "rush" followed by a prolonged period of slow linear emptying). Yet our experimental preparations were quite suited for such an experiment.

For these studies we attempted to follow on a moment-to-moment basis a monkey's eating through the 4-hr feeding period (McHugh, 1979). Food pellets (1 g each) were delivered to the animal in response to lever presses on a fixed-ratio schedule of one pellet delivered after five lever presses.

Twenty minutes before the onset of the feeding period, 150 ml of 1.0-kcal/ml glucose was infused into the stomach through the indwelling cannula. This preload was left for 20 min so as to permit the full set of gastric-emptying events to occur; namely a portion of the preload was allowed to pass into the intestine in the form of the initial rush, placing the stomach in the steady-state phase of inhibition by postpyloric glucose. We could then manipulate the gastric contents and observe the feeding behavior that began immediately afterwards under one of three different conditions.

Thus, just before the feeding period and 20 min after the infusion of the glucose preload into the stomach we could (1) remove the remnant glucose load from the stomach and observe the effects on feeding of the glucose remaining in the intestine, (2) remove the remnant glucose load from the stomach and then fill the stomach with a volume of saline (150 ml) and observe the effects of the combination of a distending nonnutrient gastric load and the intraintestinal glucose on subsequent feeding, or (3) simply leave the glucose load undisturbed in both stomach and intestine to observe and compare its effects on feeding with those seen in the other experimental conditions or with (4) controls that received an intragastric saline infusion (150 ml) just before feeding.

These comparisons would permit us to determine (1) whether the amount of glucose entering the intestine during the first 20 min would itself be sufficient to influence feeding, (2) whether a combination of this intraintestinal glucose with a distention of the stomach by infusion of saline would influence feeding, and (3) how this latter influence, if any, might compare with our often-demonstrated quantitative reduction of feeding provoked by the undisturbed glucose preload that fills both the stomach and the intestine.

The results from the first 60 min of feeding are shown in Fig. 10. If the preload was left in place undisturbed, then feeding was slow at its beginning and remained constantly less than the control right through the 4-hr feeding period. At the end of 240 min the amount of food eaten by the monkeys was 150 kcal less than what was eaten in control situations—again reduction in feeding matching the intragastric caloric infusion.

However, on those occasions in which the remnant of the preload still in the stomach was removed just before the feeding period and the stomach was left empty, we could demonstrate that a small amount of glucose had passed into the intestine (mean 16 kcal). However, when it was permitted the monkeys ate vigorously and in a fashion indistinguishable from

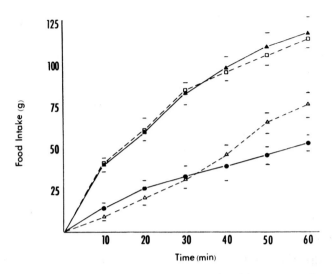

FIG. 10. Cumulative records of food intake during the first 60 min of a 4-hr feeding period of monkeys under four different conditions: (▲) intragastric saline, 150 ml saline in stomach; (□) intraintestinal glucose, glucose placed in stomach for 20 min then removed from stomach, leaving only intraintestinal glucose; (△) intraintestinal glucose + intragastric saline, after glucose removed from stomach, 150 ml saline infused into stomach; (●) intraintestinal glucose and intragastric glucose, 150 ml glucose placed in stomach and left undisturbed. (Used with permission, McHugh, 1979.)

controls. Their behavior was unaffected by this small amount of postpyloric glucose.

Finally, in the situation in which the intragastric remnant of the glucose preload was replaced with 150 ml of saline, we could again demonstrate that the intestine had received a mean of 16 kcal of glucose. Now, however, this glucose combined with the distending 150 ml of saline in the stomach had a clear influence on feeding. The animal would begin to eat only slowly just as in the situation with the load of glucose remaining in the stomach. After a variable period but usually betweeen 30 and 40 min after the beginning of feeding, the behavior changed quite abruptly: the animal began to eat with vigor and by the end of 4 hr matched the amount eaten by the controls.

The conclusion we drew from these experiments was that for a fasted monkey, glucose in physiological amounts entering the intestine from the stomach has itself little influence on feeding, but if its physiological influence on the stomach is utilized in a manipulation that provokes a sustained distention of the stomach, then a clear satiety effect is seen. The animals reduced their food intake for as long as the gastric inhibition and distention was sustained, that is, for the full 4 hr with the undisturbed glucose and for 30 to 40 min with the combination of intestinal glucose and gastric saline.

Thus, distention of the stomach inhibits feeding as Cannon and others (Janowitz and Hollander, 1956; Paintal, 1954; Towbin, 1949) demonstrated. However, this gastric satiety like gastric emptying depends on the small intestine. Nutrients in the small intestine retard gastric emptying and provoke gastric distention. The degree and duration of gastric distention produce a graded inhibition on food intake that can slow, interrupt, or postpone a meal.

D. SATIETY AND DIRECT INTRAINTESTINAL CALORIC INFUSIONS

One issue remained. The coordination between the stomach and small intestine proposed here depended on the delivery of glucose to the intestine. The experimental results indicated that the 16 kcal of glucose delivered from the preload had alone little effect on feeding. Yet we demonstrated in the experiments just reported that intraduadenal infusions can have an effect on the activity of the stomach itself, and others have demonstrated a powerful satiety effect of intestinal nutrient infusions (Liebling et al., 1975; Gibbs et al., 1981; Houpt et al., 1979). We therefore employed intraduodenal cannulas to infuse amounts of glucose that were similar to those delivered by the stomach to observe their effect on feeding.

When 15 cal of glucose were infused in the form of 1 kcal/ml solution through an intraduodenal cannula into the small intestine, there was a consistent inhibition of feeding that occurred in the first portion of the feeding period. It was prominent, obvious, and consistent in all the animals studied. In fact it was so powerful that it tended to override the influence of any gastric load added to this infusion and obscured any interaction between the intestine and the stomach.

Such a powerful effect challenged our concept of gastric distention and satiety. The results suggested that a direct intraduodenal infusion may provoke a more powerful inhibition on feeding than when glucose reaches the intestine in the more natural way, that is, from the stomach's action. To check this possibility, we carried out the following experiment.

Two animals were permitted to drink a glucose solution of 1 kcal/ml for 5 min (with phenol red added). During this time they consumed between 100 and 150 ml, which was left in the stomach for 5 min. It was then withdrawn and the amount of glucose that passed through the pylorus was

TABLE V
Cumulative Grams of Food Consumed ($\bar{x} \pm$ SE)

Feeding time (min)	Condition		
	Control ($N = 20$)	Glucose (1 kcal/ml) orally ingested, removed from stomach 5 min later (19.5 $\pm$ 1.7 kcal passed) ($N = 20$)	15 kcal Glucose (1 kcal/ml) infused into duodenum ($N = 10$)
10	35.4 $\pm$ 2.3	38.2 $\pm$ 2.6	22.9 $\pm$ 3.7[a]
20	60.1 $\pm$ 4.9	60.9 $\pm$ 4.8	39.5 $\pm$ 7.3[b]
30	77.0 $\pm$ 6.1	72.3 $\pm$ 6.0	48.9 $\pm$ 9.1[b]
40	84.9 $\pm$ 6.5	77.0 $\pm$ 5.4	54.9 $\pm$ 10.6[b]
50	90.4 $\pm$ 6.5	86.6 $\pm$ 5.6	65.2 $\pm$ 10.6
60	95.6 $\pm$ 7.9	92.5 $\pm$ 5.6	73.1 $\pm$ 10.6
120	120.1 $\pm$ 7.5	126.0 $\pm$ 8.3	114.1 $\pm$ 10.6
240	185.0 $\pm$ 9.0	187.7 $\pm$ 8.8	174.7 $\pm$ 11.9

[a] $p < 0.01$.
[b] $p < 0.05$.

estimated (19.5 $\pm$ 1.7 kcal). Again feeding of chow pellets was permitted on a lever-pulling paradigm, and, as shown in Table V, which summarizes data from 20 experiments and their controls, neither the consumption of glucose nor the passage of 19.5 kcal affected the subsequent consumption of chow. When these same animals were infused with 15 kcal of glucose directly into the duodenum, there was a prominent inhibition on chow consumption—significant through the first 40 min of the feeding period.

We conclude from these results that the study of the influences of the postpyloric compartments on satiety will require careful consideration. There is a possibility that when nutrients are directly infused into the intestine, rather than entering the postpyloric compartments by means of the stomach's own activity, some aspects of such stimuli can produce an excessively powerful inhibitory signal. An understanding of the mechanisms of inhibition produced by direct intraintestinal loads remains to be carefully examined.

VIII. Cholecystokinin and Satiety

Cholecystokinin is an intestinal hormone that inhibits gastric emptying, as we (Moran and McHugh, 1982) and others (Debas *et al.*, 1975) have shown. It is also a putative satiety agent (Gibbs *et al.,* 1973, 1976; Kissileff *et al.,* 1981). However, the mechanisms of CCK's satiety action have remained undiscerned now a decade after its proposal as an endogenous satiety factor. We have utilized the gastric-inhibitory capacity of CCK to examine the possibility that CCK-induced satiety is mediated through the stomach.

Our experiments (Moran and McHugh, 1982) were essentially the same as the previous ones in which we inhibited gastric emptying and then varied the gastric state. Here we employed an infusion of either 1.5 or 3.0 pmol/kg/min of CCK-8 as the inhibitor to gastric emptying. We chose a four-way design with monkeys equipped with both gastric and jugular vein cannulas. In design A an intravenous saline infusion was begun 60 min before the customary 4-hr feeding period. This infusion ran through the first 10 min of the feeding and was the control condition. In design B, just before the feeding began a load of 150 ml of physiological saline was introduced through the gastric cannula into the stomach. In design C we infused CCK-8 intravenously for 60 min before and 10 min into the feeding period but did not fill the stomach, seeking a direct CCK effect. In design D we combined the features of designs B and C (the infusion of CCK and the gastric load of 150 ml of saline), seeking an interaction effect.

As is clear from Table VI, there were no powerful main effects of either a saline load in the stomach or 70 min of infusion of CCK. However, there

TABLE VI

CUMULATIVE GRAMS OF FOOD EATEN WITH AND WITHOUT INTRAVENOUS CCK-8 AND INTRAGASTRIC SALINE[a,b]

Feeding time (min)	Condition			
	A (control)	B (saline)	C (CCK)	D (CCK + saline)
10	45 ± 5	48 ± 6	38 ± 8	13 ± 4[c]
20	84 ± 12	79 ± 10	73 ± 15	29 ± 9[d]
30	107 ± 13	108 ± 11	97 ± 20	47 ± 15[d]
40	128 ± 10	123 ± 13	112 ± 23	66 ± 21[c]
50	141 ± 9	136 ± 12	136 ± 27	91 ± 20
60	147 ± 13	144 ± 15	156 ± 27	105 ± 21
120	177 ± 16	162 ± 13	175 ± 28	149 ± 20
240	212 ± 16	207 ± 14	212 ± 22	198 ± 21

[a] Used with permission, Moran and McHugh (1982).
[b] Values are means ± SE.
[c] $p < 0.05$.
[d] $p < 0.01$.

was an obvious and significant interaction between a stomach load and this same dose of CCK, lasting as shown by the cumulative data out to 40 min into the feeding period.

This behavioral result can be put into perspective by recalling the effect of CCK on gastric emptying that was discussed earlier. Cholecystokinin is a potent inhibitor of gastric emptying. The inhibition is a physiological function of this intestinal hormone acting at dose ranges identical to that at which CCK stimulates pancreatic secretion (Debas *et al.*, 1975). In this dose range CCK is ineffective as an inhibitor of feeding in the fasted animal, but a potent inhibition of feeding can be produced with CCK if at this dose range its infusion is combined with a gastric load. In monkeys fasted overnight and eating a familiar food on a strict schedule, this dose range of CCK will produce a clear inhibition of feeding only when the stomach has been distended with a volume of saline. The gastric distention produced by the saline is maintained by the action of the hormone. We propose that circulating CCK has a satiety effect in its physiological range when it leads to gastric distention by restricting the flow of food from the stomach through the pylorus.

This places CCK into the integrative chain of physiological elements within the gastroduodenal system that influence feeding. When CCK secretion is provoked by the entrance of nutrients into the intestine (Meyer, 1978), it reduces gastric emptying and encourages gastric distention as feeding proceeds. Feeding continues despite the circulating CCK until the distention of the stomach provokes visceral afferent neuronal signals that interrupt the behavior.

This view resolves a paradox in the proposals of CCK as a satiety factor. If CCK acted directly on feeding, then as it is released by food entering the intestine it should arrest feeding quickly and produce brief bouts of feeding followed by short satiety periods. The stomach, however, is a storehouse for a meal, and one of its functions is to permit a single period of feeding to continue until an adequate caloric supply has been ingested. By our proposal, CCK acts to facilitate this storehouse function. CCK should thus be viewed as a satiety factor defining and delimiting a meal. It interrupts feeding when a meal has been consumed. It does not interrupt feeding directly after being secreted into the circulation. The observation that infusions of CCK in amounts thought to be physiological and extending for 70 min do not affect feeding unless combined with a distending gastric load represents our clearest evidence for this opinion.

The concept that CCK and gastric distention are linked can also explain why intermeal intervals are better predicted by the size of the preceding meal than is meal size predicted by the duration of the preceding intermeal interval (LeMagnen and Tallow, 1966). Many factors may act to influence the size of a meal taken when the animal commits itself to feeding, including schedule, taste, expectation, and past experience. However, the state of the stomach—particularly its distention if sustained by a slowing of its emptying—may provide visceral signals that render a commitment to feeding and a search for the next meal less insistent, thereby prolonging the intermeal interval after a large meal.

These concepts make CCK's action on feeding consistent with our original proposal of the linkages in the gastroduodenal system provoking satiety. The satiety that interrupts a particular meal is the behavioral outcome of a succession of physiological events: gastric emptying, hormonal secretion, and gastric distention, which occur in sequence during feeding.

The volume and caloric concentration of a given meal will also establish, via such mechanisms as CCK action, a prolonged distention of the stomach tied to a calorie-constant emptying pattern. The properties of this distention, particularly its extent and duration, can provide visceral signals to the animal about the quantity of calories ingested and held in the stomach. The signals, delivering preabsorptive information about ingestants, can reduce subsequent meal sizes and prolong subsequent intermeal intervals and thus assist in producing the caloric precision demonstrable over time with feeding. The stomach does store a meal but is also responsive to a meal's caloric content in a fashion that permits the state of the stomach to play a dynamic role in regulating the behavior of feeding.

IX. The Localization of Cholecystokinin Receptors in the Gut

In an effort to identify target sites within the gastrointestinal tract through which CCK might directly exert its effects, we turned to receptor autoradiography. We maximized conditions for the specific binding of CCK-33 and then studied samples of the GI tract from the gastroesophageal junction through to the terminal ileum in the rat (Smith et al., 1984).

A remarkably restricted site of specific CCK binding was found, in which CCK receptors were restricted to and quite densely packed on the circular muscle of the pylorus at the gastroduodenal junction, as shown in Fig. 11. There were no discernible receptors at any other gastric location or on any of the other muscular layers in the stomach or intestine. The receptors for CCK were restricted to the bundles of muscle that surround the narrow outlet of the stomach.

The discovery of this location of CCK receptors certainly increased our confidence that CCK has as one of its physiological roles the inhibition of

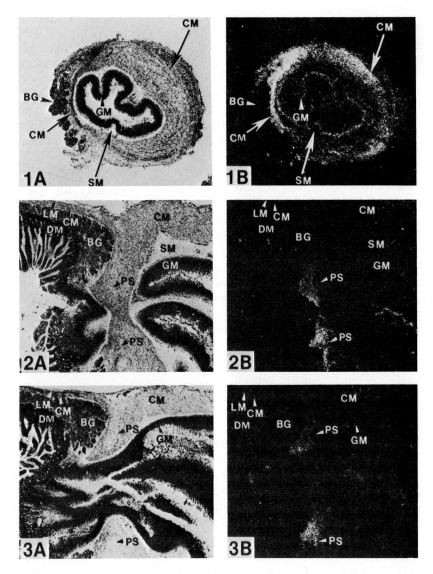

FIG. 11. Photomicrographs (A) of toluidine-blue-stained sections of pyloric sphincter and corresponding autoradiographs (B) showing CCK binding sites (white grains) after incubation in 400 pM [^{125}I]CCK-33. 1A and B: Cross section of the distal pyloric sphincter. 2A and B: Longitudinal section of the pyloroduodenal junction. 3A and B: Longitudinal section through lumen at the pyloric sphincter. Abbreviations: PS, pyloric sphincter; LM, longitudinal smooth muscle; CM, circular smooth muscle; SM, submucosa; BG, Brunner's glands; GM, gastric mucosa; DM, duodenal mucosa. (Used with permission, Smith *et al.*, 1984).

gastric emptying. Receptors for CCK were found at the very place where such a function could be easily accomplished. Cholecystokinin has been demonstrated to produce a pyloric contraction (Harvey, 1975). This localization also explained the remarkably rapid on–off effect on gastric emptying that we had discerned in our infusions of the hormone. Such a sharply localized position of its receptors right at the outflow channel from the stomach made sense of this phenomenon in a way that a more diffuse localization throughout the stomach in muscles or in nerves would not.

Finally, this was the precise localization that would support our hypothesis for a mechanism of CCK's satiety effect. The contraction of the circular muscle produced with activation of these restricted CCK sites could obstruct the pyloric outlet and so facilitate gastric distention. This observation gives the power of a structure–function analysis to our interpretation.

We have focused only on CCK satiety signals that derive from the gastroduodenal system and would act during a given meal. We not only assume but have good evidence shown earlier with fructose and xylose, that other systems of the body also must act in a coordinated fashion to control feeding behavior in the many and varied situations in which it occurs. The role of CCK in these situations is unknown. We claim for this work an advance in the sense that a proposed endogenous satiety factor has been given both a mechanism for its action and a locus for its reception appropriate to this mechanism.

X. Summary

Our overall goals were to advance a conception of the stomach and upper GI tract in the regulation of feeding and to demonstrate that there are many intriguing insights to be derived from a study of the gastric management of foodstuffs.

We were led to this research by our demonstration that feeding was, at least under certain circumstances, so regulated that the caloric intake from day to day was quite constant. Intragastric nutrient infusions reduce the day's food intake according to their calorie content and even produce this inhibition before they are completely emptied from the stomach. By employing quantitative methods to follow the passage of nutrients from the stomach, we then demonstrated that, like feeding, gastric emptying was regulated to calories. That is, the stomach would empty nutrient loads into the duodenum at a calorie-constant rate (0.4 kcal/min for the rhesus monkey and 2.1 kcal/min for humans) regardless—within certain limits—of caloric concentration, nutrient character, or meal volume. This observation led us to conceive of gastric distention—its extent and particularly its duration—as a potentially dynamic source of visceral signals that provide information on the caloric value of ingested nutrients. This information could influence subsequent food intake in a calorie-precise fashion by reducing meal size, prolonging meal intervals, or both. We explored this concept in a series of experiments with different intragastric loads and under a variety of feeding conditions and consistently demonstrated that the sustained distention of the stomach was a powerful, though not the only satiety mechanism acting on feeding.

At the same time we studied the control of gastric emptying that could lead to such caloric precision in emptying nutrients. We demonstrated a feedback inhibition on gastric emptying provoked by nutrients in the small intestine. In fact we could show that the duration of inhibition on gastric emptying (2.5 min/kcal in monkey and 0.46 min/kcal in humans) was the reciprocal of the rate of nutrient delivery from the stomach (0.4 and 2.14 kcal/min). The regulation of caloric emptying is thus a result of the establishment of a steady state between two interdependent functions: the rate at which calories empty from the stomach and the duration of gastric inhibition provoked by calories in the intestine.

Finally we have demonstrated that an intestinal hormone (CCK) released by nutrients in the intestine can, in physiological amounts, inhibit gastric emptying. This hormone, a putative satiety factor, will inhibit feeding at these doses only if it is combined with a distending volume in the stomach. We proposed that it was the natural combination of hormone secretion, inhibition of gastric emptying, and gastric distention with feeding that represented the common satiety mechanism for this hormone. In seeking a locus of action for CCK in the gastrointestinal tract, we demonstrated by autoradiography that the receptors for CCK are exclusively localized on the circular muscle of the pylorus, the very site that can reduce gastric emptying and provoke gastric filling.

Thus, the neat structure–function relationship that was the legacy of the old masters of physiology did prove itself anew when further integrative capacities and responsibilities were discerned for the stomach. It is a hopperlike structure with an intricate set of muscular, neuronal, and glandular elements. It is distendable by food that it stores and helps to digest, but it relates dynamically to both the receiving intestine and feeding behavior (Fig. 12).

The energy content of food put into the stomach affects how fast it empties. The delivery of calories to the intestine impedes gastric emptying in part through the release by some foods of the intestinal hormone CCK, which can contract the circular muscles at the pyloric sphincter.

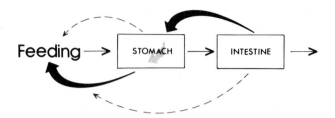

FIG. 12.   A diagram of potential satiety signals derived from the stomach and small bowel. A dynamic interaction of stomach and intestine of the sort proposed here is drawn in solid arrows.

Impedance of gastric emptying will facilitate the distention of the stomach, and a sustained distention will inhibit feeding. Mechanical, secretory, receptive, and effector elements within this gastroenteric system all act together in an integrative fashion for the regulation of behavior, a regulation that—with these and other mechanisms—can be so precisely tied to food energy that it surely is entitled to a term derived from Richter's work: homeostatic or self-regulatory behavior.

References

Brener, W., Hendrix, T. R., and McHugh, P. R. (1983). Regulation of the gastric emptying of glucose. *Gastroenterology* **85**, 76–82.

Cannon, W. B., and Washburn, A. L. (1912). An explanation of hunger. *American Journal of Physiology* **29**, 441–455.

Debas, H. T., Farrooq, O., and Grossman, M. I. (1975). Inhibition of gastric emptying as a physiological action of cholecystokinin. *Gastroenterology* **68**, 1211–1217.

Deutsch, J. A., Young, W. G., and Kalagoris, T. J. (1978). The stomach signals satiety. *Science* **201**, 165–167.

Friedman, M. I., and Stricker, E. M. (1976). The physiological psychology of hunger: A physiological perspective. *Psychological Revue* **83**, 409–431.

Geary, N., and Smith, G. P. (1982). Pancreatic glucagon and post-prandial satiety in the rat. *Physiology and Behavior* **28**, 313–322.

Gibbs, J., Young, R. C., and Smith, G. P. (1973). Cholecystokinin decreases food intake in rats. *Journal of Comparative and Physiological Psychology* **84**, 488–495.

Gibbs, J., Falasco, J. D., and McHugh, P. R. (1976). CCK decreased food intake in rhesus monkeys. *American Journal of Physiology* **230**, 15–18.

Gibbs, J., Maddison, S. P., and Rolls, E. T. (1981). The satiety role of the small intestine examined in sham feeding rhesus monkeys. *Journal of Comparative and Physiological Psychology* **95**, 1003–1005.

Halasz, B., and Pupp, L. (1965). Hormone secretion of the anterior pituitary gland after physical interruption of all nervous pathways to the hypophysiotrophic area. *Endocrinology* **77**, 533–562.

Hamilton, C. L., Ciacci, P. J., and Lewis, D. O. (1976). Feeding behavior in monkeys with and without lesions of the hypothalamus. *American Journal of Physiology* **230,** 818–830.

Harvey, R. F. (1975). Hormonal controls of gastric motility. (1975). *American Journal of Digestive Diseases* **20,** 523–539.

Houpt, T. R., Anika, S. N., and Houpt, K. A. (1979). Preabsorptive intestinal satiety controls food intake in pigs. *American Journal of Physiology* **236,** R328–R337.

Hunt, J. N. (1961). Osmotic control of gastric emptying. *Gastroenterology* **41,** 49–51.

Hunt, J. N., and Spurrell, W. R. (1951). The pattern of gastric emptying of the human stomach. *Journal of Physiology (London)* **113,** 157–168.

Hunt, J. N., and Stubbs, D. F. (1975). The volume and energy content of meals as determinants of gastric emptying. *Journal of Physiology (London)* **245,** 209–225.

Janowitz, H. D., and Hollander, F. (1956). The time factor in the adjustment of food intake to varied caloric requirement in the dog. A study of the precision of appetite regulation. *Annals of the New York Academy of Science* **66,** 56–67.

Kissileff, H. R., Pi-Sunyer, F. X., Thornton, J., and Smith, G. P. (1981). C-terminal octapeptide of cholecystokinin decreases food intake in man. *American Journal of Clinical Nutrition* **34,** 154–160.

LeMagnen, J., and Tallow, S. (1966). La peridicite spontanée de la prise d'aliments ad libitum du rat blanc. *Journal of Physiology (Paris)* **58,** 323–349.

Liebling, D. S., Eisner, J. D., Gibbs, J., and Smith, G. P. (1975). Intestinal satiety in rats. *Journal of Comparative and Physiological Psychology* **89,** 955–965.

McHugh, P. R. (1979). Aspects of the control of feeding: Application quantitation in psychobiology. *Johns Hopkins Medical Journal* **144,** 147–155.

McHugh, P. R., and Gibbs, J. (1972). Aspects of subcortical organization of feeding revealed by hypothalamic disconnections in Macaca Mulatta. *Brain* **95,** 279–292.

McHugh, P. R., and Moran, T. H. (1978). The accuracy of the regulation of caloric ingestion in the rhesus monkey: Caloric regulation in rhesus monkeys. *American Journal Physiology* **235,** R29–R34.

McHugh, P. R., and Moran, T. H. (1979). Calories and gastric emptying: A regulatory capacity with implications for feeding. *American Journal of Physiology* **236,** R254–R260.

McHugh, P. R., Gibbs, J., Falasco, J. D., Moran, T. H., and Smith, G. P. (1975a). Inhibitions of feeding examined in rhesus monkeys with hypothalamic disconnections. *Brain* **98,** 441–454.

McHugh, P. R., Moran, T. H., and Barton, C. N. (1975b). Satiety: A graded behavioral phenomenon regulating caloric intake. *Science* **190,** 167–169.

McHugh, P. R., Moran, T. H., and Wirth, J. B. (1982). Postpyloric regulation of gastric emptying in rhesus monkeys. *American Journal of Physiology* **243,** R408–R415.

Marriott, B. (1978). Feeding patterns of wild rhesus monkeys in Katmandu, Nepal. *Federation Proceedings, Federation of American Societies for Experimental Biology* **29,** 759.

Martin, J. R., and Novin, D. (1977). Decreased feeding in rats following hepatic portal infusions of glucagon. *Physiology and Behavior* **19,** 461–466.

Meyer, J. H. (1978). Release of secretin and cholecystokinin. *In* "Endocrinology of the Gut" (S. R. Bloom, ed.). Churchill Livingston, Edinburgh.

Moran, T. H., and McHugh, P. R. (1981). Distinctions amongst three sugars in their effects on gastric emptying and satiety. *American Journal of Physiology* **241,** R25–R30.

Moran, T. H., and McHugh, P. R. (1982). Cholecystokin suppresses food intake by inhibiting gastric emptying. *American Journal of Physiology* **242,** R491–R497.

Novin, D., Sanderson, J. D., and VanderWeele, D. A. (1974). The effect of isotonic glucose on eating as a function of feeding condition and infusion site. *Physiology and Behavior* **13,** 3–7.

Paintal, A. S. (1954). A study of gastric stretch receptors: Their role in the peripheral mechanisms of satiation of hunger and thirst. *Journal of Physiology* (*London*) **126,** 255–270.

Panksepp, J. (1971). Is satiety mediated by the ventromedial hypothalamus? *Physiology and Behavior* **7,** 381–384.

Rayford, P. L., Fender, H., Ramus, N. I., Reeder, D. D., and Thompson, J. C. (1975). Release and half life of CCK in man. *In* "Gastrointestinal Hormones—A Symposium" (J. C. Thompson. ed.). Univ. of Texas Press, Austin.

Richter, C. P. (1942–1943) Total self-regulatory functions in animals and human beings. *Harvey Lecture Series* **38,** 63–103.

Rowland, N., and Stricker, E. M. (1979). Differential effects of glucose and fructose infusions on insulin induced feeding in rats. *Physiology and Behavior* **22,** 387–389.

Smith, G. T., Moran, T. H., Coyle, J. T., Kuhar, M. J., O'Donahue, T. L., and McHugh, P. R. (1984). Anatomical localization of cholecystokinin receptors to the pyloric sphincter. *American Journal of Physiology* **246,** R127–R130.

Thomas, D. W., and Mayer, J. (1968). Meal taking and regulation of food intake on normal and hypothalamic hyperphagic rats. *Journal of Comparative and Physiological Psychology* **66,** 642–653.

Towbin, E. J. (1949). Gastric distention is a factor in the satiation of thirst in esophagustomized dogs. *American Journal of Physiology* **159,** 533–541.

Wirth, J. B., and McHugh, P. R. (1983). Gastric distension and short-term satiety in rhesus monkeys. *American Journal of Physiology* **245,** R174–R180.

Woods, S. C., Delke, E., and Vasselli, J. R. (1974). Metabolic hormones and regulation of body weight. *Psychological Revue* **81,** 26–43.

Wyngaarden, J. P., Segal, S., and Foley, J. B. (1958). Physiological disposition and metabolic fate of infused pentosis in man. *Journal of Clinical Investigation* **37,** 1695–1407.

Functional Organization of the W-, X-, and Y-Cell Pathways in the Cat: A Review and Hypothesis

S. Murray Sherman

Department of Neurobiology and Behavior
State University of New York at Stony Brook
Stony Brook, New York

I. Introduction

Our contemporary understanding of the mammalian retinogeniculocortical pathways rests largely on the pioneering work of Hubel and Wiesel (1962, 1965). Their receptive field studies of single cells in cats emphasized the serial and hierarchical organization of these pathways. Hubel and Wiesel (1962, 1965) concluded that, as the hierarchy is ascended from retinal ganglion cells to neurons of the lateral geniculate nucleus, to and through cells that represent the presumed hierarchical levels of visual cortex (e.g., simple, complex, and hypercomplex cells), receptive field properties become more complex and specific for stimulus parameters. They suggested that this increasing complexity and specificity is the process by which the visual system abstracts and analyzes features of the visual environment. Each local portion of visual space is thus analyzed by a single chain of neurons from the retina through the lateral geniculate nucleus to the visual cortex.

Although certain aspects of this hypothesis have been challenged and some modifications of it have been required to accommodate new observations made during the past two decades, it still serves as the major theoretical framework for research into the neuronal organization of the mammalian visual pathways. Perhaps the major theoretical challenge to this hypothesis stems from evidence that emphasized the parallel organization of these pathways. Actually, two complementary and important concepts of such parallel organization have emerged. The first, elucidated originally by Sprague (1966), Diamond and Hall (1969), and Schneider (1969), emphasized the functional significance of multiple thalamocortical pathways (e.g., retinogeniculocortical and retinotectothalamocortical). This type of parallel processing is not considered further here (for reviews of this, see Sprague *et al.,* 1981; Diamond, 1982). The second type of parallel processing, which is the focus of the rest of this article, is the parallel organization evident within the retinogeniculocortical pathways. That is, at least three separate, functionally independent, retinogeniculocortical pathways have been identified. These have been called the W-, X-, and Y-cell pathways, although other terminology has also been used.

A. TERMINOLOGY

A brief clarification of the terminology used here is in order. It is generally accepted that X- and Y-cells are each a fairly homogeneous neuronal class, based on morphological and physiological properties, and that each can be distinguished from W-cells (e.g., Rodieck, 1979; Stone *et al.,* 1979;

Lennie, 1980b; Sherman and Spear, 1982; Rodieck and Brening, 1983). However, W-cells, at least in the retina, are not homogeneous and almost certainly represent several distinct classes (Rodieck, 1979; Rodieck and Brening, 1983). "W-Cell" here refers to retinal ganglion or geniculate neurons that are neither X- nor Y-cells. The term W-cell is preferred, despite its shortcomings, over others suggested for the various classes thought to be subsumed by this phrase for two reasons. First, it is not yet clear how many classes (and thus terms) apply to these cells, nor has it yet been demonstrated beyond a reasonable doubt that retinal W-cells are not a single class with considerable variability. Second, this article is mainly concerned with retinogeniculocortical pathways, and as will be noted later, the subset of W-cells that is involved in this pathway may well prove to be a single class.

Several alternate terms have been used in the classification of retinal ganglion and geniculate cells. It is not always clear that these are isomorphic with one another or to the "W-, X-, and Y-cell" terminology used here. However, to a first approximation, the following terms are more or less interchangeable (Enroth-Cugell and Robson, 1966; Cleland *et al.,* 1971; Cleland and Levick, 1974a,b; Fukada and Saito, 1972; Hoffmann *et al.,* 1972; Stone and Hoffmann, 1972; Stone and Fukuda, 1974; Hochstein and Shapley, 1976a; Stevens and Gerstein, 1976; Bullier and Norton, 1979a,b). For W-cells these are "sluggish," "sluggish-sustained," or "sluggish-transient." For X-cells these are "sustained," "brisk-sustained," "tonic," "group II," "heterogeneous," or "linear." For Y-cells these are "transient," "brisk-transient," "phasic," "group I," "homogeneous," or "nonlinear." The "W-, X-, and Y-cell" terminology is used here because it is the one most commonly used and widely accepted. It is a neutral terminology that by itself conveys no implicit suggestion as to functional significance (Rowe and Stone, 1977). Also, while "W-cell" will probably be replaced with several other terms when these cells are unambiguously classified, it is preferred as a conservative alternative until such classification is available.

B. Hypothesis for Significance of W-, X-, and Y-cell Pathways

It has often been suggested that these W-, X-, and Y-cell pathways independently analyze different aspects of the same visual scene, and that these different analyses are combined to form the neural representation of the visual environment. Thus, instead of a single hierarchical chain of neurons to represent each portion of visual space, at least three such functionally distinct chains do so independently and in parallel, each chain responsible for a particular feature (e.g., form, movement, color, brightness, and depth or distance).

The purpose of this article is to describe a hypothesis for the functional organization of these W-, X-, and Y-cell pathways in cats. The hypothesis can be summarized as follows. Y-Cells are responsible for the analysis of basic forms and represent a sufficient and probably necessary pathway for good form vision, whereas X-cells provide higher spatial resolution to the basic form analysis accomplished by the Y-cell pathway. These suggestions derive from consideration of X- and Y-cell response properties, the anatomical organization of the X- and Y-cell pathways, and psychophysical studies of experimental cats with different levels of abnormality in the X- and Y-cell pathways. No detailed, specific hypothesis can be provided as yet for the W-cell pathway, but by reason of poor W-cell responsiveness and relative lack of influence of W-cells on neurons in visual cortex, this pathway may play a minor role in conscious perception of visual patterns (see also Stone *et al.*, 1979).

This hypothesis has already appeared for the X- and Y-cell pathways in a brief and superficial form (Sherman, 1979, 1982; see also Sherman and Spear, 1983). A consideration of other mammalian species, including primate, will also be included. The hypothesis is speculative and incomplete. It is offered in the spirit of providing a theoretical framework for existing data and perhaps also directing future investigations. Because detailed reviews of W-, X-, and Y-cells have already appeared (Rodieck, 1979; Stone *et al.*, 1979; Lennie, 1980b; Sherman and Spear, 1982, 1983), this article will simply summarize some of the major features of these neuronal classes.

II. General Overview of the Visual Pathways

The focus of this article is the retinogeniculocortical pathways, which represent the largest well-defined portion of the visual system; however, other clearly important pathways exist. Some of these extrageniculate pathways will be considered here in the context of geniculate pathways. For reviews of these pathways, see Rodieck (1979), Sherman and Spear (1982), Rosenquist *et al.* (1982), and Raczkowski and Rosenquist (1983).

The largest terminus of retinofugal fibers is the dorsal division of the lateral geniculate nucleus (hereafter, unless otherwise noted, "lateral geniculate nucleus" refers only to this dorsal division), and most of the remaining retinal fibers terminate in the superior colliculus. Other sites of termination include the ventral division of the lateral geniculate nucleus (in the thalamus), regions of the pretectum, the accessory optic nucleus (in the midbrain tegmentum), and the suprachiasmatic nucleus (in the hypothalamus). Other brain stem visual pathways strongly implicated in sensory processing include those from the midbrain to the thalamus. The superior colliculus projects to the medial portion of the lateral posterior nucleus as well as to portions of the lateral geniculate nucleus; the parabigeminal nucleus (also located in the midbrain) projects to portions of the lateral geniculate nucleus, and the pretectal nuclei project visual fibers to the pulvinar nucleus as well as to portions of the lateral geniculate nucleus.

Tusa and colleagues (reviewed in Tusa *et al.*, 1981; Tusa, 1982) have elucidated many separate, retinotopically organized visual areas of cerebral cortex (see Fig. 1), and each of these receives input from the lateral geniculate, lateral posterior, and/or pulvinar nuclei (see Table I). Also, rich interconnections exist among these visual areas, and large projections have been described from many of these areas to the midbrain and visual thalamus. The central visual pathways are obviously complexly interconnected and functionally interdependent. Indeed, further research may continue to increase the number of distinct visual areas of cortex. For instance, Olson and Graybiel (1981) and Mucke *et al.* (1982) described a visual area in the ventral bank of the anterior ectosylvian sulcus; this is not shown in Fig. 1. Any attempt, such as the present article, to suggest the functional organization of a subset of these pathways, such as the retinogeniculocortical pathways, needs to be recognized for the simplification that it is.

III. Physiological Classification of W-, X-, and Y-Cells

Retinal ganglion and geniculate cells in the cat can be functionally classified into at least three main groups, called W-, X-, and Y-cells. However, as noted in Section I,A, the W-cell term probably subsumes several distinct groups that are arbitrarily thrown together. In any case, these ganglion cell classes represent the peripheral point of departure for any consideration of the W-, X-, and Y-cell pathways, because very little is yet known related to any differences in retinal circuitry that applies to these neuronal classes (but see Hochstein and Shapley, 1976a,b; Kolb, 1979). The available evidence suggests that each geniculate neuron receives retinal input from a small number of W-, X-, or Y-cells, with practically no mixture of classes among the retinal afferents (for X- and Y-cells, see Cleland *et al.*, 1971; Hoffmann *et al.*, 1972; for W-cells, this must be inferred from Cleland *et al.*, 1975b; Wilson *et al.*, 1976; Bowling

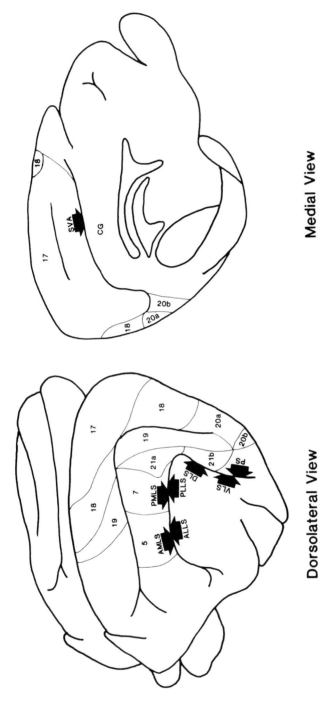

Dorsolateral View

Medial View

FIG. 1.   Visual cortical areas in the cat as shown in dorsolateral and medial views of the left hemisphere. In addition to the nine areas designated by Brodmann numbers (5, 7, 17, 18, 19, 20a, 20b, 21a, 21b) are nine additional areas abbreviated as follows: AMLS, anterior medial lateral suprasylvian area; PMLS, posterior medial lateral suprasylvian area; VLS, ventral lateral suprasylvian area; ALLS, anterior lateral lateral suprasylvian area; PLLS, posterior lateral lateral suprasylvian area; DLS, dorsal lateral suprasylvian area; CG, cingulate gyrus; PS, posterior suprasylvian area; SVA, splenial visual area. Thirteen of these areas (17, 18, 19, 20a, 20b, 21a, 21b, AMLS, PMLS, VLS, ALLS, PLLS, and DLS) seem to be purely visual and exhibit retinotopic organization. The remaining five (5, 7, CG, PS, SVA) have some visual neurons but may not be exclusively visual, and no retinotopic organization has yet been demonstrated for any of them. (Redrawn from Tusa et al., 1981; Tusa, 1982; Symonds et al., 1981; Raczkowski and Rosenquist, 1983.)

238

TABLE I
INNERVATION OF VISUAL CORTICAL AREAS[a]

Subcortical afferent pathways[b]	Cortical areas[c]																	
	17	18	19	20a	20b	21a	21b	AMLS	PMLS	VLS	ALLS	PLLS	DLS	5	7	CG	PS	SVA
Retina → LGN (A,A1) →	+++	+++																
Retina → LGN (C_m) →	+	++	+++															
Retina → LGN (C_p) →	+	++	+++	+					+	+								
Retina → LGN (MIN) →	+	+++	+++	+			++	++	++			+	+					
Retina → LGN (GW) →		++	++				++	++	++									
Visual cortex → LP_l →	++	++	+++	+++	+++	+++	+++	+++	+++	+	+	+	+					
Retina → SC → LP_m →			+	++	++	+	+		+	+++	+++	+++	+++					
Retina → PT → pulvinar →		++	++	+	+	+	+	+	+	+	+	+	+	+++	+++	+++		+++
Retina → PT → CLN →		++	++	+	+	+	+	+	+	+	+	+	+	+	+	+	+++	
CLN → claustrum →	+++	+++	+++	+++	+++	+	+	+	+	+	+	+	+	+	+	+	+++	+++

[a] Adapted from Raczkowski and Rosenquist (1983) and Rosenquist (1984).

[b] Abbreviations for subcortical afferents: A,A1, laminae A and A1; CLN, central lateral nucleus; C_m, magnocellular lamina C; C_p, parvocellular C laminae; GW, geniculate wing; LGN, lateral geniculate nucleus; LP_m and LP_l, medial and lateral divisions, respectively, of the lateral posterior nucleus; MIN, medial interlaminar nucleus; PT, pretectum; SC, superior colliculus. For abbreviations of cortical areas, see Fig. 1.

[c] Key: +, Light innervation; ++, moderate innervation; +++, heavy innervation.

and Michael, 1980, 1984; Sur and Sherman, 1982a,b; Leventhal, 1982). It
is thus possible to refer to geniculate W-, X-, or Y-cells as those neurons
receiving retinal input from W-, X-, or Y-cells, respectively. Indeed, except for subtle differences (Hubel and Wiesel, 1961; Sanderson *et al.*,
1971; Suzuki and Takahashi, 1973; Bullier and Norton, 1979a; Kaplan *et
al.*, 1979; So and Shapley, 1981), response properties of geniculate neurons closely match those of their retinal inputs (Cleland *et al.*, 1971).
Details of these response properties in the retina and the lateral geniculate
nucleus can be found elsewhere (Kuffler, 1953; Hubel and Wiesel, 1961;
Enroth-Cugell and Robson, 1966; Cleland *et al.*, 1971, 1975b; Hoffmann
et al., 1972; Fukada and Saito, 1972; Stone and Hoffmann, 1972; Cleland
and Levick, 1974a,b; Fukuda and Stone, 1974; Stone and Fukuda, 1974;
Bullier and Norton, 1979a,b; Hochstein and Shapley, 1976a,b; Stevens
and Gerstein, 1976; Wilson *et al.*, 1976; Lehmkuhle *et al.*, 1980a; Lennie,
1980a; Sur and Sherman, 1982a, 1984; Thibos and Levick, 1983; Troy,
1983; for reviews, see Rodieck, 1979; Stone *et al.*, 1979; Lennie, 1980b;
Sherman and Spear, 1982, 1983) and are summarized in the following
paragraphs.

A. MEASUREMENT OF RESPONSE PROPERTIES USED IN CLASSIFICATION

Before considering response properties of W-, X-, and Y-cells, it is
worth describing the two related approaches used to describe neuronal
responses to visual stimuli. The first is the classic use of geometric stimuli
like bars and spots to plot the structure of the receptive field. Neuronal
response is measured as a function of stimulus shape, position, and contrast to determine this structure.

The second approach focuses on the neuronal response to stimuli consisting of one-dimensional sine wave gratings (Cornsweet, 1970; Braddick
et al., 1978; Sekuler *et al.*, 1978) that are drifted or sinusoidally counterphased. Such gratings are characterized by a homogeneous luminosity
profile along one axis (typically vertical) and a sinusoidal profile along the
orthogonal axis (usually horizontal). The stimulus contrast is defined by
the luminance values of the peak (L_{max}) and trough (L_{min}) of the sinusoidal luminance profile as $(L_{max} - L_{min})/(L_{max} + L_{min})$. Mean luminance is
$\frac{1}{2}(L_{max} + L_{min})$. Spatial frequency is the number of stimulus cycles of the
sine wave luminance profile per degree of visual angle. Temporal frequency in cycles per second or hertz (Hz), for a drifting grating, is the
drift speed in degrees per second multiplied by the spatial frequency in
cycles per degree. For a counterphased grating, this value is simply the
counterphase rate. Figure 2 illustrates the spatial and temporal luminance
changes for a sinusoidally counterphased sine wave grating. Finally, the

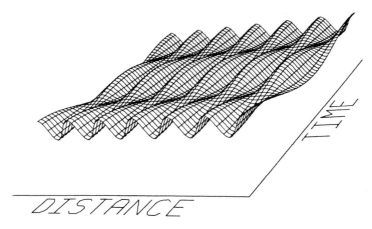

FIG. 2.   Luminance profile in space and time for a sinusoidally counterphased sine wave grating. Luminance is plotted on the Z axis. Along the spatial axis, the luminance profile is always sinusoidal, although contrast changes with time such that no contrast is evident at certain times. Along the temporal axis, troughs of luminance become peaks, and vice versa, with a sinusoidal temporal profile. Spatial and temporal frequency can be independently adjusted. Note that mean luminance remains constant during the modulation. (From Sekuler *et al.*, 1978, with permission of the authors.)

spatial (or temporal) phase angle describes the relative spatial (or temporal) position of the grating as a fraction of a complete spatial (or temporal) stimulus cycle of 360°. For instance, a spatial phase difference of 90° between two otherwise equivalent gratings means that they are spatially offset by one-quarter of a spatial cycle. Typically, the neuronal response is plotted as a function of contrast, spatial, and/or temporal parameters. The minimum contrast needed to evoke a threshold response from the neuron can be measured as a function of spatial and temporal parameters, and contrast sensitivity is defined as the inverse of the minimum contrast needed to evoke a threshold response. One can plot either the contrast sensitivity or the response (at a fixed, generally high, contrast) as a function of spatial or temporal frequency. Because response and sensitivity are closely related and their respective functions similar in form for those retinal and geniculate neurons thus far studied (cf. Lehmkuhle *et al.*, 1980a; So and Shapley, 1981), the two measures are often considered interchangeable and are often termed spatial or temporal tuning functions.

Such response measures evoked by sinusoidal stimuli permit the use of linear systems analysis (including Fourier analysis), and the advantages of such an analysis have been described previously (Cornsweet, 1970; Braddick *et al.*, 1978; Sekuler *et al.*, 1978). Briefly, as Fig. 3 illustrates, any complex waveform can be created by the linear addition of sine waves

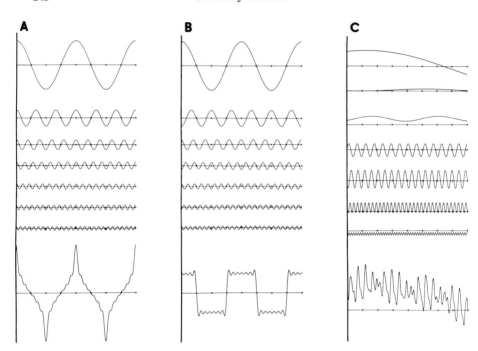

FIG. 3.   Examples of Fourier analysis and synthesis. The bottom row shows three complex waveforms synthesized from the linear addition of seven different sine waves. Amplitude and frequency are in arbitrary units. (A) Formation of an approximately triangular
waveform from sine waves. If the top sine wave has frequency F with amplitude A, the
succeeding ones are $3F$ with $\frac{1}{3}A$, $5F$ with $\frac{1}{5}A$, $7F$ with $\frac{1}{7}A$, $9F$ with $\frac{1}{9}A$, $11F$ with $\frac{1}{11}A$, and $13F$
with $\frac{1}{13}A$. A precise triangle wave would continue to have odd components added, and the
nth component would have frequency nF and amplitude A/n. Note that the peaks and
troughs of the top sine wave are lined up with peaks and troughs of others, and this
establishes their phase relationships. (B) Formation of an approximately square waveform
from sine waves. Note that the only difference between this and (A) is the phase relationships of the component sine waves. Here, the peaks and troughs of the top sine wave are
lined up with peaks and troughs of the third, fifth, and seventh sine waves, but not with the
troughs and peaks of the second, fourth, and sixth sine waves. Phase is thus an important
parameter in Fourier synthesis. (C) Formation of arbitrary, complex waveform from seven
different sine waves that differ in both modulation amplitude and mean amplitude, in frequency, and in phase. Given enough sine waves with appropriate parameters, any complex
waveform can be so analyzed and synthesized.

appropriately chosen for phase, frequency, modulation amplitude (or contrast), and mean amplitude. The importance of phase is emphasized in the
comparison between Fig. 3A and B, in which the only difference in the
component sine waves is one of phase, yet the resultant complex waveforms are quite different. The determination of the component sine waves
of a complex waveform is Fourier analysis, and the creation of a complex

waveform from the linear addition of sine waves is Fourier synthesis. Since the luminosity of any visual scene can be described along any dimension as a complex waveform of luminosity versus distance across the scene, the luminosity values of any scene can be analyzed or synthesized in terms of its component sine wave gratings. These sine wave gratings thus represent a basic visual stimulus, and a description of a neuron's responsiveness to a range of sine wave stimuli provides a useful first approximation of the neuron's responsiveness to more complex stimuli. Because Fourier analysis depends on the linear addition of sine waves, this analysis works well for neurons that respond linearly to visual stimuli (i.e., the response to two simultaneously presented stimuli equals the sum of the responses to each alone) and poorly for neurons that respond nonlinearly.

In practice, two measures have proved most useful in the analysis of retinal and geniculate cell responsiveness: a measure of response linearity and determination of sensitivity (or responsiveness) as a function of spatial or temporal frequency. Spatial linearity is determined by the neuron's sensitivity to the spatial phase of a counterphased grating, as shown by Fig. 4A. A neuron with linear spatial summation exhibits a response that varies sinusoidally with spatial phase, the period of variation being equal to a spatial cycle of the stimulus. Although many forms of nonlinearity are possible, a retinal or geniculate neuron with nonlinear summation tends to exhibit a response that is not phase dependent in this manner, and in practice, is often phase independent (Fig. 4B). Linearity of temporal summation is determined by the Fourier components of the response to a counterphased grating (Fig. 5). A linear response is one that occurs at the fundamental temporal frequency of the stimulus frequency (Fig. 5A), and a nonlinear response occurs at higher harmonics (usually the second harmonic) of the stimulus frequency (Fig. 5B). That is, modulation of a linear response is sinusoidal at the same frequency as the stimulus, while a nonlinear response is modulated at higher harmonics, often manifested as a "frequency-doubled" (i.e., twice the stimulus frequency) response.*

---

* Movshon *et al.* (1978) have shown that some visual cells with more complex receptive fields than retinal ganglion or geniculate cells (e.g., cortical neurons) may require more sophisticated tests to determine their linear or nonlinear summation properties. What has been described here may not generally apply to visual neurons other than retinal ganglion and geniculate cells in the cat. Even for these simpler retinal ganglion and geniculate neurons, two different types of nonlinearities can exist that should be distinguished from one another. In practice, the noticeable frequency doubled response, which seems to result from full-wave rectification in spatial pooling of inputs to the cell under study, results in a prominent second harmonic component (plus other higher order, even components) in the response (Hochstein and Shapley, 1976b). However, if a "linear" cell's mean or spontaneous discharge level is too low to permit complete expression of a fundamental, sinusoidal re-

The second measure, spatial or temporal tuning functions, simply plots contrast sensitivity or response as a function of spatial or temporal frequency. The response measure plotted can be either the linear (fundamental) or nonlinear (usually a second harmonic) component of the neuron's response as a function of spatial or temporal frequency. Figure 6 shows spatial contrast sensitivity functions representative of geniculate W-, X-, and Y-cells, and Fig. 7 shows the analogous temporal functions. Figure 8 shows analogous spatial response functions for retinal X- and Y-cells.

B. W-Cell Response Properties

W-Cells were recognized as a distinct and major class (or classes) of retinal and geniculate neurons only during the last 5–10 years, and consequently relatively little is known about them. In the retina, they comprise a heterogeneous physiological group that has led some authors (Cleland and Levick, 1974a,b; Rodieck, 1979; Rodieck and Brening, 1983) to conclude that several distinct neuronal classes actually occupy the W-cell grouping. However, limited evidence from geniculate W-cells (Sur and Sherman, 1982a; Stanford *et al.*, 1983) suggests that these may be a single functional class that displays considerable functional variation. Thus, we can tentatively conclude that the subset of retinal W-cells that innervates the lateral geniculate nucleus and participates in the retinogeniculocortical W-cell pathway may be a single neuronal class. Preliminary evidence suggests that the other retinal "W-cells," which innervate other brain stem structures—for example, the superior colliculus (Hoffmann, 1973), ventral division of the lateral geniculate nucleus (Spear *et al.*, 1977), and pretectum (Hoffmann and Schoppmann, 1975—do indeed form separate neuronal classes (see Rodieck, 1979; Rodieck and Brening, 1983).

W-Cells can be distinguished from X- and Y-cells by a number of response properties (see Table II). W-Cells have the slowest axonal conduction velocities among retinal ganglion cells and geniculate neurons. Most geniculate W-cells have a classic, antagonistic center–surround receptive

---

sponse to a stimulus (i.e., the trough of the response is cut off at zero response, since a negative response cannot be exhibited), the result is a half-wave rectification of the response. Fourier analysis of this, too, yields second and higher order, even harmonics, but such a response in terms of cell classification would be regarded as linear (Movshon *et al.*, 1978a). Full- and half-wave rectification in the response can still be distinguished, because the former has little or no power in the odd harmonics, whereas the latter does. Thus, if a ratio is computed between the sizes of the second harmonic and fundamental components of response, a low ratio indicates relative linearity, with the possibility of half-wave rectification, and a high ratio indicates relative nonlinearity, with full-wave rectification (Hochstein and Shapley, 1976a; Movshon *et al.*, 1978a).

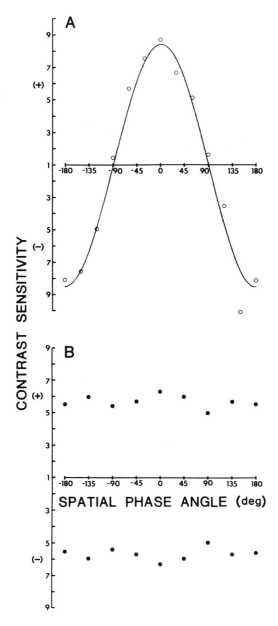

FIG. 4. Contrast sensitivity versus spatial phase angle for two geniculate neurons. (A) Linear W-cell, showing a sinusoidal sensitivity to the phase of a sine wave grating of 0.2 cycles/degree counterphased at 2 Hz. The response occurs at the fundamental counterphase frequency, and negative values imply a response 180° shifted in *temporal* phase from a positive response. At spatial phase angles of ± 90° the neuron exhibits minimal response; these are the "null positions" for the grating. (B) Nonlinear W-cell, showing little or no phase sensitivity to a 0.1 cycles/degree sine wave grating counterphased at 2 Hz. The response shows frequency doubling (i.e., it occurs at twice the counterphase rate), and thus each point is plotted twice as a positive and negative value. (From Sur and Sherman, 1982a.)

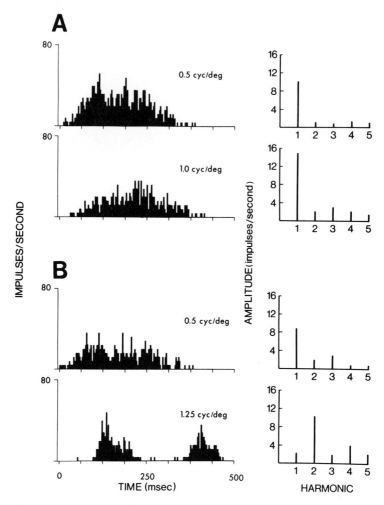

FIG. 5. Responses to counterphased gratings of a linear and nonlinear cell in the lateral geniculate nucleus. On the left are shown average response histograms to a single cycle of a sine wave grating counterphased at 2 Hz; the spatial frequency of each is also indicated. On the right is shown the first five Fourier components of this response, the first component equaling the 2-Hz counterphase rate of the grating. (A) Responses of an X-cell (linear cell). At both the lower and higher spatial frequencies, the response is dominated by the fundamental Fourier component. (B) Responses of a Y-cell (nonlinear cell). At lower spatial frequencies (upper), the response is linear and dominated by the fundamental Fourier component. At higher spatial frequencies (lower), for which the linear component is less sensitive (Fig. 6C), the response is nonlinear and dominated by higher harmonics, mostly the second harmonic. (From Mangel et al., 1983).

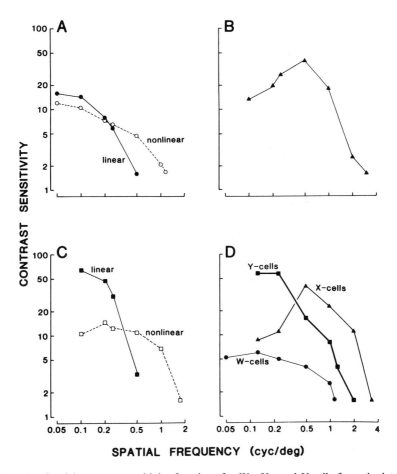

FIG. 6. Spatial contrast sensitivity functions for W-, X-, and Y-cells from the lateral geniculate nucleus. All cells illustrated had receptive fields between 5° and 15° of the area centralis. These functions were generated by measuring contrast sensitivity as a function of spatial frequency to sine wave gratings that were sinusoidally counterphased at 2 Hz. (A) Functions for two W-cells in the parvocellular C-laminae. One responded linearly and the other did not. Thus, the function in the latter case was generated from a second harmonic response (see Fig. 5B). These W-cell examples represent relatively responsive W-cells. (B) Function for a typical X-cell in the A-laminae. (C) Function for a typical Y-cell in the A-laminae. Two components are seen: a linear component that is more sensitive to lower spatial frequencies, and a nonlinear component (second harmonic response) that is more sensitive to higher spatial frequencies. The linear component is sensitive to spatial phase, and the nonlinear component is not (Fig. 4). The nonlinear component was generated at a spatial phase position of the grating for which no linear response was evident (i.e., the "null" position). (D) Mean contrast sensitivity functions for 10–15 cells of each class. No distinction is made here between linear and nonlinear responses. At least at 2 Hz, on average, W-cells are relatively insensitive to all spatial frequencies, X-cells are the most sensitive to higher spatial frequencies (and thus have the best resolution), and Y-cells are the most sensitive to lower spatial frequencies.

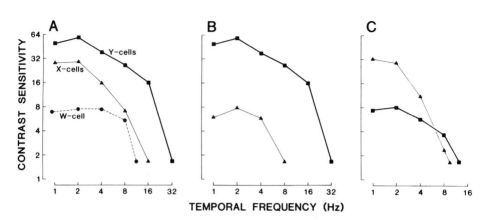

FIG. 7. Temporal contrast sensitivity functions for W-, X-, and Y-cells from the lateral geniculate nucleus. For a given spatial frequency of a sine wave grating, contrast sensitivity is plotted as a function of the sinusoidal counterphase frequency. Shown are mean data from the same X- and Y-cells as are illustrated in Fig. 6D plus a single W-cell (similar population data are not presently available for W-cells). (A) Functions in response to the spatial frequency to which the cell was most sensitive. This is a higher spatial frequency for X-cells than for W- and Y-cells (see Fig. 6D). (B) Functions taken at the same lower spatial frequency of 0.125 cycles/degree. (C) Functions taken at the same higher spatial frequency of 1.0 cycle/degree. Only at these higher spatial and lower temporal frequencies do X-cells tend to exhibit better contrast sensitivity than do Y-cells.

field arrangement, with either an ON center and OFF surround or OFF center and ON surround, and these receptive fields are relatively large. Some W-cells respond tonically to appropriate standing contrasts (e.g., a bright spot centered in an ON center field or a dark spot centered in an OFF center field), and others respond in a phasic manner. Likewise, some W-cells sum spatial and temporal parameters linearly, and others do so nonlinearly (Fig. 4). W-Cells exhibit poor and inconsistent responsiveness to visual stimuli, which has led some authors to name these cells "sluggish" (Cleland and Levick, 1974a,b; Thibos and Levick, 1983). Probably related to this, contrast sensitivity functions of these cells (Fig. 6) demonstrate poor sensitivity that is nearly a log unit worse than that for X- or Y-cells. W-Cells are most sensitive to lower spatial and temporal frequencies (Figs. 6 and 7) and exhibit poor spatial or temporal resolution, which is defined as the highest spatial or temporal frequency to which the neuron responds. Finally, W-cells with center–surround receptive field organization can be distinguished from X- and Y-cells by the following test (Cleland and Levick, 1974a): an ON center W-cell fails to respond to a dark spot removed from its center, and an OFF center W-cell likewise fails to

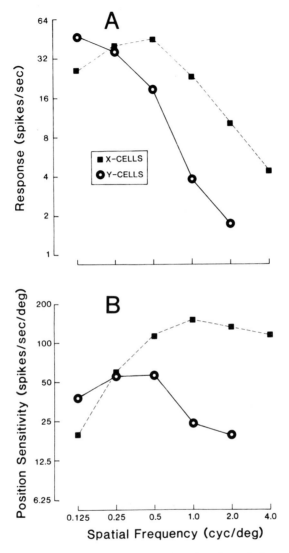

FIG. 8. Spatial tuning and position sensitivity functions for retinal ganglion X- and Y-cells averaged as in Fig. 6 and 7. The functions were obtained from 13 X- and 14 Y-cells in response to sine wave gratings drifted at 2 Hz. (A) Average spatial-tuning functions for X- and Y-cells. These represent the fundamental response component as a function of spatial frequency. (B) Average position sensitivity functions for X- and Y-cells. These represent maximum spatial phase or position sensitivity as a function of spatial frequency. This sensitivity equals $2\pi \cdot F_1 \cdot SF$, where F_1 is the fundamental response component at the spatial frequency (SF) under study. (Data taken from Sur and Sherman, 1984.)

TABLE II

PROPERTIES OF RETINAL AND GENICULATE W-, X-, AND Y-CELLS

Property	W-Cells[a]	X-Cells	Y-Cells
Axonal conduction velocity	Slow	Medium	Fast
Spatial and temporal summation properties to visual stimuli	Some linear, others nonlinear	Linear	Linear to lower spatial frequencies, nonlinear to higher ones
Receptive field organization	Mostly center–surround[a]	Center–surround	Linear center–surround with small nonlinear subunits distributed throughout
Receptive field size	Large	Small	Medium
Contrast sensitivity	Poor	Good to medium and higher spatial frequencies	Excellent to lower spatial frequencies
Spatial resolution	Poor	Excellent	Linear component fair, nonlinear component good
Temporal resolution	Poor	Fair	Good
Approximate retinal ratio	10–20%[a]	75–85%	5–7%
Approximate LGN ratio	10%[a]	40–50%	40–50%

[a] Here we refer only to the subset of W-cells that seem to be involved in retinogeniculate innervation (see text). This includes mainly cells with center–surround receptive fields.

respond to removal of a centered bright spot; X- and Y-cells respond vigorously to such stimuli.

The observation just made refers to those W-cells that appear to project to the lateral geniculate nucleus. However at least four other neuronal types have been distinguished among the cat's retinal ganglion cells. These are clearly not X- or Y-cells and may be functionally distinct from the W-cells described earlier (Stone and Fabian, 1966; Rodieck, 1967; Stone and Hoffmann, 1972; Cleland and Levick, 1974a,b; Stone and Fukuda, 1974). These all have very slowly conducting axons and generally poor or inconsistent responses to visual stimuli. These four general types include (1) cells that are differentially sensitive to different wavelengths of light (2) cells that are sensitive to the direction of stimulus motion (3) cells that are inhibited by any contrast located in the receptive field, and (4) cells that are excited by any contrast in the receptive field. The color-coded cells exhibit receptive fields with a classic center–surround organization, but the last three have diffusely organized fields with no obvious center–surround arrangement. These four types of ganglion cells that do not seem to form a prominent input to the lateral geniculate nucleus are not further considered in this article.

C. X-CELL RESPONSE PROPERTIES

X-Cell axons conduct at velocities intermediate between the slower ones of W-cells and the faster ones of Y-cells. Receptive fields of X-cells have a classic center–surround organization and are smaller than those of W- and Y-cells. X-Cells generally exhibit tonic responses to standing contrasts as well as linear summation in response to visual stimuli. These cells respond briskly and sensitively to most visual stimuli. However, spatial contrast sensitivity or response functions (Figs. 6 and 8) show that these cells are most sensitive to middle spatial frequencies, since their sensitivity falls off for lower and higher ones. Generally, X-cells are most sensitive to lower temporal frequencies (Lehmkuhle *et al.,* 1980a), although there may be a sensitivity peak near 2–4 Hz (Lennie, 1980a). The best spatial resolution of X-cells, which occurs at low temporal frequencies, generally exceeds that of W- and Y-cells (Figs. 6 and 7). The best temporal resolution of X-cells (at middle spatial frequencies) falls between the poorer values of W-cells and better ones of Y-cells (Fig. 7). However, Fig. 7 shows that at higher spatial frequencies, X-cells exhibit better temporal resolution than do Y-cells, and at higher temporal frequencies, Y-cells exhibit better spatial resolution than do X-cells. W-Cells are consistently worst on these measures.

From spatial-tuning functions similar to those in Figs. 6 and 8, it is possible to infer the cell's maximum sensitivity to small changes in stimulus position or spatial phase, which we call "position sensitivity." For drifting gratings at constant temporal frequency, this phase or position sensitivity (in spikes per second per degree) equals the product of 2π, the spatial frequency, and the amplitude of the fundamental response component at that frequency (Sur and Sherman, 1984). Since for these cells only the fundamental response component is sensitive to spatial phase (Hochstein and Shapley, 1976a), it is only this component that can confer phase sensitivity to the cell. Figure 8 plots this for retinal X- and Y-cells. The greatest position sensitivity is exhibited by X-cells at higher spatial frequencies. At lower ones, Y-cells are more sensitive than are X-cells, although this sensitivity is generally less than that observed for X-cells at higher frequencies.

D. Y-CELL RESPONSE PROPERTIES

Among retinal ganglion cells and geniculate neurons, Y-cells have the fastest-conducting axons. Y-Cells tend to have receptive fields intermediate in size between the larger ones of W-cells and smaller ones of X-cells. Y-Cells generally respond transiently to standing contrasts and are sensitive to most visual stimuli.

Y-Cells show a complex pattern of response linearity to visual stimuli: they have both linear and nonlinear response components, each of which exhibits characteristic response properties (Hochstein and Shapley, 1976b; Lehmkuhle *et al.*, 1980a; So and Shapley, 1981). The linear component is most sensitive to lower spatial frequencies and exhibits spatial resolution that is slightly better than that of W-cells but much poorer than that of X-cells (Figs. 6 and 8). Also, as noted earlier and shown in Fig. 8, the fundamental response component provides better position sensitivity for Y-cells than for X-cells only at lower spatial frequencies. The nonlinear component, which is relatively insensitive to lower spatial frequencies, is more sensitive than the linear component to higher spatial frequencies. Indeed, the nonlinear component is nearly as good as X-cells in terms of spatial resolution (Fig. 6). These and similar data led Hochstein and Shapley (1976b) to propose a two-part model for the Y-cell receptive field. One part consists of a linear, center–surround component that is relatively large to account for the relatively poor spatial resolution of the linear response. The second part is a collection of small, nonlinear subunits scattered throughout the center and surround to account for the relatively good spatial resolution of the nonlinear responses. No data have yet been published regarding the separate contributions of the linear and nonlinear response components to temporal contrast sensitivity functions. However, at low spatial frequencies, for which the linear component dominates, Y-cells exhibit better temporal resolution than do W- or X-cells (Fig. 7). Also, at all spatial frequencies Y-cells are generally more sensitive to lower temporal frequencies than to higher ones (Fig. 7; and Lehmkuhle *et al.*, 1980a), although there may be a moderate sensitivity peak near 2–4 Hz (Lennie, 1980a).

E. SUMMARY OF W-, X-, AND Y-CELL RESPONSE PROPERTIES

Table II and Figs. 6–8 summarize many of the functional properties that distinguish W-, X-, and Y-cells from one another. Axonal conduction velocities increase from W-cells to X-cells to Y-cells, and receptive-field sizes tend to increase from X-cells to Y-cells to W-cells. Generally, X-cells respond tonically to standing contrasts and Y-cells respond in a phasic manner; some W-cells are tonic and others are phasic. X- and Y-cells respond much better and more consistently to most visual stimuli than do W-cells. X-Cells and some W-cells exhibit predominantly linear response summation to visual stimuli. Other W-cells respond nonlinearly. Y-Cells have both linear and nonlinear response components, the former being more sensitive to lower spatial frequencies and the latter to higher ones. As shown by Figs. 6 and 7, W-cells respond relatively poorly at all temporal and spatial frequencies. At lower spatial and higher temporal frequencies, Y-cells are the most responsive neurons. Conversely, X-cells are the most responsive neurons at higher spatial and lower temporal frequences, particularly if only linear response components are considered. Finally, X-cells display their best position sensitivity at higher spatial frequencies, and this sensitivity generally exceeds that exhibited by Y-cells (Fig. 8). All of these response features suggest that Y-cells are important for the analysis of lower spatial frequencies and X-cells become increasingly important for higher ones, a distinction that will be reiterated in the consideration of the role these neuronal classes play in visual perception.

IV. Anatomical Organization and Distribution of the W-, X-, and Y-Cell Pathways

Until relatively recently, studies of the W-, X-, and Y-cell pathways were by necessity essentially unidimensional. Since these neuronal classes could be identified only by electrophysiological criteria, knowledge about them was largely confined to their response properties. As a first step toward a multidisciplinary approach to the study of these pathways, a number of investigators have attempted to establish the morphological correlates of these cell types. Such a multidisciplinary approach, which ultimately should include a range of biological disciplines such as pharmacology, biophysics, biochemistry, and embryology, is needed not only for a thorough understanding of these pathways, but also because any single approach without validation from others is subject to difficulties of interpretation. For instance, the uncertainties of electrode sampling render doubtful any attempt to describe the distributions of the W-, X-, and Y-cell pathways. If these distributions can be verified anatomically, they can be more surely specified. Indeed, the anatomical correlates of the W-, X-, and Y-cell pathways to be described here have greatly enhanced our understanding of the functional organization of these pathways.

A. RETINA

1. Morphological Classification of Ganglion Cells

Nearly a century ago, Ramón y Cajál (translated in Rodieck, 1973) drew attention to the different morphological types of ganglion cells in the cat retina that could be discerned from Golgi impregnations. Mainly on the basis of dendritic branching patterns in the inner plexiform layer, he described some 20–30 classes. Unfortunately, this classification cannot be readily correlated with the physiological classification of W-, X-, and Y-cells.

Boycott and Wassle (1974) also used the Golgi technique to provide the first hypothesis of specific morphological correlates for W-, X-, and Y-cells. They described alpha, beta, and gamma morphological types (see Fig. 9) and suggested from indirect evidence that these represent Y-, X-, and W-cells, respectively. *Alpha* cells have the largest somata, fairly extensive dendritic arbors, and the thickest axons. *Beta* cells have medium-sized somata, small but densely branched dendritic arbors, and axons of intermediate thickness. *Gamma* cells, according to the original description of Boycott and Wassle (1974), have the smallest somata, extensive but sparsely branched dendritic arbors, and the thinnest axons. One analysis of optic nerve axons has successfully demonstrated these components of the axon diameter spectrum: a small-diameter mode probably belonging to gamma-cell axons, a medium-diameter mode probably belonging to beta-cell axons, and a large-diameter tail probably belonging to alpha-cell axons (Williams and Chalupa, 1983).

Other morphological types have been described that have somata in the

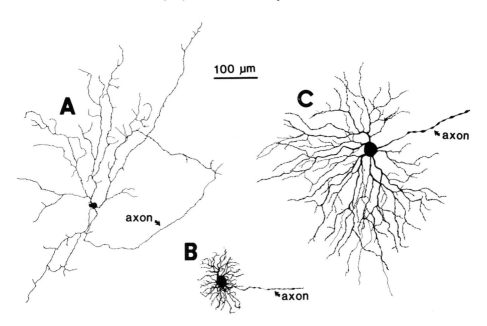

FIG. 9.   Camera lucida drawings of ganglion cells in the retina as viewed in a flat mount. Each neuron was intracellularly filled with HRP after physiological identification. (A) W-Cell with gamma morphology; (B) X-cell with beta morphology; (C) Y-cell with alpha morphology. (From Stanford and Sherman, 1984.)

beta-cell range but that are clearly not beta cells. These may be variants of gamma cells [e.g., the *delta* cells of Boycott and Wassle (1974) and the medium-sized *gamma* cells of Stone and Clarke (1980)], or they may represent other morphological classes [e.g., the *epsilon, g1,* and *g2* cells of Leventhal (1982)]. At present, it is no easier to decide how many morphological classes are subsumed within the "gamma"-cell population (i.e., neither alpha nor beta cells) than it is to decide how many physiological classes are represented by "W-cells" (i.e., neither X- nor Y-cells).

The best published evidence for correlations among morphological and physiological types is the series of experiments by Wassle and colleagues (Cleland *et al.,* 1975a; Wassle *et al.,* 1975, 1981a,b; Peichl and Wassle, 1981; Wassle, 1982), which make a strong case that alpha cells are Y-cells. The evidence that beta cells are X-cells and that gamma cells are W-cells is rather less direct and secure. The more direct approach of labeling a single physiologically identified cell with an intracellular injection of Lucifer yellow or horseradish peroxidase (HRP) has produced preliminary data that largely support these correlations (Saito, 1983; Stanford and Sherman, 1984). This has shown that alpha cells are Y-cells, beta cells are

X-cells, and most gamma cells are W-cells. More data of this sort should eventually establish the structure–function correlations quite firmly.

2. Distribution of Cell Types

A number of laboratories have made use of the structure–function correlates just described to survey with histological techniques the distribution of the W-, X-, and Y-cell classes across the retina (Boycott and Wassle, 1974; Fukuda and Stone, 1974; Cleland et al., 1975a; Wassle et al., 1975, 1981b; Stone, 1978; Peichl and Wassle, 1979; Illing and Wassle, 1981; Leventhal, 1982; Williams and Chalupa, 1983). These proposed distributions must be qualified partly because of a degree of uncertainty in the structure–function correlates, particularly for W- and X-cells, and partly because of a degree of controversy regarding the estimated values for the distributions (Fukuda and Stone, 1974; Wassle et al., 1981a,b; Wassle, 1982; Leventhal, 1982). Indeed there is as yet no agreement regarding the actual number of ganglion cells, regardless of classification (Hughes and Wassle, 1976; Hughes, 1981; Stone, 1978; Stone and Campion, 1978). Nonetheless, these distributions offer the best approximation of W-, X-, and Y-cell patterns across the retina independent of electrode-sampling problems. Of approximately 200,000 ganglion cells, roughly 5% are alpha cells (or Y-cells), one-half to two-thirds are beta cells (or X-cells), and one-third to one-half are gamma, delta, epsilon, g1, and g2 cells (or W-cells). Of this last group of presumed W-cells, only about 40% (or roughly 15–20% of the ganglion cell total) appear to project to the lateral geniculate nucleus (Illing and Wassle, 1981; Leventhal, 1982).

The relative ratios of cell types vary with eccentricity. The density of both X- and Y-cells peaks at the area centralis, but this peak is much sharper for X-cells. Thus, the relative ratio of X- to Y-cells, which on average is roughly 10:1, decreases with increasing eccentricity from the area centralis (Hoffmann et al., 1972; Fukuda and Stone, 1974; Wassle et al., 1975, 1981a; Peichl and Wassle, 1979, 1981; Wassle, 1982; Leventhal, 1982). W-Cell density is fairly uniform across the retina with a slight increase along the horizontal streak, which is an elongated horizontal region passing through the area centralis (Rowe and Stone, 1976).

3. Central Projections

Every retinal X- and Y-cell and an as yet unspecified subset of W-cells projects to the lateral geniculate nucleus (Fukuda and Stone, 1974; Bowling and Michael, 1980, 1984; Illing and Wassle, 1981; Leventhal et al., 1980a,b; Sur and Sherman, 1982b; Rowe and Dreher, 1982). As noted above, retrograde labeling of retinal ganglion cells from HRP injections into the lateral geniculate nucleus (Illing and Wassle, 1981; Rowe and Dreher, 1982) suggests that roughly 40% of the W-cells project to that nucleus. The details of the retinogeniculate projection of W-, X-, and Y-cells with respect to the various geniculate laminae is described in the following section. A meager projection from X-cells seems to be directed outside the lateral geniculate nucleus (Fukuda and Stone, 1974). Horse-radish peroxidase labeling of individual X-cell axons in the optic tract occasionally reveals an axonal branch that can be traced for a short dis-tance beyond the lateral geniculate nucleus (Sur and Sherman, 1982b), and some X-cell input to the midbrain has been suggested (Hoffmann and Stone, 1973; Leventhal *et al.*, 1980b; Wassle and Illing, 1980). Single Y-cell axons branch to innervate the lateral geniculate nucleus, superior colliculus, and perhaps other brain stem sites (Bowling and Michael, 1980; Wassle and Illing, 1980; Sur and Sherman, 1982b). Different popula-tions of W-cells seem to innervate the lateral geniculate nucleus, the superior colliculus, the ventral division of the lateral geniculate nucleus, the pretectum, and perhaps other brain stem sites (Hoffmann, 1973; Fu-kuda and Stone, 1974; Cleland *et al.*, 1975b; Wilson *et al.*, 1976; Spear *et al.*, 1977; Leventhal *et al.*, 1980a,b). The retinogeniculate W-cells appar-ently have larger somata on average than do those W-cells that innervate extrageniculate structures (Leventhal *et al.*, 1980a,b; Leventhal, 1982; Rowe and Dreher, 1982).

B. Lateral Geniculate Nucleus

1. Gross Topography

a. Lamination. The cat's lateral geniculate nucleus is a laminated structure, and as Figs. 10 and 11A and B illustrate, the laminae are defined in terms of ocular input (Hickey and Guillery, 1974; Guillery *et al.*, 1980). The contralateral nasal retina innervates laminae A, C, C2, and 1 of the medial interlaminar nucleus (which is a subdivision of the lateral genicu-late nucleus), and the geniculate wing.* The ipsilateral temporal retina

---

* Guillery *et al.* (1980) have called this retinofugal terminal zone the "geniculate wing," although others (e.g., Leventhal *et al.*, 1980a) have called this the "retinal recipient zone" of the pulvinar. One can logically define the (dorsal) lateral geniculate nucleus as that collection of neurons that receives direct retinal input and projects to cerebral cortex. This region would thus better be called "geniculate wing" rather than a division of the pulvinar. Note that, by this reasoning, lamina C3 of the lateral geniculate nucleus should indeed not be considered a part of that nucleus, because it receives no direct retinal input (Hickey and Guillery, 1974).

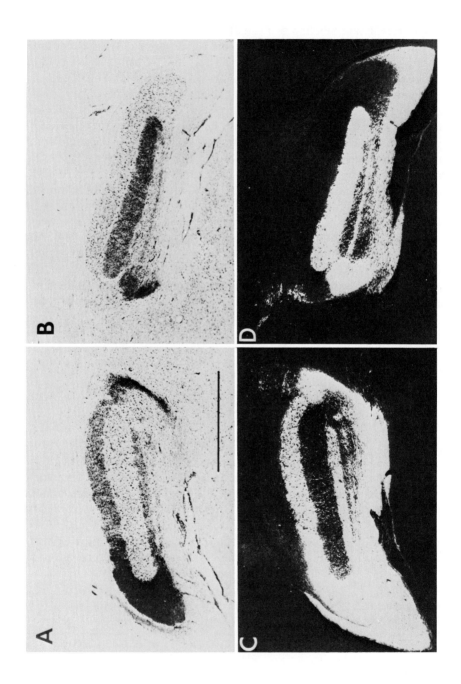

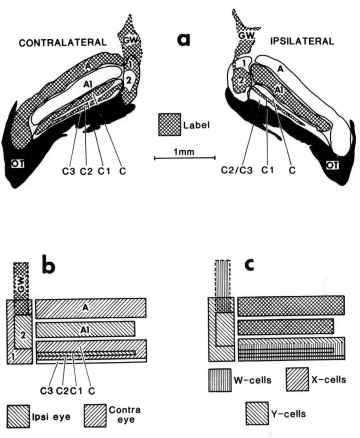

FIG. 11. Laminar arrangements of the cat's lateral geniculate nucleus. (a) Camera lucida drawings of the sections shown in Fig. 10, with autoradiographic label from the right eye cross-hatched. The contralateral eye innervates laminae A, C, C2, and 1 (of the medial interlaminar nucleus), and the geniculate wing (GW). The ipsilateral eye innervates laminae A1, C1, and 2 (of the medial interlaminar nucleus), and the geniculate wing. Thus, neither eye innervates lamina C3, and the geniculate wing is the only geniculate region to receive innervation from both eyes. (b) Schematic representation of ocular inputs in relation to the laminae. (c) Schematic representation of W-, X-, and Y-cell inputs and distributions in relation to the laminae (see text for details).

FIG. 10. Photomicrographs of coronal sections through the left and right lateral geniculate nuclei of a cat. The cat previously had an injection of tritiated proline placed into its right eye, and these sections were treated for autoradiography. (A) and (C) Bright-field and dark-field photomicrographs, respectively, of the same view of the left nucleus. (B) and (D) Bright-field and dark-field photomicrographs, respectively, of the same view of the right nucleus. Inputs from the right (injected) eye are labeled darkly in the bright-field views, and brightly in the dark-field views. Figure 11 shows the laminar relationships of these sections. The scale in (A) is 1 mm and applies as well to (B)–(D).

innervates laminae A1, C1, and 2 of the medial interlaminar nucleus, and the geniculate wing. Thus, the geniculate wing is the one region that receives binocular input, and lamina C3 is the one lamina that appears to receive no direct retinal afferents (Fig. 11B). Not shown in Figs. 10 and 11A and B is lamina 3 of the medial interlaminar nucleus (Guillery *et al.*, 1980; Rowe and Dreher, 1982), because it occupies a more caudal region than is illustrated there. Lamina 3 is innervated by the contralateral temporal retina and thus maps the "wrong" hemifield.

b. Retinotopic Organization. The lateral geniculate nucleus exhibits a precise point-to-point map such that neighboring geniculate neurons have receptive fields adjacent to each other in visual space. The retinotopic maps are best understood for the A- and C-laminae (Laties and Sprague, 1966; Sanderson 1971a). These laminae are stacked in register such that a line of cells oriented perpendicular to the laminar borders (or across the short axis of each lamina) maps the same single point in visual space. These have been termed the "projection lines." The vertical meridian of the visual field (which, in the retina, passes vertically through the area centralis) is mapped at the medial edge of the A- and C-laminae, and lateral locations along these laminae map progressively more peripheral visual field. Note, for example, that lamina A extends further laterally than does lamina A1 (Figs. 10 and 11A and B), because the nasal retina (which innervates lamina A) extends further from the vertical meridian than does the temporal retina (which innervates lamina A1). Finally, vertical directions in visual space are represented by anteroposterior directions in the nucleus such that more elevated (or less elevated) visual coordinates are mapped more posteriorly (or anteriorly). Maps in the medial interlaminar nucleus and geniculate wing are understood in less detail and have only recently been described (Guillery *et al.*, 1980).

The visuotopic map in the lateral geniculate nucleus, while continuous, is distorted by the fact that more neural tissue is devoted to more central visual regions than to more peripheral ones. This distortion has been called the "magnification factor." For instance, near the anteroposterior middle of the nucleus where the horizontal midline of the visual field is represented, the medial half of lamina A maps only the central 5° of visual field, and the lateral half maps the remaining 85–90° of visual field.

Sanderson (1971b) has suggested that this distortion is a reflection of that already present among ganglion cells, since these are more densely aggregated nearer the area centralis. Optical constraints of the eye and the predominant direction of information flow across the layers through the retina require that ganglion cells be located at or very near their receptive field positions. Thus regions that require more neurons for more detailed analysis (e.g., the area centralis) must have a greater density of cells. The lateral geniculate nucleus (and other visual areas of the brain) have no such optical constraints and are thus able to form neural circuits in the framework of a fairly uniform density of neurons. This could result in retinal regions of greater ganglion cell density being represented by larger volumes of geniculate tissue with constant neuronal density. Magnification factors such as that seen in the lateral geniculate nucleus might thus occur.

Of course, if one wishes to relate ganglion cell density to magnification factor in a given brain locus (e.g., lateral geniculate nucleus, superior colliculus, or one of the visual cortical areas), one must include only the subset of ganglion cells that participate in innervation of that locus. For instance, magnification factor of the geniculate A-laminae, which contain X- and Y-cells but not W-cells (see later), should be compared with some combination of the density distribution of retinal X- and Y-cells; for superior colliculus, magnification factor should be compared against the combined density of retinal Y-cells and those W-cells that innervate the superior colliculus. To date, such comparisons have not been made in any systematic fashion, although a superficial comparison of the visuotopic map for the A-laminae (Sanderson, 1971a) with alpha and beta ganglion cell density distributions (Peichl and Wassle, 1979; Leventhal, 1982) suggest the plausibility of this hypothesis.

2. Afferent Input

a. Retinal Afferents. As mentioned before, most retinal ganglion cells, including every X- and Y-cell and many W-cells, project to the lateral geniculate nucleus. This projection has a strong differential laminar pattern. Figure 11C shows the laminar distribution of geniculate W-, X-, and Y-cells, which in turn reflects laminar differences in the retinogeniculate projection along these pathways (Fig. 12). Most information relevant to these laminar differences in afferent projection patterns stems from physiological studies of single geniculate neurons, since each of these neurons seems to receive input from a single class of ganglion cell. These studies have largely focused on the A-laminae (Cleland *et al.,* 1971; Hoffmann *et al.,* 1972; So and Shapley, 1981; Lehmkuhle *et al.,* 1980a), although several studies of the C-laminae (Cleland *et al.,* 1975b; Wilson *et al.,* 1976; Sur and Sherman, 1982a) and laminae 1 and 2 of the medial interlaminar nucleus (Mason, 1975; Kratz *et al.,* 1978; Dreher and Sefton, 1979) have been reported. Laminae A and A1 contain a mixture of X- and Y-cells without W-cells. The dorsal part of lamina C contains Y-cells and perhaps some W- and X-cells (Wilson *et al.,* 1976; Friedlander *et al.,* 1981), and the remainder of the C-laminae contain only W-cells (Wilson *et*

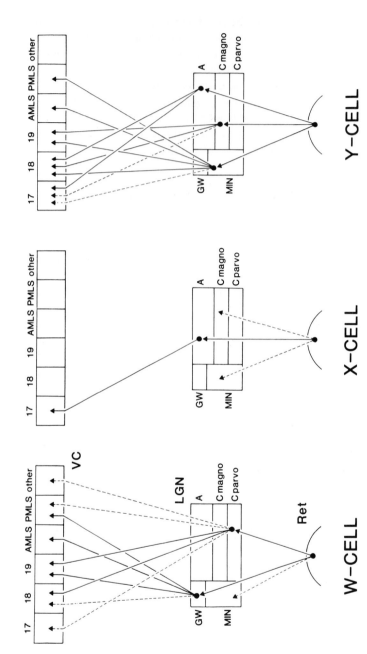

FIG. 12. Schematic summary diagram of W-, X-, and Y-cell pathways from retina through the lateral geniculate nucleus to various areas of visual cortex (for further details, see Fig. 1 and Table I). Abbreviations: Ret, retina; LGN, lateral geniculate nucleus; A, A-laminae; C, C-laminae; Cparvo, parvocellular C-laminae; GW, geniculate wing; MIN, medial interlaminar nucleus; VC, visual cortex; 17–19, areas 17–19; AMLS, anterior medial lateral suprasylvian area; PMLS, posterior medial lateral suprasylvian area; other, areas 20a, 20b, 21a, and 21b plus the ventral lateral suprasylvian, posterior lateral lateral suprasylvian, and dorsal lateral suprasylvian areas. Solid lines represent relatively dense projections, and dashed lines represent relatively sparse projections.

al., 1976; Stanford *et al.,* 1981, 1983; Sur and Sherman, 1982a). The dorsal part of lamina C that contains Y-cells has large somata and is termed magnocellular lamina C; the remainder of the C-laminae, which contain only W-cells, has small somata and is termed the parvocellular C-laminae. Laminae 1 and 2 of the medial interlaminar nucleus predominantly contain Y-cells, although rare W- and X-cells may also exist there (Mason, 1975; Kratz *et al.,* 1978; Dreher and Sefton, 1979; Rowe and Dreher, 1982). No recordings from the geniculate wing and lamina 3 of the medial interlaminar nucleus have yet been reported, but indirect anatomical evidence suggests that the former contains mostly W-cells, and the latter, mostly Y-cells (Guillery *et al.,* 1980). Figure 12 summarizes our current, somewhat incomplete understanding: retinal W-cells innervate the parvocellular C-laminae, the geniculate wing, and possibly the medial interlaminar nucleus; X-cells innervate the A-laminae and possibly magnocellular lamina C and the medial interlaminar nucleus; and Y-cells innervate the A-laminae, magnocellular lamina C, and the medial interlaminar nucleus.

Several laboratories (Bowling and Michael, 1980, 1984; Sur and Sherman, 1982b) have labeled with HRP individual, physiologically identified, optic tract axons to illustrate the pattern of single-cell terminations in the lateral geniculate nucleus. Figure 13 shows examples for an X-cell axon and a Y-cell axon. X-Cell axons innervate essentially only lamina A or A1, depending on the eye of origin, and every X-cell axon does so. The terminal fields are relatively small and densely packed with terminal boutons that represent the retinal synapses (Robson and Mason, 1979; Hamos *et al.,* 1983). An occasional X-cell axon emits a collateral branch that sparsely innervates magnocellular lamina C or the medial interlaminar nucleus, but even for these the number of terminal boutons outside of the A-laminae represent less than 1% of the number in the A-laminae (Sur and Sherman, 1982b). Finally, most X-cell axons have a branch that bypasses the lateral geniculate nucleus and approaches the brachium of the superior colliculus (Sur and Sherman, 1982b); what, if any, extrageniculate structures these axons innervate is open to question (but see Hoffmann and Stone, 1973; Leventhal *et al.,* 1980; Wassle and Illing, 1980). Every Y-cell axon innervates lamina A or A1. The typical Y-cell terminal volume for the A-laminae is 5–10 times larger with roughly 3 times as many boutons as the typical X-cell terminal region (Sur and Sherman, 1982b). Also, most Y-cell axons branch to innervate densely the medial interlaminar nucleus, and, if from the contralateral eye, magnocellular lamina C. Clearly, each Y-cell axon much more extensively innervates the lateral geniculate nucleus than does each X-cell axon. Virtually all Y-cell axons continue past the lateral geniculate nucleus to innervate other

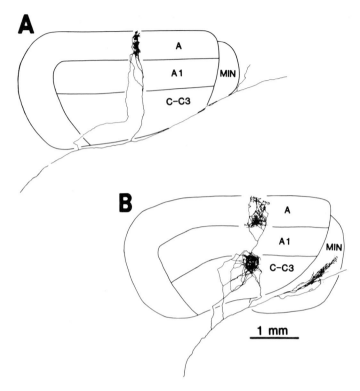

FIG. 13. Camera lucida drawings of terminal patterns for retinogeniculate axons as viewed in the coronal plane. Each axon was intracellularly filled with HRP after physiological identification, and each of these drawings was reconstructed from several consecutive 100-μm-thick sections. (A) X-Cell axon; (B) Y-cell axon. Abbreviations: A, Al, and C–C3, laminae; MIN, medial interlaminar nucleus. (Unpublished data from M. Sur and S. M. Sherman; see also Sur and Sherman, 1982b.)

brain stem sites, particularly the superior colliculus (Bowling and Michael, 1980). There are as yet no published descriptions of successfully labeled W-cell axons.

b. Extraretinal Afferents. Although this lateral geniculate nucleus is the largest terminus of retinofugal projections, this nucleus also receives afferent input from areas 17, 18, 19, and PMLS of the visual cortex (Beresford, 1962; Guillery, 1967; Garey *et al.*, 1968; Hollander, 1970, 1972; Niimi *et al.*, 1971; Kawamura *et al.*, 1974; Updyke, 1975, 1977, 1981), the perigeniculate nucleus (Alhsen and Lindstrom, 1978), the midbrain (Niimi *et al.*, 1970; Graybiel, 1972; Graham, 1977; Graybiel and Berson, 1980; Torrealba *et al.*, 1981), and probably portions of the brain stem reticular formation, including the locus coeruleus (see reviews by

Singer, 1977; Burke and Cole, 1978; see also Rogawski and Aghajanian, 1980). The perigeniculate nucleus is a collection of neurons lying just dorsal to lamina A, and perigeniculate neurons receive input from axon collaterals of geniculocortical relay cells as these axons pass en route to cortex (Dubin and Cleland, 1977; Ahlsen *et al.*, 1978; Friedlander *et al.*, 1981; Stanford *et al.*, 1983). The perigeniculate nucleus is also innervated by cerebral cortex (Niimi *et al.*, 1971; Updyke, 1975, 1977) and possibly also to a very minor degree by the retina (Laties and Sprague, 1966; Ide, 1982). The midbrain afferents terminate mainly in the C-laminae and medial interlaminar nucleus, while the other afferents seem to innervate all geniculate subdivisions.

The retinal input seems functionally dominant, since it powerfully excites geniculate target neurons and response properties of geniculate cells so closely match those of their retinal inputs (Hubel and Wiesel, 1961; Cleland *et al.*, 1971; Hoffmann *et al.*, 1972; Bullier and Norton, 1979a, Kaplan *et al.*, 1979; So and Shapley, 1981). However, retinal synapses comprise only about one-fifth of the synapses found in the lateral geniculate nucleus (Guillery, 1969), although it is not known what proportion of the remainder originates from sources extrinsic or intrinsic to the nucleus. Cortical input seems also to be excitatory (Kalil and Chase, 1970; Tsumoto *et al.*, 1978) but much less powerfully so than the retinal input, and activity of the perigeniculate neurons probably inhibits geniculate cells (Lindstrom, 1982). Because perigeniculate cells receive input from a geniculocortical relay cells, this presumed inhibition represents a feedback loop. The actions of the other inputs to the lateral geniculate nucleus are presently unknown.

3. Geniculate Neuronal Classes

As noted already, response properties of geniculate neurons closely resemble those of retinal ganglion cells, because each geniculate neuron seems to receive retinal input from very few (or one) ganglion cells of a single W-, X-, or Y-cell, ON or OFF center class. Consequently, nearly every geniculate neuron can be classified as a W-, X-, or Y-cell.

a. Relay Cells and Interneurons. A different classification of geniculate neurons is that of relay cells and interneurons. The former possess axons that project to cortex, whereas the latter have axons that are strictly intrinsic to the lateral geniculate nucleus. It should be noted that many relay cells contribute to local geniculate circuitry by means of axon collaterals (Friedlander *et al.*, 1981; Stanford *et al.*, 1983), and thus the potential for local circuits can theoretically exist without interneurons. Also, perigeniculate cells can be considered as interneurons, since they form a feedback loop from relay cells back to the lateral geniculate nucleus, but strictly speaking, their somata are outside of the lateral geniculate nucleus.

Estimates of the percentage of interneurons with somata within the lateral geniculate nucleus range from practically none (Lin *et al.*, 1977) to roughly 25% (LeVay and Ferster, 1979; Geisert, 1980). The discrepancy and source of uncertainty stem from the fact that attempts to demonstrate the presence of interneurons are based on negative evidence or the inability to demonstrate an extrinsic axon. Physiologically, this usually results from a failure to activate the recorded geniculate neuron antidromically from electrical stimulation of the cortex (e.g., Dubin and Cleland, 1977) and anatomically from a failure to label cells retrogradely with markers (such as HRP) injected into cortex (e.g., LeVay and Ferster, 1977, 1979). It is not yet safe to conclude that every relay cell can be antidromically stimulated from cortex or that each will retrogradely transport HRP; such observations may not unambiguously identify interneurons.

Two more recent lines of evidence further confuse the issue. First, Friedlander *et al.* (1981) injected HRP into physiologically identified geniculate cells (see also later). They found some cells that could not be antidromically activated from cortex but that clearly possessed axons projecting to cortex. They also reported cells that had morphological features normally associated with interneurons but that were antidromically activated from cortex. Likewise, Meyer and Albus (1981) retrogradely labeled cells with morphological features usually associated with interneurons from HRP placed into visual cortex. Second, Fitzpatrick *et al.* (1984) found that virtually all geniculate cells could be labeled either retrogradely from HRP placed into cortex or with an antibody to glutamic acid decarboxylase (GAD), which is a synthetic enzyme for the presumed inhibitory transmitter, γ-aminobutyric acid (GABA). No cell was labeled for both substances. It seems implausible, though possible, that only those relay cells that failed to transport HRP retrogradely also contain GAD (e.g., Einstein *et al.*, 1983). Perhaps because of their short axons, interneurons do not generate action potentials (as is the case for many retinal interneurons) and could consequently have been overlooked in the physiological recordings on which Friedlander *et al.* (1981) based their sample. In any case, although the presence of interneurons seems most likely, it is still based on circumstantial evidence. Because every recorded cell apparently receives direct retinal afferents and can be classified as a W-, X-, or Y-cell (cf. Dubin and Cleland, 1977), and because the vast majority of geniculate neurons are in any case relay cells that can be similarly classified, the ensuing discussion is organized around these neuronal classes.

b. Structure–Function Correlates. As was the case for retina, attempts to establish structural correlates for geniculate W-, X-, and Y-cells began with studies of Golgi-impregnated neurons. In such a study of the A- and C-laminae, Guillery (1966) noted four general morphological classes, although he pointed out that the plurality of impregnated neurons in his sample could not be placed into any of these four classes. Nonetheless, other workers used a variety of indirect approaches to suggest the correlation of each of these four morphological classes with W-cells, X-cells, Y-cells, or interneurons (Wilson *et al.*, 1976; LeVay and Ferster, 1977).

Structure–function correlates have subsequently been established with the more direct approach of HRP iontophoresis into physiologically identified geniculate neurons (Friedlander *et al.*, 1979, 1981; Stanford *et al.*, 1981, 1983). From these data, Fig. 14 summarizes many of the morphological features of geniculate W-, X-, and Y-cells in the A- and C-laminae. This sort of structure–function correlation has not yet been extended to neurons of the medial interlaminar nucleus or the geniculate wing. W-Cells were found in the parvocellular C-laminae and have small somata, thin axons, and fairly thin dendrites. The dendrites occasionally have complex appendages and often are beaded or varicose in appearance. Their dendritic arbors are roughly disk-shaped and oriented parallel to the geniculate laminar borders, and typically part of each arbor crosses laminar borders. X-Cells were found in the A-laminae and have small somata, intermediate-sized axon diameters, and thin dendrites. For most X-cells, the dendrites are rather sinuous and have numerous stalked appendages. Their dendritic arbors are cylindrical, with the long axis oriented perpendicular to the laminar borders (i.e., along the previously mentioned projection lines), and each arbor is wholly contained within lamina A or A1. As noted earlier, several X-cells that were confirmed as relay cells had morphological features previously associated with interneurons (Friedlander *et al.*, 1981). Y-Cells were found in the A-laminae and magnocellular lamina C. These have large somata, thick axons, and thick, fairly straight dendrites. A few simple spinelike appendages extend from some of the dendrites. The dendritic arbors tend to display approximately spherical symmetry, and some dendrites of each Y-cell cross laminar borders.

4. Relative Numbers of Geniculate W-, X-, and Y-Cells

A number of factors conspire to confound estimates of the relative numbers of geniculate W-, X-, and Y-cells. These factors include the

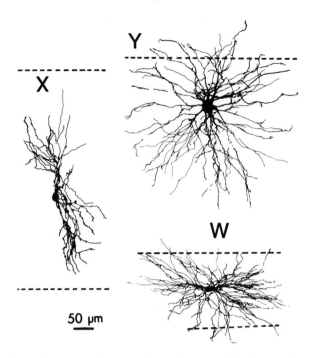

FIG. 14.   Camera lucida drawings of a W-cell, X-cell, and Y-cell in the lateral geniculate nucleus as viewed in the coronal plane. The location and orientation of laminar boundaries are also shown relative to each cell. Each neuron was intracellularly filled with HRP after physiological identification, and each was reconstructed from several consecutive 100-μm-thick sections. The W-cell was located in lamina C2 and/or C3 (laminar borders here were determined by autoradiography following an injection of tritiated proline into the ipsilateral eye), the X-cell was located in lamina A, and the Y-cell was located in lamina A1. (From Stanford *et al.*, 1983.)

differential distributions of these cell classes with laminar location (Fig. 11C), differential distributions with receptive-field eccentricity (cf. Hoffmann *et al.*, 1972), and uncertainties regarding the interpretation of electrophysiological data due to uncontrolled electrode-sampling biases. Nonetheless, the available evidence to be outlined suggests that, at least for X- and Y-cells, the geniculate ratios are quite different from those in retina. This, in turn, suggests an important role for retinogeniculate circuitry beyond a simple relay of visual information. That is, this circuitry alters the relative weight of the geniculocortical limbs of these parallel pathways compared to their representation among the retinogeniculate limbs.

a. W-Cells. Estimates of relative W-cell numbers are especially tenu-
ous because so few relevant data are available. Wilson *et al.* (1976), in an
electrophysiological study of the A- and C-laminae, reported that only
11% of the neurons recorded were W-cells. Although it is often suggested
that neurons with small somata (i.e., W-cells) are underrepresented in
physiological samples, studies that have combined physiological and morphological analyses of single neurons (Friedlander *et al.,* 1981; Stanford *et
al.,* 1983) suggest that little or no such underrepresentation exists for the
A- and C-laminae. However, while W-cells may represent a small neuronal segment of these laminae, their unknown numbers in the geniculate
wing and medial interlaminar nucleus render uncertain any estimate of
their overall proportion in the lateral geniculate nucleus.

b. X- and Y-Cells. Two separate lines of evidence offer rather similar
estimates for the X- to Y-cell ratios in the A-laminae. First, LeVay and
Ferster (1977) showed that a particular morphological type, the class 1
cell described by Guillery (1966), represents roughly one-third of the neurons in these laminae. Friedlander *et al.* (1981) subsequently demonstrated that nearly all of these class 1 cells are Y-cells, although some Y-
cells have other morphological features. Thus, the evidence of LeVay and
Ferster (1977) suggests an X- to Y-cell ratio of no more than 2:1. Second,
in an analysis of A-laminae neurons, Friedlander *et al.* (1981) compared
the soma size distributions of their HRP-labeled X- and Y-cells with those
seen in Nissl preparations, and from this deduced an X- to Y-cell ratio of
roughly 2:1. Since Y-cells are far more numerous than are X-cells in
magnocellular lamina C and the medial interlaminar nucleus, these authors suggested that the overall X- to Y-cell ratio in the lateral geniculate
nucleus approaches unity.

This estimate of a geniculate X- to Y-cell ratio approaching 1:1 contrasts sharply with the retinal estimate of roughly 10:1. If these estimates
are correct, and it is important to remember that neither the retinal nor the
geniculate estimates are confirmed, then the retinogeniculate innervation
patterns must be quite different for the X- and Y-cell pathways. That is,
each retinal Y-cell axon must innervate nearly 10 times as many geniculate neurons on average as does each X-cell axon. A consideration of the
relative numbers of retinal ganglion cells and geniculate neurons led
Friedlander *et al.* (1981) to suggest that each retinal Y-cell axon on average innervates 30–40 geniculate neurons, whereas each X-cell axon innervates only two to four cells. As shown in Fig. 13, morphological analysis of single X- and Y-cell optic tract axons (Bowling and Michael, 1980;
Sur and Sherman, 1982b) is consistent with this suggestion, since a typical
Y-cell axon branches to innervate a zone of the lateral geniculate nucleus

that is roughly an order of magnitude larger than the zone innervated by a typical X-cell axon.

Regardless of the specifics of retinogeniculate circuitry, these retinal and geniculate estimates of X- and Y-cell numbers suggest a powerful relative amplification of the Y-cell pathway in this circuitry. This relative amplification forms one of the bases of the hypothesis to be presented here for X- and Y-cell functioning.

5. Central Projections

Figure 12 summarizes the main features of the geniculocortical projections. The many different target areas in the cerebral cortex are indicated in terms of both the W-, X-, and Y-cell pathways and the different geniculate laminae. Many of the data represented here for the W-, X-, and Y-cells are indirect and inferred from a combination of pathway-tracing studies that reveal the geniculocortical projection for each lamina (Garey and Powell, 1967; Rosenquist et al., 1974; Hollander and Vanegas, 1977; Garey and Blakemore, 1977; Lin and Sherman, 1978; Itoh et al., 1979; Leventhal, 1979; Geisert, 1980; Raczkowski and Rosenquist, 1980, 1983; Tong et al., 1982) plus a knowledge of the laminar distribution of W-, X-, and Y-cells.

a. W-Cells.   Geniculate W-cells seem to contribute to the innervation of every cortical area that receives geniculate afferents. The most prominent of the presumptive W-cell projections innervates areas 18, 19, and the AMLS and PMLS areas of the lateral suprasylvian cortex (for details of this terminology, see the legend to Fig. 1; and Symonds et al., 1981; Tusa et al., 1981; Tusa, 1982). As noted already, it is not yet clear that these W-cells form a homogeneous neuronal class. For instance, W-cells of the C-laminae may prove to be distinct from those thought to exist in the geniculate wing. Different classes of W-cell could thus have distinct patterns of geniculocortical innervation.

It is also not clear to what extent the W-cell innervation of multiple visual areas reflect multiple innervation of several areas by single branching axons or differential innervation of single areas by different pools of W-cells. Geisert (1980) has obtained evidence that many individual C-laminae neurons, which are presumably W-cells, innervate multiple cortical areas.

b. X-Cells.   A combination of evidence, both electrophysiological (Stone and Dreher, 1973; Mitzdorf and Singer, 1978, 1980; Bullier and Henry, 1979a–c) and anatomical (Ferster and LeVay, 1978; Gilbert and Wiesel, 1979; Humphrey et al., 1984a,b), demonstrates that geniculate X-cells nearly exclusively innervate the striate cortex (area 17). While it is diffcult to exclude the possibility of some direct extrastriate input from geniculate X-cells, it seems safe to conclude that, if such a projection exists, it is exceedingly sparse.

c. Y-Cells. Like W-cells, Y-cells seem to innervate many areas of visual cortex. Relatively dense Y-cell input seems to exist for areas 17, 18, 19, plus the AMLS and PMLS areas of the lateral suprasylvian cortex. Both electrophysiological (Stone and Dreher, 1973) and anatomical (Geisert, 1980) data indicate that many individual Y-cells of the A-laminae innervate both areas 17 and 18 via branching axons, although only a minority of Y-cells do so (Humphrey *et al.,* 1984a,b). It is not clear to what extent the multiple terminal zones of geniculocortical Y-cells from magnocellular lamina C and the medial interlaminar nucleus result from an analogous pattern of branching axons.

It follows from the preceding discussion that the small minority of retinal ganglion cells that are Y-cells (roughly 5%) innervates a much larger fraction of geniculate relay cells (see earlier). These geniculate Y-cells, in turn, innervate a large region of many areas of visual cortex. In contrast, the majority of retinal ganglion cells that are X-cells have a geniculocortical representation that is limited to only one area, area 17, of visual cortex. This contrast between the X- and Y-cell pathways will be considered again later.

C. Visual Cortex

Because this article focuses on the W-, X-, and Y-cell pathways and because so little is presently known regarding the manner by which the various areas of visual cortex process information from these pathways, the discussion of visual cortex will be brief and somewhat narrowly limited. For a more general consideration of mammalian visual cortex, the reader is directed to several publications (Henry, 1977; Gilbert, 1977, 1983; Kaas, 1978, 1980; Hubel and Wiesel, 1977; Van Essen, 1979; Diamond, 1979; Lund *et al.,* 1979; Merzenich and Kaas, 1980; Lund, 1981; Tusa *et al.,* 1981; Tusa, 1982).

As noted earlier and illustrated in Fig. 1, no fewer than 13 distinct visual areas of cerebral cortex have been mapped in the cat, and Fig. 12 summarizes the distribution of geniculocortical W-, X-, and Y-cell inputs to these areas. Others not yet completely mapped may also exist, such as areas 5, 7, CG, PS, and SVA of Fig. 1 and the anterior ectosylvian area (Olson and Graybiel, 1981; Mucke *et al.,* 1982). Nearly all of the data relevant to intracortical processing of these separate geniculate inputs derives from studies of the striate cortex.

1. Striate Cortex

a. Cell Types. The main morphological cell types found in striate cortex, and indeed throughout neocortex, are stellate cells, pyramidal cells, and fusiform cells (O'Leary, 1941; Lorente de No, 1949; Sholl, 1955; Lund, 1973; Lund *et al.*, 1979). Stellate cells have small, star-shaped somata and small but densely branched dendritic arbors. Their axons usually ramify locally, although Gilbert and Wiesel (1983) have described several spiny stellate cells with axons that travel up to 2 mm along the cortical layers (see also Martin and Whitteridge, 1984). Pyramidal cells have large, pyramid-shaped somata with the apex pointing toward the pial surface. A single long apical dendrite ascends from the apex, often with branches, and equally long basilar dendrites fan out from the base of the soma in a direction more or less parallel to the pial surface. The axon derives from the base of the soma and typically but not always enters the white matter, although branches often contribute to intracortical circuitry (Gilbert and Wiesel, 1983). Fusiform cells have a variety of shapes but are often elongated with tufts of dendrites emanating from each end of an ovoid-shaped soma. The axon usually enters white matter after emitting locally ramifying collaterals. Other rarely encountered cellular shapes have also been described (e.g., Peters and Regidor, 1981). Thus, stellate cells are thought to be the major class of cortical interneuron, whereas pyramidal and fusiform cells represent the major cortical efferents.

The two generally recognized physiological cell classes of striate cortex, simple and complex cells, were originally described by Hubel and Wiesel (1962). These classes are defined in terms of their receptive field properties. In two general ways, simple and complex receptive fields are strikingly different from those of geniculate neurons. These cortical cells usually have binocular receptive fields (i.e., a receptive field for the homonymous portion of each retina). These cells also tend to be particularly selective for the shape or orientation of visual stimuli and often for the direction of moving targets. The major differences between simple and complex cells are twofold: first, simple cells tend to have separate, spatially offset ON or OFF discharge zones (i.e., discharges at onset or offset of a small spot stimulus), while complex cells tend to have a single ON–OFF discharge zone (i.e., discharges at onset and offset of a small spot stimulus); second, simple cells tend to show fairly linear summation within their discharge zones while complex cells do not. The more subtle differences between simple and complex cells are beyond the scope of this article (for reviews, see Henry 1977; Stone *et al.*, 1979; Lennie, 1980b; Sherman and Spear, 1982; Dean and Tolhurst, 1983).

Precisely how these morphological and physiological cell classes relate to one another and to the W-, X-, and Y-cell pathways is a matter of intense interest and some controversy. Earlier suggestions that stellate cells are simple cells and pyramidal cells are complex cells (Kelly and Van Essen, 1974) seem not to be borne out by subsequent data (Gilbert and Wiesel, 1979; Lin *et al.*, 1979; Martin and Whitteridge, 1984), suggesting no relationship between these pairs of physiological and morphological classes. Likewise, earlier suggestions that X-cells innervate simple cells while Y-cells innervate complex cells (Hoffmann and Stone, 1971) have been discarded in view of evidence that individual simple and complex cells can receive X- or Y-cell input, but not both (Bullier and Henry, 1979a–c). Interestingly, these latter studies suggest that a given simple or complex cell is part of the X- or Y-cell pathway and that no significant convergence of these pathways occurs in striate cortex (see also Mullikin *et al.*, 1981; Tanaka, 1983a,b; Ferster and Lindstrom, 1983; Martin and Whitteridge, 1984). Although anatomical data clearly implicate W-cell input to striate cortex, little physiological evidence of this input has been seen (Mitzdorf and Singer, 1978, 1980; Bullier and Henry, 1979a–c; Tanaka 1983b). In combination with the poor responsiveness of geniculate W-cells, this suggests a rather limited influence of the W-cell pathway on striate cortex, and perhaps other areas of visual cortex as well.

b. Lamination. Like other regions of neocortex, the striate cortex is composed of six layers aligned parallel to the pial surface and numbered I–VI from the pial surface to the white matter. These layers generally differ in the composition of their cellular elements, although each cell type can be found in any layer. Layer I is mainly a cell-poor, synaptic plexiform layer. Stellate cells tend to concentrate in layers II and IV, pyramidal cells in layers III and V, and fusiform cells in layer VI (O'Leary, 1941; Sholl, 1955; Lund *et al.*, 1979). Also, simple cells are concentrated in deep layer III, layer IV, and layer VI, whereas complex cells are numerous in all layers except layers I and IV (Hubel and Wiesel, 1962; Gilbert, 1977; Leventhal and Hirsch, 1978).

Another important feature of the cortical layering is the distinctive laminar arrangement of the afferents to striate cortex, the best studied among these being the geniculocortical afferents (Rosenquist *et al.*, 1974; LeVay and Gilbert, 1976; Ferster and LeVay, 1978; Leventhal, 1979; Gilbert, 1983; Humphrey *et al.*, 1984a,b). Most of these afferents terminate in layer IV, although substantial inputs exist to layers I, lower layer

III, and layer VI. W-Cells seem to terminate predominantly in layer I, lower layer III, and the layer V–VI border; X-cells, in the lower half of layer IV (i.e., layer IVb) and layer VI, although substantial X-cell input is also seen in upper layer IV (i.e., layer IVa); and Y-cells, in the upper half of layer IV (i.e., layer IVa) and layer VI. Thus, there is limited overlap in the laminar distribution of geniculocortical W-, X-, and Y-cell terminals. Iontophoresis of HRP into single X- or Y-cell axons (Gilbert and Wiesel, 1979; Humphrey *et al.*, 1984a,b) has shown that each typically innervates both layers IV and VI; also, as is the case for retinogeniculate axons, the Y-cell axons innervate a much larger volume of area 17 than do the X-cell axons (see also Ferster and LeVay, 1978). Typically, each Y-cell axon seems to innervate several ocular dominance columns (see later), whereas each X-cell axon seems to limit its innervation to a single such column. No morphological description of single W-cell geniculocortical axons has yet been published.

  c. Columnar Organization. Hubel and Wiesel (1962) first demonstrated the columnar organization of the cat's striate cortex. That is, the functional unit of this cortex seems to be a column several cells in diameter that extends vertically across the layers.

  Two related columnar systems have been clearly demonstrated, and others have been suggested. First are the orientation columns (Hubel and Wiesel, 1962; Albus, 1979; Schoppmann and Stryker, 1982): cells within a column are selective for the same stimulus orientation in visual space (e.g., vertical), whereas cells in a neighboring column share the same, slightly different preferred orientation (e.g., 10° from vertical). There is an orderly progression of preferred orientations as neighboring columns are sampled across cortex. The second columnar system is for ocular dominance (Shatz *et al.*, 1977; Shatz and Stryker, 1978). Alternating patches of layers IV and VI that are roughly 500 μm in width receive geniculocortical input related strictly to one eye or the other (i.e., either from laminae A, C, 1, etc., or from laminae A1, 2, etc.). Although most cells of area 17 are binocular, ocular dominance columns nonetheless signify cortical zones in which one or the other eye has the dominant input. Also, many of the layer IV simple cells only have monocular fields, and the dominant eye for these matches the cells' location with respect to the ocular dominance columns (Shatz and Stryker, 1978). Hubel and Wiesel (1977) defined the "hypercolumn" as the slab of cortex that contains adjacent ocular dominance columns plus the full cycle of orientation columns necessary to map all stimulus orientations around the clock; each slab extends through all the layers and occupies roughly 1 mm^2 of cortical surface. In addition to these types of functional columns, for which a wealth of evidence is available, limited data suggest that columnar or laminar arrangements may also exist for other functional properties, such as spatial-frequency tuning and stereopsis or target distance from the eyes (Blakemore, 1970; Maffei and Fiorentini, 1977; Tootell *et al.*, 1980; Tolhurst and Thompson, 1982).

2. Extrastriate Visual Areas

Although receptive-field studies have been reported for many of the extrastriate areas of visual cortex, including areas 18, 19, and PMLS (Hubel and Wiesel, 1965, 1969; Dreher and Cottee, 1975; Spear and Baumann, 1975; Camarda and Rizzolatti, 1976; Orban and Callens, 1977; Sherk, 1978; Movshon *et al.*, 1978; Guedes *et al.*, 1983; von Grunau and Frost, 1983), few of these offer data that can be readily interpreted in the context of the W-, X-, and Y-cell pathways. Figure 12 summarizes a somewhat speculative treatment of the direct geniculocortical pathways. Those to extrastriate cortex involve only W- or Y-cells, because the X-cell input is essentially limited to area 17. However, since area 17 projects to many other regions of visual cortex, this raises the possibility that the X-cell pathway is well represented and important throughout extrastriate visual cortex.

Several studies offer preliminary clues that such an indirect X-cell input to areas 18 and 19, if it exists at all, is not of enormous import. First, electrical stimulation is often used to determine the conduction velocity of the geniculocortical afferents that are part of the pathway leading to the innervation of a cortical cell. W-, X-, and Y-cell input can be inferred from afferent conduction velocity, and such data from neurons in areas 18 and 19 have failed to reveal significant X-cell input, either direct or indirect via area 17 (Tretter *et al.*, 1975; Dreher *et al.*, 1980; Harvey, 1980), although failure to find indirect inputs from electrical stimulation may be of limited significance. Second, functional removal of area 17 by ablation or cooling has surprisingly little effect on response properties of area 18 neurons (Dreher and Cottee, 1975; Sherk, 1978; but see Donaldson and Nash, 1975), which suggests that the W- and/or Y-cell inputs normally dominate the functional properties of area 18. Unfortunately, no published data address the possible role of indirect X-cell inputs via area 17 to extrastriate visual areas other than areas 18 and 19. Although this is a substantial qualification, the X-cell pathway in cortex may nonetheless be largely limited to area 17.

Even within area 17, the importance of the X-cell pathway may be limited. This is suggested by Malpeli's study (1983) of neuronal response properties in striate cortex during reversible blockade of geniculate lamina A. This blockade was effected by iontophoresis of cobaltous chloride into lamina A, a procedure that essentially eliminates from striate cortex all X-cell and probably most Y-cell input representing the contralateral eye. During such blockade, little effect was seen on receptive field properties from the contralateral eye for most area 17 cells in supragranular layers and many in layer V. Normal activity here must depend on W- and Y-cell inputs (although the responsiveness of these cortical cells seems greater than can plausibly be supported by W-cell input alone) from routes outside lamina A, such as via the C-laminae, medial interlaminar nucleus, or more circuitous pathways.

D. SUMMARY

The somewhat speculative picture painted here for the functional organization of the W-, X-, and Y-cell pathways suggests that they remain largely parallel through much of the visual cortex and that the relative cortical representations of these pathways does not reflect their retinal distribution. Every retinal X- and Y-cell innervates the lateral geniculate nucleus. X-Cells are dominant in the retina, but their central representation can be followed only to the A-laminae of the lateral geniculate nucleus and from there to area 17 of visual cortex. The relay of X-cell information from area 17 to extrastriate cortex remains a possibility that has yet to be demonstrated. Y-Cells, which represent a small minority of retinal ganglion cells, innervate increasingly large neuronal pools in the lateral geniculate nucleus and visual cortex. It is likely that most of the visual cortical areas are dominated by the Y-cell pathway. Least is known about the W-cell pathway, but only a subset of retinal W-cells is related to geniculocortical pathways. Geniculate W-cells probably innervate most or all areas of visual cortex (Fig. 12). However, their importance to cortical function is difficult to gauge, although limited electrophysiological evidence suggests weak functional input to striate cortex.

It thus appears that the functional organization of the central visual pathways is such that a small minority of retinal ganglion cells (Y-cells) may come to dominate cortex, while the vast majority (X- and W-cells) may play a relatively minor role in cortical function. It should be noted that the presumed minor roles for W- and X-cells differ, since X-cells powerfully influence cells in a limited region (area 17) while W-cells seem to influence cells weakly throughout most of visual cortex. These conclusions are far from firm and require considerably more data than are presently available to assess the relative importance of the W-, X- and Y-cell pathways to the many areas of visual cortex.

V. Perceptual Correlates for W-, X-, and Y-Cells

A. QUALIFICATIONS IN INTERPRETING BEHAVIORAL DATA

Large gaps persist despite attempts to relate the behavioral visual capacities of cats with the response properties of their visual neurons. For instance, most behavioral data have until recently consisted of a stimulus–response measure, the ability to learn to discriminate among various geometric shapes (e.g., Smith, 1938; Winans, 1967; Spear and Braun, 1969; Doty, 1971, 1973; Sprague *et al.*, 1977), that is difficult to relate to most neuronal receptive field properties. This gap has been bridged somewhat with the introduction of psychophysical techniques that make use of a stimulus–response paradigm similar to a paradigm used neurophysiologically. That is, a cat's contrast sensitivity to sine wave gratings can be psychophysically established as a function of spatial and temporal frequency by determining the minimum contrast needed for the cat to detect the grating (Blake and Camisa, 1977; Blake and DiGianfillipo, 1980; Lehmkuhle *et al.*, 1982, 1984). This is analogous to the contrast sensitivity functions that have been described already for visual neurons.

Even with this most favorable condition for deriving correlations between behavior and neurophysiology, several important qualifications and assumptions must be noted. First, it is not at all clear how one correlates a contrast threshold for a cell with that determined psychophysically. The techniques used to determine the cellular and psychophysical thresholds require different and somewhat arbitrary measures of responsiveness. Second, the animals' states (alert behavior versus anesthetized and paralyzed) are quite different during the psychophysical and neurophysiological determinations. Third, it is not clear what measure of neuronal responsiveness relates to the psychophysical thresholds. For instance, if, as is often assumed, the most sensitive cells for a given stimulus set the psychophysical threshold, then less sensitive neurons such as W-cells (see Figs. 6 and 7) should play little or no role in behavioral contrast sensitivity under normal conditions. As noted later, normal cats are sensitive to stimuli of sufficiently low contrast that few if any W-cells would respond to that stimulus. Thus, W-cells may contribute significantly to vision only for suprathreshold, higher-contrast targets, and measurements of behavioral contrast sensitivity functions cannot address such a hypothetical suprathreshold function. Many other difficulties with these correlations between behavior and neurophysiology could also be listed.

Finally, while spatial contrast sensitivity functions determined psychophysically for a subject may be of inherent interest, it is not yet clear how these functions relate to the quality of form or spatial vision of which the subject is capable. Form vision can be defined as the ability to detect and recognize the spatial content of visual stimuli. While the definition of form vision may be straightforward, its measure is not. The most widely used measure of form vision has been one of spatial acuity, but it is now clear that this is inadequate (see later; see also Hess and Howell, 1977; Ginsburg, 1978; Berkley and Sprague, 1979; Lehmkuhle *et al.*, 1982). The other widely used measure of form vision is imprecise and depends on the ability to discriminate or recognize arbitrarily defined stimuli, such as circles versus crosses for cats and faces for humans. Although imprecise, this latter operational measure for the quality of form vision leads to interesting parallels between spatial vision deficits and deficient spatial contrast sensitivity functions. These parallels will be described in some detail here, but it is important to remember that these parallels reflect a limited evaluation of the quality of form vision.

Despite these qualifications, some surprisingly clear correlations emerge between a comparison of the neurophysiological and behavioral data based on contrast sensitivity functions. This section will therefore concentrate on these functions for normal cats and cats with experimental manipulations that interfere with the W-, X-, or Y-cell pathways.

B. NORMAL CATS

Blake and Camisa (1977) first reported spatial and temporal contrast sensitivity functions of normal cats and interpreted these results in the context of X- and Y-cell pathways. [W-Cell participation in geniculocortical innervation was not known when Blake and Camisa (1977) reported their results, and in any case, the insensitivity of W-cells makes it unlikely that they are significantly involved in the behavioral thresholds of the sort measured.] A description of the parameters of spatial and temporal frequency can be found in Section III,A; the value of sensitivity is simply the inverse of the minimum contrast needed for the cat to detect the stimulus (i.e., the threshold contrast). Figure 15 shows spatial functions at different temporal frequencies, including stationary presentation ($\triangle$), ON–OFF flicker at 1.5 Hz ($\square$), and ON–OFF flicker at 10 Hz ($\bigcirc$). Note that, for both stationary presentation and flicker at the lower temporal rate, sensitivity peaks at middle spatial frequencies and falls off for higher and lower ones. At the higher flicker rate, the sensitivity monotonically drops with increasing spatial frequency.

Blake and Camisa (1977) reasoned as follows. Y-Cells would dictate sensitivity to higher temporal rates as well as to lower spatial frequencies (regardless of rate), because X-cells are less sensitive to such stimuli. On the other hand, X-cells would determine the sensitivity to the higher

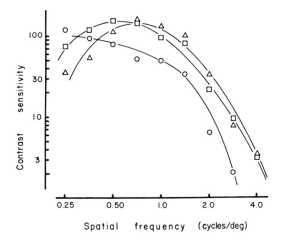

FIG. 15. Psychophysically determined contrast sensitivity as a function of spatial frequency for a normal cat. Functions are shown for stationary presentation of a sine wave grating (△), ON–OFF flicker (i.e., interchanging of the grating with a uniform field of equal average luminance) at 1.5 Hz (□), and ON–OFF flicker at 10 Hz (○). (From Blake and Camisa, 1977, with permission of the authors.)

spatial frequencies at lower rates. Figures 6 and 7 support this reasoning. Thus, the psychophysical function at 10 Hz would be Y-cell dominated, which explains why there is no sensitivity loss to lower spatial frequencies (Fig. 6). At 1.5 Hz, the significant X-cell activity would raise sensitivity to all but the lower spatial frequencies (Fig. 6), which explains why the behavioral sensitivity function at that rate peaks around the middle spatial frequencies.

C. Cats with Cortical Lesions

1. Lesions to Striate Cortex

From Fig. 12 it should be clear that a bilateral removal of area 17 in cats effectively eliminates all cortical representation of the X-cell pathway and spares much of the W- and Y-cell pathways. Doty (1971), and Sprague and colleagues (Sprague, 1966; Sprague et al., 1976, 1977, 1981; Berkley and Sprague, 1978, 1979; Berlucchi and Sprague, 1981) were the first to establish that lesions limited to area 17 and parts of area 18 produce remarkably mild deficits in visually guided behavior. Visual deficits were limited to suprisingly small reductions in spatial resolution (including moderate losses in orientation and grating resolutions and a marked loss in vernier acuity), while visual capacities on a wide range of other visual tasks were affected little or not at all by the lesions. Thus, by the operational measure of form vision noted in Section V,A, these cats without area 17 and the X-cell pathway exhibit excellent form vision despite reduced acuity. Also, Kaye *et al.* (1981) reported that although bilateral lesions of areas 17, 18, and part of 19 had surprisingly little effect on a cat's acuity, these lesions almost totally eliminate binocular depth discrimination. While area 17 and the X-cell pathway do not seem essential for basic form vision, they might be needed for other functions beyond inproved acuity, such as stereopsis or a variety of visually guided behaviors not yet tested in destriate cats.

Lehmkuhle *et al.* (1982) confirmed and extended some of these observations by obtaining preoperative and postoperative contrast sensitivity functions for destriate cats. The lesion affects sensitivity only to higher spatial frequencies and lower temporal ones (Fig. 16). At higher rates little or no difference between preoperative and postoperative performance could be detected. The contrast sensitivity found after bilateral removal of striate cortex almost certainly reflects activity in the remaining Y-cell pathways.

A more detailed consideration of Y-cell response properties further supports this conclusion. As described in Section III,D and illustrated in Fig. 6C, Y-cell responsiveness can be divided into a linear component, which dominates at lower spatial frequencies, and a nonlinear component, which dominates at higher spatial frequencies (Hochstein and Shapley, 1976b; Lehmkuhle *et al.,* 1980a). The linear component is sensitive to the spatial phase, or position, of the stimulus, whereas the nonlinear component is not (see Fig. 4; and Hochstein and Shapley, 1976b). Thus, while the nonlinear response component can signal the presence of a stimulus, the linear component is needed to signal precise stimulus position (see also, Sur and Sherman, 1984). In normal cats, for which X-cells probably determine psychophysical thresholds at higher spatial frequencies, spatial resolution of both stimulus presence and stimulus position is signaled by the same linear response mechanism. If removal of the X-cell pathway by a bilateral area 17 ablation leaves Y-cells to determine spatial resolution, one would expect a greater deficit in spatial resolution for stimulus position than for stimulus presence. That is, compared to Y-cells, X-cells are much more sensitive to position or spatial phase (Fig. 8) and only moderately more sensitive to higher spatial frequencies (Lehmkuhle *et al.,* 1980a; So and Shapley, 1981). As noted before, destriate cats suffer more of a resolution loss for vernier acuity, which requires positional information to determine the spatial offset of line segments, than for simple grating resolution, which requires only information about the presence or absence of the stimulus (Berkley and Sprague, 1979).

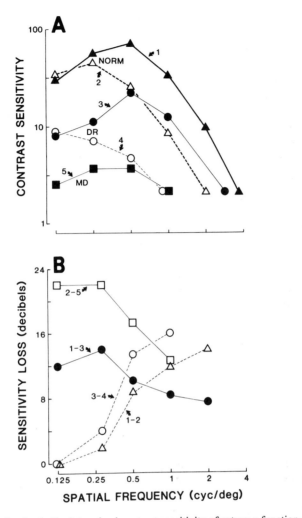

FIG. 16. Psychophysically determined contrast sensitivity of cats as a function of spatial frequency. The stimuli consisted of sine wave gratings counterphased at 1.0 or 1.5 Hz. (A) Contrast sensitivity functions for five types of cats; each curve represents an average from two subjects. (▲, △) Data from the same two normally reared cats before (curve 1) and after (curve 2) bilateral removal of cortical area 17 and part of area 18. (●, ○) Data from the same two dark-reared cats before (curve 3) and after (curve 4) bilateral removal of cortical area 17 and part of area 18. (■, curve 5) Data from the deprived eyes of two cats reared with monocular lid suture. (With their nondeprived eyes, these cats exhibited sensitivity indistinguishable from that of the normal cats.) (B) Differences in sensitivity (sensitivity loss) between various pairs of curves in (A) as a function of spatial frequency. Sensitivity loss was computed in decibels as 20 times the logarithm of the ratio of the higher to the lower sensitivity. Where differences are attributed mostly to X-cell losses (i.e., lesions to area 17; curves 1 minus 2 and 3 minus 4), sensitivity losses mostly occur at higher spatial frequencies. Where differences are attributed mostly to Y-cell losses (i.e., normal versus dark reared and normally reared with lesions to area 17 versus monocularly deprived; curves 1 minus 3 and 2 minus 5), sensitivity losses mostly occur at lower spatial frequencies. (Redrawn from Lehmkuhle et al., 1982, 1984.)

While this does offer an interesting correlation between the visual capacity of cats and of their X- and Y-cells, it would be better to have available a detailed psychophysical analysis of spatial phase or position sensitivity for normal and destriate cats.

The surprisingly normal visual capacity of cats after removal of striate cortex suggests that the X-cell pathway is not necessary for basic form vision. The remaining Y-cell and perhaps W-cell pathways seem sufficient for excellent form vision, albeit with a reduced level of spatial resolution.

2. Lesions to Extrastriate Cortex

Although no one has yet reported contrast sensitivity measurements of cats with lesions of extrastriate areas of visual cortex, Sprague *et al.* (1977) have provided a description of visual behavior in such cats that can be tied in a general way to the W-, X-, and Y-cell pathways. Bilateral lesions that include area 17 and extend to most of area 18 do not interfere with basic form vision (Spear and Braun, 1969; Sprague *et al.*, 1976, 1977, 1981). Only when the lesions encroach significantly into area 19 and the lateral suprasylvian visual areas does pattern vision become severely compromised (Sprague *et al.*, 1977, 1979; Baumann and Spear, 1977; Loop and Sherman, 1977; Berlucchi and Sprague, 1981). Interpreted in the context of Fig. 12, it follows that a substantial loss in all of the geniculocortical pathways is needed to preclude reasonable form vision. It should also be noted that such lesions also destroy the projection zones of the extrageniculate visual thalamus (e.g., retinotectothalamocortical pathways; cf. Berlucchi and Sprague, 1981).

D. Cats Raised with Visual Deprivation

There have been several psychophysical studies of contrast sensitivity of cats raised with various forms of visual deprivation, particularly with lid suture and dark-rearing. Because the status of the X- and Y-cell pathways, and to a lesser extent the W-cell pathway, has been assessed in such cats, these data permit further correlates between neurophysiology and behavior. The neurological status of visually deprived cats has been reviewed by Movshon and Van Sluyters (1981) and Sherman and Spear (1982).

1. Monocularly Sutured Cats

a. Deficits in the Visual Pathways. In monocularly sutured cats, retinal ganglion cells of all classes respond fairly normally to visual stimuli (Sherman and Stone, 1973; Kratz *et al.*, 1979a; Cleland *et al.*, 1980).

However, a substantial deficit develops in the Y-cell pathway that is apparent in all appropriate regions of the lateral geniculate nucleus receiving Y-cell afferents from the deprived eye (Sherman *et al.*, 1972; for a review of this subject, see Sherman and Spear, 1982). Because of the pattern of geniculocortical innervation (Fig. 12), a failure of geniculate Y-cells to develop properly would affect practically all of the known visual areas of cortex. Apparently, much of the loss of geniculate Y-cells is due to the failure of many Y-cell axons from the deprived retina to innervate geniculate cells properly (Friedlander *et al.*, 1982; Sur *et al.*, 1982). On the other hand, deprived geniculate X-cells develop fairly normal responsiveness to visual stimuli, although there may be a deficit in their spatial resolution (Lehmkuhle *et al.*, 1980b; Shapley and So, 1980; Derrington and Hawken, 1981; Mower and Christen, 1982; Mangel *et al.*, 1983). Interestingly, the Y-cell deficits are limited to the deprived binocular segment of the lateral geniculate nucleus,* since Y-cells in the deprived monocular segment develop normally (Sherman *et al.*, 1972, 1975b; Lehmkuhle *et al.*, 1980b). However, the subtle deficit claimed for deprived geniculate X-cells, a loss of resolution, is found equally in the binocular and monocular segments (Lehmkuhle *et al.*, 1980b). No studies have specifically tested responsiveness of deprived W-cells, although histological measurements of the deprived parvocellular C-laminae suggest little or no deficit for these neurons (Hickey, 1980; Murakami and Wilson, 1980; Leventhal and Hirsch, 1983).

Presumably correlated to this pattern of geniculate deficits are recordings of evoked potentials in cortical areas 17 and 18 that reveal a dramatic loss of Y-cell input and much less of a loss of X-cell input (Snyder and Shapley, 1979; Mitzdorf and Singer, 1980; Jones and Berkley, 1983; Freeman *et al.*, 1983). That is, there is a much greater loss of the faster-conducting input that exhibits peak sensitivity to higher temporal and lower spatial frequencies. While X-cell input may reach layer IV of area 17 (Shatz and Stryker, 1978), the fact that nearly all cells beyond layer IV are insensitive to visual stimulation of the deprived eye (Wiesel and

---

* The binocular segment of visual field is that central portion normally viewed by both eyes; the monocular segments are those peripheral portions that are normally viewed only by the ipsilateral eye. Temporal retina sees only binocular segment, and monocular segment is viewed by the most peripheral nasal retina. For the cat, the binocular segment is the central 90° of visual field, whereas each monocular segment is represented roughly 45 to 90° laterally from the fixation point. Because the visual field is retinotopically mapped onto the lateral geniculate nucleus and areas of visual cortex, it is possible to define binocular and monocular segments of these structures. For example, the geniculate A-laminae have both segments represented: the monocular segment is mapped where lamina A extends laterally beyond lamina A1, and the binocular segment is mapped in lamina A1 and the corresponding portion of lamina A.

Hubel, 1963; Shatz and Stryker, 1978; and many others) suggests that the X-cell pathway is eventually lost as well within the level of striate cortex. W-Cell input to visual cortex is difficult to demonstrate with these techniques, even in normal cats.

Deficits due to visual deprivation have also been described in visual regions other than the lateral geniculate nucleus and striate cortex. However, most primary deficits seem to occur in the geniculocortical pathways, since these other deficits are largely secondary to those in the geniculocortical pathways (for a more detailed discussion of the primary sites of deprivation-induced deficits, see Sherman and Spear, 1982). Consequently, many of the neural abnormalities due to rearing with monocular suture may have as their basis the failure of geniculate Y-cells to develop normally.

b. Behavioral Deficits. Although some early reports suggested that a monocularly sutured cat using its deprived eye was practically blind (Wiesel and Hubel, 1963, 1965), later studies succeeded in demonstrating some rudimentary visual capacity for that eye (Ganz and Fitch, 1968; Dews and Wiesel, 1970; Rizzolatti and Tradari, 1971; Spear and Ganz, 1975), particularly its monocular segment (Sherman, 1973; Sherman and Sprague, 1979).

Figure 16A shows the psychophysically determined contrast sensitivity for the deprived eye (Lehmkuhle *et al.*, 1982). Severe sensitivity losses are evident for all spatial frequencies, particularly lower ones (Fig. 16B). This is consistent with the substantial abnormalities among geniculate Y-cells and also among area 17 neurons that presumably reflect deficits in the X-cell pathway as well. It seems likely that the additional visual deficits of the deprived eye versus those seen in the destriate cats (e.g., sensitivity losses to lower spatial frequencies) correlate with the added loss of the Y-cell pathway due to the deprivation. It is not clear whether the extremely limited spatial vision of the deprived eye reflects a fairly normal geniculocortical W-cell pathway, fairly normal W- and Y-cell subcortical pathways (cf. Hoffmann and Sherman, 1974), or some normal development of geniculocortical pathways in the deprived monocular segment (Guillery and Stelzner, 1970; Sherman, 1973; Sherman *et al.*, 1974; Wilson and Sherman, 1977). Incidentally, on all tests of visual performance, these cats using the nondeprived eye exhibit normal visual capabilities (Dews and Wiesel, 1970; Sherman, 1973; Lehmkuhle *et al.*, 1982).

2. Binocularly Deprived Cats

Two types of binocularly deprived cats have been extensively studied: one raised with binocular lid suture and the other raised in total darkness.

Although these are clearly different rearing conditions and there may well be significant differences among their neuronal abnormalities, for the purposes of this article they will be treated together because of their obvious similarities (see Sherman and Spear, 1982, for a more complete discussion of these forms of binocular deprivation).

a. Deficits in the Visual Pathways. As is the case with monocular suture, retinal ganglion cells after binocular suture seem normal (Sherman and Stone, 1973); these cells have not yet been studied in dark-reared cats. Following both forms of binocular deprivation, a substantial deficit is seen among geniculate Y-cells in both monocular and binocular segments (Sherman *et al.,* 1972; Kratz *et al.,* 1979b; see Sherman and Spear, 1982, for the significance of the differences in the pattern of deficits following monocular and binocular deprivation). Geniculate X-cells respond fairly normally in these cats (but see Mower *et al.,* 1981; Kratz, 1982), and the effects of binocular deprivation on W-cells have not yet been studied. Many cells in striate cortex remain binocularly responsive after this deprivation, although their normal specificity for stimulus orientation and direction of movement is largely absent (Wiesel and Hubel, 1965; Pettigrew, 1974; Blakemore and Van Sluyters, 1975; Buisseret and Imbert, 1976; Fregnac and Imbert, 1978; Watkins *et al.,* 1978; Leventhal and Hirsch, 1980). Leventhal and Hirsch (1980) have interpreted this pattern of cortical physiology in terms of fairly normal development of X-cell input with more serious abnormalities in Y-cell input. Although the relevant data for binocularly deprived cats are relatively sketchy, they suggest serious abnormalities in the Y-cell pathway and fairly normal development of the X-cell pathway. As is the case with monocular deprivation, deficits outside of the geniculocortical pathways may be secondary to those occurring in these pathways (e.g., Hoffmann and Sherman, 1975).

b. Behavioral Deficits. Many papers have emphasized the seriously deficient form vision in binocularly deprived cats (Wiesel and Hubel, 1965; Sherman, 1973; Blake and DiGianfillipo, 1980; Lehmkuhle *et al.,* 1982, 1984), and this is supported by studies of their contrast sensitivity. Figure 16 shows similar psychophysical functions and sensitivity losses for binocularly sutured and dark-reared cats (Lehmkuhle *et al.,* 1982). Sensitivity losses are seen for all spatial frequencies, especially for lower ones. This is a similar pattern to that seen after monocular suture, although the sensitivity losses are less severe after binocular deprivation.

The difference in sensitivity between binocularly and monocularly deprived cats may be due to a less abnormal X-cell pathway in the former than in the latter. As noted before (Sections V,D,1,a and V,D,2,a), the deprived X-cell pathway is completely disrupted in area 17 of monocularly sutured cats, but, according to Leventhal and Hirsch (1980), may

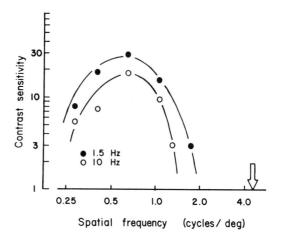

FIG. 17. Psychophysically determined contrast sensitivity as a function of spatial frequency for a dark-reared cat. Stimuli consisted of a sine wave grating sinusoidally counterphased at 1.5 Hz (●) or 10 Hz (○). The arrow along the abscissa indicates the high-spatial-frequency intercept seen in normal cats to the 1.5-Hz stimulus. (From Blake and DiGianfillipo, 1980, with permission of the authors.)

largely survive intact in area 17 of binocularly deprived cats. Indeed, Blake and DiGianfillippo (1980) have provided evidence that the reduced contrast sensitivity of dark-reared cats is mostly due to remaining X-cell activity. Unlike the case in normal cats (see Blake and Camisa, 1977; and Fig. 15), dark-reared cats exhibit attenuation to lower spatial frequencies both at low and high temporal rates (Fig. 17). It thus seems that Y-cell activity, which exhibits no sensitivity reduction at lower spatial frequencies, is not available to dominate the behavioral responses at higher temporal rates after dark-rearing, a situation that does occur in normal cats. Indeed, removal of striate cortex in these cats (and thus any useful X-cell function) seriously compromises the contrast sensitivity of these cats, and the losses are evident mainly in higher spatial frequencies as is the case in normally reared cats with such lesions (Fig. 17; and Lehmkuhle et al., 1984).

E. CONCLUSIONS

Figure 16 suggests several interesting conclusions. First, the behavioral data correlate in a general way with what is known of the functional status of W-, X-, and Y-cells in normal, cortically lesioned, and visually deprived cats. These correlations by no means prove a cause-and-effect relationship, but they seem worth pursuing.

Second, the general visual capabilities of these cats correlate much more accurately with their sensitivity to lower spatial frequencies than to higher ones. Thus, cats with good sensitivity to lower spatial frequencies (e.g., normal and destriate cats) have excellent form vision, and those with poor sensitivity to these frequencies (e.g., monocularly and binocularly deprived cats) have at best rudimentary form vision. Sensitivity to higher spatial frequencies is less crucial to basic form vision than is sensitivity to lower frequencies. Indeed the dark-reared cats on average have slightly better spatial resolution (i.e., sensitivity to higher spatial frequencies) than do the destriate cats (Fig. 16), yet the destriate cats have obviously superior form vision. Clearly, spatial resolution alone is an inadequate and often misleading measure of overall visual performance. These data suggest that sensitivity to the lower spatial frequencies is necessary and sufficient for excellent form vision and that sensitivity to the higher spatial frequencies adds an appreciation of fine detail and raises resolution. This conclusion has already been reached for human visual performance (Kabrisky *et al.*, 1970; Ginsburg *et al.*, 1976; Ginsburg, 1978; Hess and Garner, 1977; Hess and Howell, 1977; Hess and Woo, 1978).

Finally, even though the vast majority of studies of the cat's central visual pathways in normal and visually deprived cats have concentrated on striate cortex, Fig. 16 illustrates some of the logical limitations of these studies. The excellent form vision of destriate cats makes it rather obvious that area 17 is not essential to this behavioral capability. Also, the fact that destriate cats have significantly better form vision than do visually deprived cats implies that deprivation-induced deficits seen in striate cortex (or the X-cell pathway), no matter how severe, cannot account for the behavioral deficits in the deprived cats. Obviously, severe deprivation-induced abnormalities must exist outside and independent of any seen in area 17 (or the X-cell pathway), and a likely source of these deficits are the geniculate Y-cells that innervate so many regions of visual cortex. While studies of cat striate cortex are obviously useful in understanding the geometry of connections in a part of the brain, the functional significance of these connections has yet to be elucidated.

VI. Hypothesis for the Functional Organization and Role of the W-, X-, and Y-Cell Pathways

The dearth of information about the W-cell pathway makes it difficult to ascribe any specific function to this pathway. However, the poor and inconsistent responses of W-cells, their large, diffuse receptive fields, and the inability of many investigators to demonstrate a powerful influence of the W-cell pathway on neurons in striate cortex suggest that these cells do not play a significant role in basic form vision. No specific role for the W-cell pathway can yet be suggested (but see Stone *et al.*, 1979), and this is obviously a weakness in the hypothesis. Much more knowledge of W-cells is needed. Also, the possibility exists that the reported insensitivity of W-cells is an artifact of the physiological preparation (e.g., due to anesthesia or paralysis) and that these cells are normally responsive and crucial to normal pattern vision.

However, most attention regarding functional significance for spatial vision has focused on X- and Y-cells. Figures 6 and 8 summarize several major differences between these neuronal classes regarding their responses to spatial visual patterns. Y-Cells are considerably more responsive or sensitive to lower spatial frequencies, whereas X-cells are more responsive to higher ones and generally more sensitive to changes in position or spatial phase. Evidence from psychophysical studies cited in Section V underscores the primacy of lower spatial frequencies to form vision. Indeed, it has been suggested (Kabrisky *et al.*, 1970; Ginsburg *et al.*, 1976; Ginsburg, 1978; Hess and Woo, 1978) that basic form information is carried by the lower spatial frequencies and that the higher ones merely add detail to the basic forms. Thus, a loss of higher frequencies is not nearly so devastating to form vision as is a loss of lower ones (Fig. 16). From this and a comparison of response properties (Figs. 6 and 8), the following hypothesis logically emerges: *the Y-cell pathway is responsible for analysis of basic forms, and the X-cell pathway adds detail and raises spatial resolution and position sensitivity to this basic form analysis.*

This hypothesis for X- and Y-cell function differs significantly from many others, the most prominent and popular of which suggests that X-cells analyze spatial patterns while Y-cells analyze temporal patterns (Ikeda and Wright, 1972; Kulikowski and Tolhurst, 1973; Stone *et al.*, 1979). Other hypotheses have also been suggested (e.g., Lennie, 1980b; Troy, 1983). Most of these other hypotheses emphasize the relative paucity of Y-cells versus X-cells in the retina to argue for the relatively minor role in vision for Y-cells compared to X-cells. Implicit in these arguments seems to be the notion that the X-cell pathway remains dominant with respect to the Y-cell pathway throughout the lateral geniculate nucleus and visual cortex. One key to the hypothesis presented in the present article is the evidence that, compared to the X-cell pathway, the Y-cell pathway dominates the visual cortex, at least partly because of dramatically different extents of axonal arborizations between X- and Y-cell axons along these pathways.

The behavioral evidence summarized in Figs. 16 and 17, while far from definitive, clearly supports the hypothesis presented here rather than the separation into spatial processing for X-cells and temporal processing for Y-cells, or indeed any major role in basic form vision dependent on X-cells. Essentially complete interruption of the X-cell pathway by area 17 lesions does not destroy spatial vision, as these other hypotheses would suggest. Conditions in which significant Y-cell activity exists (e.g., normal and destriate cats) provide excellent form vision. Conditions in which the Y-cell pathway is deficient (e.g., monocular and binocular deprivation) result in poor form vision, even in the case of dark-reared cats that may have fairly normal X-cell activity (Fig. 17). These data suggest but by no means prove that the Y-cell pathway is necessary and sufficient for good form vision.

The importance attributed by this hypothesis to Y-cells seems at first glance to be at variance with the low percentage of Y-cells in the retina (see earlier). As noted already and summarized schematically in Fig. 18, the Y-cell pathway starts as a small minority of retinal ganglion cells, captures a much larger fraction of geniculate neurons, and becomes a dominant input to the many areas of visual cortex. In contradistinction, the X-cell pathway starts as the majority of retinal ganglion cells, becomes a much smaller fraction of geniculate neurons, and influences perhaps a half or less of a single area (area 17) of visual cortex.

This difference in the functional connections and relative importance of the X- and Y-cell pathways at peripheral and central levels actually fits neatly with the hypothesis of X- and Y-cell function suggested in this article. Note here that peripheral and central refers to hierarchical stages of processing rather than to locations in the visual field. In order to encode the lower spatial frequencies at the sensory periphery or retina, relatively few neurons are needed. Thus, few Y-cells need exist in the retina. However, the importance of these lower spatial frequencies to form analysis dictates that most of the visual cortex be devoted to them. Thus, a tremendous amplification of the Y-cell pathway occurs centrally. In order to encode the higher spatial frequencies peripherally in the retina (e.g., to maximize spatial resolution and position sensitivity), many more neurons are needed than are required for the lower frequencies. Thus, X-cells abound in retina. However, since the X-cell pathway is used to add detail to a basic form analysis already provided by the Y-cell pathway, relatively little cortex is devoted to X-cells. Thus, relatively little divergence and amplification occurs centrally in the X-cell pathway.

This hypothesis for the functional organization and significance of the W-, X-, and Y-cell pathways is little more than a sketchy notion that might be useful as a theoretical framework against which to test future data. There are many untested assumptions and gaps in our knowledge. Nonetheless, this hypothesis does serve to unify a large and diverse body

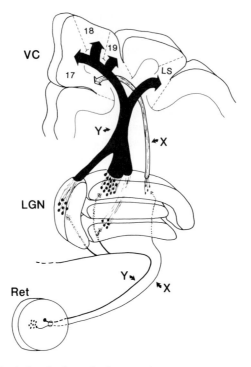

Fig. 18.   Hypothetical and schematic diagram of the retinogeniculocortical X- and Y-cell pathways; for simplicity, only pathways from the contralateral eye are illustrated. VC, Visual cortex; LGN, lateral geniculate nucleus; Ret, retina. Each retinogeniculate and geniculocortical Y-cell axon branches to innervate many more neurons than does each of the analogous X-cell axons. Also, the X-cell pathway is essentially limited to the A-laminae and area 17, whereas the Y-cell pathway occupies most regions of the lateral geniculate nucleus and visual cortex. Consequently, a small minority of retinal ganglion cells (Y-cells) come to dominate visual cortex, whereas the much greater number of retinal ganglion cells (X-cells) come to control much less cortical tissue. For details and the functional significance of this schema, see text.

of presently available data even if future experimentation might require its abandonment.

VII. W-, X-, and Y-Cells in Mammalian Species Other Than the Cat

All of the discussion in the previous sections has been limited to the functional organization of the cat's retinogeniculocortical pathways. A natural question is, how generally are these organizational features found in other species? More specifically, do neurons and pathways homologous to W-, X-, and Y-cells and their pathways even exist in species other than the cat? Despite several years of interest in these and related questions, clear answers have yet to emerge.

A. HOMOLOGY AND CLASSIFICATION

Ideally, one would like to determine if in species other than cats neurons and pathways exist that are homologous to W-, X-, and Y-cells and their pathways. Campbell and Hodos (1970) have thoroughly discussed the concept of homology in the nervous system and define the term as follows: "Structures and other entities are homologous when they could, in principle, be traced back through a geneological series to a stipulated common ancestral precursor irrespective of morphological similarity" (Campbell and Hodos, 1970, p. 358). In other words, primate homologs to cat X- and Y-cells must have evolved from cell classes in an ancestor that was also ancestral to cats, and these same ancestral X- and Y-cells must have evolved into those classes recognized as X- and Y-cells in cats. Direct determination of homology is impractical, since extinct ancestral species cannot be studied, and indirect determinations of homology from living species require much more evidence of possible retinal and geniculate cell classes across mammalian species than is presently available. Instead of this, most studies have concentrated on more limited aspects of the similarities in the physiology and morphology of neurons and pathways across species, and this reflects analogy. Analogy can be defined as "correspondence between structures or entities due to similarity in function whether or not they can be traced to a stipulated common precursor" (Campbell and Hodos, 1970, p. 359). Too many examples of analogy from convergent evolution exist to distinguish between homology and analogy when such similarities are noted between neuronal types.

While the question of homology versus analogy must be put aside, at least for the present, it is still of considerable interest to determine the extent to which the central visual pathways of different species, including primates and humans, are organized functionally like the cat's. The conclusion one reaches in such phylogenetic comparisons usually reflects the manner by which one classifies neurons.

As a hypothetical example, consider the classification of Y-cells. In the cat such cells can be characterized both by fast axonal conduction and by nonlinear spatial and temporal summation of certain visual stimuli. If a cell type in another species possesses fast axonal conduction (a Y-cell characteristic) but linear summation of visual stimuli (an X-cell characteristic), such a cell might be identified as a Y-cell if conduction velocity were considered to be the "essential" characteristic or as an X-cell if linearity of summation were considered to be "essential." Since the choice of "essential" features to establish homologies or analogies is artificial and arbitrary, it seems better to rely on a range of characteristics for classification of cell types (cf. Rowe and Stone, 1977). As Campbell and Hodos (1970) note, "nature has not provided us with a 'touchstone' for the recognition of homology" (p. 362). If neuronal types in two species share most of a constellation of properties and have relatively few differences, these cell types could be considered functionally similar, and their differences could be viewed as relatively minor properties for which strong evolutionary pressures to conform did not exist. If cell types in two species do not share a majority of properties, the hypothesis of homology or analogy would not be supported. Many of these problems of establishing similar cell types are exemplified in comparisons between cats and primates.

B. Primate Visual System

A detailed description of the primate visual system is beyond the scope of this article. Instead the focus will be on a brief overview of the classification in primates of retinal and geniculate neurons into categories that can be compared to W-, X-, and Y-cells in the cat. Studies of primate retinal ganglion cells have suggested a threefold division into classes with properties in some ways similar to those of the cat's W-, X-, and Y-cells (deMonasterio and Gouras, 1975; deMonasterio, 1978a–c; Schiller and Malpeli, 1977), but the main points about these pathways can be made from a consideration of the lateral geniculate nucleus.

1. Lateral Geniculate Nucleus

a. Monkeys. In the monkey this nucleus is composed of a dorsal collection of several laminae of smaller cells called the parvocellular laminae, a ventral pair of magnocellular laminae with larger cells, and neurons in the interlaminar zones and in the "S"-laminae lying ventral to the magnocellular laminae. Several groups have suggested that the parvocellular cells are X-like, the magnocellular are Y-like, and the remainder (interlaminar and S-laminae) are W-like. In favor of this classification are the following observations (Hubel and Wiesel, 1972; Dreher *et al.,* 1976; Sherman *et al.,* 1976; Leventhal *et al.,* 1981; Fitzpatrick *et al.,* 1981, 1983; Weber *et al.,* 1983; Blasdel and Lund, 1983). Larger retinal ganglion cells with rapidly conducting axons (somewhat like cat alpha cells) project to the cells in the magnocellular laminae. These geniculate cells have larger receptive fields, respond well to rapidly moving targets, and exhibit transient responses to visual stimuli. Also, these geniculate cells project to layer IVC-alpha of area 17, which is the dorsal half of the major geniculate recipient zone and presumably corresponds to the Y-cell termination in the dorsal half of layer IV of the cat. The cells in the parvocellular laminae are innervated by more slowly conducting axons of smaller ganglion cells (somewhat like cat beta cells), have smaller receptive fields, respond poorly to rapidly moving targets, exhibit sustained responses to visual stimuli, and innervate layer IVC-beta of area 17, which is just ventral to the magnocellular terminal zone and presumably corresponds to the X-cell termination in the ventral half of layer IV of the cat. Least is known about the interlaminar and S-laminae cells, but like W-cells in the cat, these cells project to layers I and III of striate and extrastriate cortex.

However, in several important ways, only some of which are outlined here, these comparisons can be criticized. First, no one has yet reported response properties for neurons in the S-laminae or the interlaminar zones, so evidence for the W-cell analogy is particularly thin. Second, the parvocellular (but not magnocellular) laminae of many or most monkeys (e.g., rhesus monkeys) are dominated by cells selective for color, a property not associated with cat X-cells. However, some monkeys (e.g., owl monkeys) may not have significant wavelength sensitivity among parvocellular neurons. Third, tests of spatial and temporal linearity (Kaplan and Shapley, 1982) indicate that all parvocellular and many of the magnocellular cells sum linearly, an X-cell property. The remainder of magnocellular cells sum nonlinearly, as do Y-cells. This has led Kaplan and Shapley (1982) to suggest that the magnocellular cells as a group are analogous to X- and Y-cells of the cat intermixed as in the A-laminae and that the parvocellular cells represent a class for which no clear analogy exists in the cat. However, Derrington and Lennie (1984) and Sherman *et al.* (1984) have recently suggested that these magnocellular cells as a population are actually continuously variable for the property of linearity and that the division into linear (X) and nonlinear (Y) classes is an arbitrary division of a continuum; on average, magnocellular cells exhibit greater nonlinearity than do parvocellular cells. Also, it should be noted that W-cells in the cat can be either linear or nonlinear (Sur and Sherman, 1982a), so that these properties are not uniquely linked to X- or Y-cells.

Obviously, it is not at all clear what, if any, specific analogies exist in the monkey for the cat's X- and Y-cells. On balance, many similarities can be listed for an X- and Y-cell analogy to parvocellular and magnocellular cells, respectively. The chief problem with this conclusion is that certain details of the spatial and temporal summation properties are not equivalent between X-cells and parvocellular cells or between Y-cells and magnocellular cells. However, it seems possible that the "linear" magnocellular cells may be analogous to Y-cells that never developed or evolved powerful nonlinear subunits. In kittens, these subunits develop relatively late, so that immature Y-cells are often rather linear (Wilson *et al.*, 1982; Mangel *et al.*, 1983). Perhaps in this regard, the linear magnocellular cells of the monkey are similar to immature Y-cells in the cat.

b. Galogos. A similar argument has been made by Norton and Casagrande (1982) for geniculate neurons in the galago, or bush baby. This prosimian primate has three pairs of geniculate laminae: a pair with small cells that exhibit response properties rather like W-cells, a pair with medium-sized cells that exhibit response properties, including linear summation, rather like X-cells, and a pair with large cells that exhibit response properties rather like Y-cells, although most exhibit linear summation. Norton and Casagrande (1982) concluded that the last type represents neurons more like Y-cells without nonlinear subunits than like X-cells.

2. Functional Correlates

A consideration of psychophysical data from monkeys in the context of their presumptive analogs to W-, X-, and Y-cell pathways offers interesting parallels to the cat. In monkeys, the projection of nearly all parvocellular and magnocellular cells (e.g., all presumptive X-like and Y-like neurons, regardless of which analogy proves correct) is limited to area 17 (Tigges *et al.*, 1977; Hendrickson *et al.*, 1978). Thus nothing comparable is seen in monkeys to the massive extrastriate projection of geniculate Y-cells of the cat, which may be taken as another criticism of the proposed analogy between cat Y-cells and monkey magnocellular cells. However, cells of the monkey's S-laminae and interlaminar zones plus perhaps a small minority of parvocellular and magnocellular cells exhibit an extrastriate projection (Wong-Riley, 1976; Yukie and Iwai, 1981; Benevento and Yoshida, 1981; Fitzpatrick *et al.*, 1981), perhaps analogous to the cat's W-cell pathway. Thus a bilateral ablation of area 17 in a monkey, which severely compromises the animal's spatial vision (Weiskrantz, 1972; Schilder *et al.*, 1972; Keating, 1980; Dineen and Keating, 1981), would completely eliminate nearly all cortical representation of presumptive X-like and Y-like cells. Miller *et al.* (1980) have shown the devastating effects of such a lesion on the animal's contrast sensitivity (Fig. 19).

Perhaps the reason that striate cortex is essential to satisfactory form vision in monkeys and not in cats is that all or nearly all of the cortical representation of the Y-cell pathway passes through this area in monkeys but not in cats. The main difference between species is not area 17 per se but rather the pattern of Y-cell projections. As long as significant Y-cell projections remain (the destriate cat), excellent form vision results, but

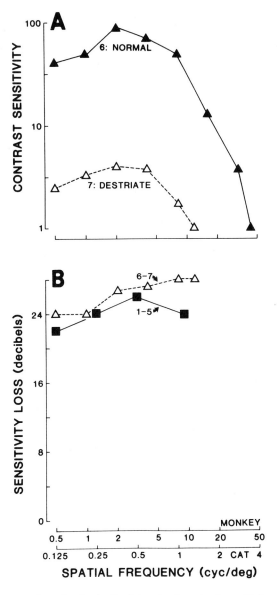

Fig. 19. Average of psychophysically determined contrast sensitivity as a function of spatial frequency for four rhesus monkeys. The stimuli consisted of stationary sine wave gratings that had to be discriminated from a gray target of equal luminance. (A) Spatial contrast sensitivity functions before (curve 6) and after (curve 7) bilateral removal of area 17. (Curves 1–5 appear in Fig. 16.) (B) Sensitivity loss as a function of spatial frequency (cf. Fig. 16). Compared are the losses of monkeys due to area 17 lesions (curve 6 minus 7) and those of cats due to rearing with monocular deprivation (curve 1 minus 5 from Fig. 16). Note the similarity in these losses that may be attributed to similar losses of geniculocortical X- and Y-cell pathways. (Data for rhesus monkeys redrawn from Miller *et al.*, 1980.)

when the Y-cell pathway is substantially interrupted (the visually deprived cat and destriate monkey), extremely poor vision results. Figure 19B shows the similarity in deficits between the destriate monkey and monocularly deprived cat. In both animals, subcortical pathways and/or W-cell pathways reaching cortex are presumably the major substrates for the remaining visual capacity.

3. Conclusions

Clearly, the primate's retinogeniculocortical pathways are organized into at least three parallel and largely separate pathways. It is not yet possible to decide whether this represents a pattern similar to the cat's W-, X-, and Y-cell pathways, and if so, what the precise homologies or analogies are. It might prove particularly interesting to discern primate analogs to the cat's Y-cell pathway, given the importance this article has suggested for the Y-cell pathway's role in the cat's visual capacities. However, one candidate for geniculate Y-like cells in monkeys and *Galago* species (i.e., cells of the magnocellular laminae) often exhibits linear summation and does not possess an extrastriate projection. Perhaps this neuronal class, which in the cat may be the latest to develop ontogenetically and is most susceptible to the postnatal visual environment (see review in Sherman and Spear, 1982), exhibits more variation in properties across species than do other classes. In any case, if Y-like cells do exist in the monkey's geniculostriate pathways, the difference in behavioral consequences of striate cortex ablation between cats and monkeys can be readily explained by the hypothesis presented in this article for Y-cell function and the differences in geniculocortical Y-cell projection patterns between cats and monkeys.

C. Other Mammalian Species

In general, insufficient data are available to be certain that neurons analogous to W-, X-, and/or Y-cells exist in other mammalian species, but in those species studied, it seems clear that retinal ganglion cells and/or geniculate neurons are organized into functionally distinct classes. Furthermore, some of the functional differences are remarkably similar to those found among cat W-, X-, and Y-cells. Mammalian species other than primates for which such differences have been reported include the tree shrew (Sherman *et al.*, 1975a), rat (Fukuda *et al.*, 1979; Lennie and Perry, 1981), and rabbit (Caldwell and Daw, 1978; Molotchnikoff and Lachapelle, 1978; So, 1983). While a positive statement cannot yet be made, the available evidence does not rule out the notion that the parallel organization of W-, X-, and Y-cell pathways seen in the cat is a general mammalian feature.

It should be noted that data from the tree shrew are somewhat at variance with some of the specific speculations just outlined. In this species, little or no extrastriate component exists in the geniculocortical projection (Diamond *et al.*, 1970; Harting *et al.*, 1973), yet form vision remains excellent after complete removal of area 17 (Snyder and Diamond, 1968; Killackey *et al.*, 1971; Ware *et al.*, 1972). Thus, although monkeys and tree shrews exhibit a similar pattern of geniculocortical connections, the behavioral consequences of striate cortex lesions are quite different between these species. The excellent form vision of the destriate tree shrew has been attributed to retinocolliculothalamocortical pathways that provide visual input to extrastriate cortex independently of the geniculostriate projection. The tree shrew superior colliculus is remarkable for its size,* and Norton (1982) has suggested that collicular neurons in tree shrews have response properties similar in many ways to those of Y-cells in cats. In any case, this serves as an example of the difficulty in inferring the functional significance of visual pathways in different species from notions developed in cats.

VIII. General Conclusions

This article has focused on the division of the cat's retinogeniculocortical system into W-, X-, and Y-cell pathways. A number of independent lines of research have suggested a functional hypothesis for these pathways. This hypothesis is incomplete. It is intended as a theoretical framework for present data and should be tested for future validation or dismissal.

Least is known specifically about the W-cell pathway, but largely because of the poor responsiveness of W-cells, this pathway is not assigned a specific role in conscious visual perception (see also Stone *et al.*, 1979). This is the weakest part of the hypothesis and the most likely one to require change. The Y-cell pathway is assigned the most prominent role in form vision. This pathway with its cortical representation seems sufficient and probably necessary for reasonable spatial vision. The X-cell pathway is assigned a role in maximizing spatial acuity and position sensitivity,

* Norton (1982) has pointed out that the ratio of volumes of the superficial gray layer of the superior colliculus and the lateral geniculate nucleus is 6 for tree shrews and only 0.2 for monkeys. By this measure the collicular pathways versus the geniculocortical pathways are roughly 30 times more prominent in tree shrews than in monkeys.

thereby providing greater detail in the analysis of the visual scene than that provided by the Y-cell pathway. The X-cell pathway may also play a crucial role in stereopsis. This hypothesis is substantially different from previous suggestions for these pathways, particularly those pertaining to X- and Y-cells (cf. Ikeda and Wright, 1972; Stone *et al.*, 1979; Lennie, 1980b).

There is still considerable controversy and confusion regarding the homologs or analogs of W-, X-, and Y-cells in species other than the cat. While it is clearly premature to extend this hypothesis to other species, it does offer an attractively simple explanation for some of the different deficits caused by cortical ablations. For instance, removal of the striate cortex in cats leaves much of the Y-cell pathway relatively undisturbed, and good spatial vision results. The same cortical lesion in monkeys obliterates the presumptive Y-like pathway, and poor spatial vision ensues. However, so many obvious differences can be seen between the cat's and the monkey's (and other species') neurons, it is quite possible that no specific analogy to W-, X-, and Y-cells exists outside of cats.

Whether or not correct, the hypothesis presented here offers a different way of interpreting ablations or other disruptions (e.g., abnormal development) of the visual system. One should of course attend to specific anatomical levels or areas of cortex damaged, but attention should also be directed to abnormalities in the W-, X-, or Y-cell pathways irrespective of the anatomical level or cortical area affected.

References

Ahlsen, G., and Lindstrom, S. (1978). Projection of perigeniculate neurons to the lateral geniculate body in the cat. *Meeting of European Association for Neuroscience, 3rd* S367.

Ahlsen, G., Lindstrom, S., and Sybirska, E. (1978). Subcortical axon collaterals of principal cells in the lateral geniculate body of the cat. *Brain Research* **156**, 106–109.

Albus, K. (1979). 14C-deoxyglucose mapping of orientation subunits in the cat's visual cortical areas. *Experimental Brain Research* **37**, 609–613.

Baumann, T. P., and Spear, P. D. (1977). Role of the lateral suprasylvian visual area in behavioral recovery from effects of visual cortex damage in cats. *Brain Research* **138**, 445–468.

Benevento, L. A., and Yoshida, K. (1981). The afferent and efferent organization of the lateral geniculo-prestriate pathways in the macaque monkey. *Journal of Comparative Neurology* **203**, 455–474.

Beresford, W. A. (1962). A Nauta and Gallocyanin study of the cortico-lateral geniculate projection in the cat and monkey. *Journal fur Hirnforschung* **5**, 210–228.

Berkley, M. A., and Sprague, J. M. (1978). Behavioral analysis of the geniculocortical ampbell, C. B. G., and Hodos, W. (1970). The concept of homology and the evolution of the nervous system. *Brain, Behavior and Evolution* **3,** 353–367.

leland, B. G., and Levick, W. R. (1974a). Brisk and sluggish concentrically organised ganglion cells in the cat's retina. *Journal of Physiology (London)* **240,** 421–456.

leland, B. G., and Levick, W. R. (1974b). Properties of rarely encountered types of ganglion cells in the cat's retina and an overall classification. *Journal of Physiology (London)* **240,** 457–492.

leland, B. G., Dubin, M. W., and Levick, W. R. (1971). Sustained and transient neurones in the cat's retina and lateral geniculate nucleus. *Journal of Physiology (London)* **217,** 473–496.

leland, B. G., Levick, W. R., and Wassle, H. (1975a). Physiological identification of a morphological class of cat retinal ganglion cells. *Journal of Physiology (London)* **248,** 151–171.

leland, B. G., Morstyn, R., Wagner, H. G., and Levick, W. R. (1975b). Long-latency retinal input to lateral geniculate neurones of the cat. *Brain Research* **91,** 306–310.

'leland, B. G., Mitchell, D. E., Gillard-Crewther, S., and Crewther, D. P. (1980). Visual resolution of retinal ganglion cells in monocularly-deprived cats. *Brain Research* **192,** 261–266.

ornsweet, T. N. (1970). "Visual Perception." Academic Press, New York.

ean, A. F., and Tolhurst, D. J. (1983). On the distinctness of simple and complex cells in the visual cortex of the cat. *Journal of Physiology (London)* **344,** 305–325.

eMonasterio, F. M. (1978a). Properties of concentrically organized X and Y ganglion cells of Macaque retina. *Journal of Neurophysiology* **41,** 1394–1417.

eMonasterio, F. M. (1978b). Center and surround mechanisms of opponent-color X and Y ganglion cells of retina of Macaques. *Journal of Neurophysiology* **41,** 1418–1434.

eMonasterio, F. M. (1978c). Properties of ganglion cells with atypical receptive-field organization in retina of Macaques. *Journal of Neurophysiology* **41,** 1435–1449.

eMonasterio, F. M., and Gouras, P. (1975). Functional properties of ganglion cells of the rhesus monkey retina. *Journal of Physiology (London)* **251,** 167–195.

errington, A. M., and Hawken, M. J. (1981). Spatial and temporal properties of cat geniculate neurones after prolonged deprivation. *Journal of Physiology (London)* **314,** 107–120.

errington, A. M., and Lennie, P. (1984). Spatial and temporal contrast sensitivities of neurons in lateral geniculate nucleus of macaque. *Journal of Physiology (London)* **357,** 219–240.

ews, P. B., and Wiesel, T. N. (1970). Consequences of monocular deprivation on visual behavior in kittens. *Journal of Physiology (London)* **206,** 437–455.

iamond, I. T. (1979). The subdivisions of neocortex: A proposal to revise the traditional view of sensory, motor, and association areas. *In* "Progress in Psychobiology and Physiological Psychology" (J. M. Sprague and A. N. Epstein, eds.), Vol. 8, pp. 1–43. Academic Press, New York.

iamond, I. T. (1982). Changing views of the organization and evolution of the visual pathways. *In* "Changing Concepts of The Nervous System" (A. R. Morrison and P. L. Strick, eds.), pp. 201–233. Academic Press, New York.

iamond, I. T., and Hall, W. C. (1969). Evolution of neocortex. *Science* **164,** 251–262.

iamond, I. T., Snyder, M., Killackey, H., Jane, J., and Hall, W. C. (1970). Thalamo-cortical projections in the tree shrew (*Tupaia glis*). *Journal of Comparative Neurology* **139,** 273–306.

ineen, J., and Keating, E. G. (1981). The primate visual system after bilateral removal of striate cortex. *Experimental Brain Research* **41,** 338–345.

system in form vision. *In* "Frontiers in Visual Science" (S. J. Coo
eds.), pp. 220–239. Springer-Verlag, Berlin and New York.

Berkley, M. A., and Sprague, J. M. (1979). Striate cortex and visual acu
cat. *Journal of Comparative Neurology* **187,** 679–702.

Berlucchi, G., and Sprague, J. M. (1981). The cerebral cortex in visual
ory, and interhemispheric transfer in the cat. *In* "The Organizatio
Cortex" (F. O. Schmitt, F. G. Worden, G. Adelman, and J. G. Den
440. MIT Press, Cambridge, Massachusetts.

Blake, R., and Camisa, J. M. (1977). Temporal aspects of spatial vision
mental Brain Research **28,** 325–333.

Blake, R., and DiGianfilippo, A. (1980). Spatial vision in cats with select
Journal of Neurophysiology **43,** 1197–1205.

Blakemore, C. (1970). The representation of three-dimensional visual
striate cortex. *Journal of Physiology (London)* **209,** 155–178.

Blakemore, C., and Van Sluyters, R. C. (1975). Innate and environme
development of the kitten's visual cortex. *Journal of Physiology (l*
716.

Blasdel, G. G., and Lund, J. S. (1983). Termination of afferent axons i
cortex. *Journal of Neuroscience* **3,** 1389–1413.

Bowling, D. B., and Michael, C. R. (1980). Projection patterns of sing
characterized optic tract fibers in cat. *Nature (London)* **286,** 899–90

Bowling, D. B., and Michael, C. R. (1984). Terminal patterns of sing
characterized optic tract fibers in the cat's lateral geniculate nu
Neuroscience **4,** 198–216.

Boycott, B. B. and Wassle, H. (1974). The morphological types of gan
domestic cat's retina. *Journal of Physiology (London)* **240,** 397–419.

Braddick, O., Campbell, F. W. and Atkinson, J. (1978). Channels in visic
In "Handbook of Sensory Physiology, Vol. VIII, Perception" (R. H
witz, and H.-L. Teuber, eds.), pp. 3–38. Springer-Verlag, Berlin and

Buisseret, P., and Imbert, M. (1976). Visual cortical cells: Their developm
normal and dark-reared kittens. *Journal of Physiology (London)* **255**

Bullier, J., and Henry, G. H. (1979a). Ordinal position of neurons in c
Journal of Neurophysiology **42,** 1251–1263.

Bullier, J., and Henry, G. H. (1979b). Neural path taken by afferent stream
of the cat. *Journal of Neurophysiology* **42,** 1264–1270.

Bullier, J., and Henry, G. H. (1979c). Laminar distribution of first-order n
ent terminals in cat striate cortex. *Journal of Neurophysiology* **42,** 1

Bullier, J., and Norton, T. T. (1979a). X and Y relay cells in cat lateral ge
Quantitative analysis of receptive-field properties and classification. *J
physiology* **42,** 244–273.

Bullier, J., and Norton, T. T. (1979b). Comparison of receptive-field prop
ganglion cells with X and Y lateral geniculate cells in the cat. *Journal
ogy* **42,** 274–291.

Burke, W., and Cole, A. M. (1978). Extraretinal influences on the lateral ge
Review of Physiology Biochemistry and Experimental Pharmacology

Caldwell, J. H., and Daw, N. W. (1978). New properties of rabbit retin
Journal of Physiology (London) **276,** 257–276.

Camarda, R., and Rizzolatti, G. (1976). Visual receptive fields in the lat
area (Clare-Bishop area) of the cat. *Brain Research* **101,** 423–443.

Donaldson, I. M. L., and Nash, J. R. G. (1975). The effect of a chronic lesion in cortical area 17 on the visual responses of units in area 18 of the cat. *Journal of Physiology (London)* **245,** 325–332.

Doty, R. W. (1971). Survival of pattern vision after removal of striate cortex in the adult cat. *Journal of Comparative Neurology* **143,** 341–369.

Doty, R. W. (1973). Ablation of visual areas in the central nervous system. *In* "Handbook of Sensory Physiology, Vol. VII/3B"(R. Jung, ed.), pp. 483–541. Springer-Verlag, Berlin and New York.

Dreher, B., and Cottee, L. J. (1975). Visual receptive-field properties of cells in area 18 of cat's cerebral cortex before and after acute lesions of area 17. *Journal of Neurophysiology* **38,** 735–750.

Dreher, B., Fukada, Y., and Rodieck, R. W. (1976). Identification, classification and anatomical segregation of cells with X-like and Y-like properties in the lateral geniculate nucleus of old-world primates. *Journal of Physiology (London)* **258,** 433–452.

Dreher, B., and Sefton, A. J. (1979). Properties of neurons in cat's dorsal lateral geniculate nucleus: A comparison between medial interlaminar and laminated parts of the nucleus. *Journal of Comparative Neurology* **183,** 47–64.

Dreher, B., Leventhal, A. G., and Hale, P. T. (1980). Geniculate input to cat visual cortex: A comparison of area 19 with areas 17 and 18. *Journal of Neurophysiology* **44,** 804–826.

Dubin, M. W., and Cleland, B. G. (1977). Organization of visual inputs to interneurons of lateral geniculate nucleus of the cat. *Journal of Neurophysiology* **40,** 410–427.

Einstein, G., Davis, T. L., and Sterling, P. L. (1983). Ultrastructural evidence that two types of X-cell project to area 17. *A.R.V.O. Abstracts, Supplement to Investigative Ophthalmology and Visual Science* **24,** 266.

Enroth-Cugell, C., and Robson, J. G. (1966). The contrast sensitivity of retinal ganglion cells of the cat. *Journal of Physiology (London)* **187,** 517–552.

Ferster, D., and LeVay, S. (1978). The axonal arborizations of lateral geniculate neurons in the striate cortex of the cat. *Journal of Comparative Neurology* **182,** 923–944.

Ferster, D., and Lindstrom, S. (1983). An intracellular analysis of geniculo-cortical connectivity in area 17 of the cat. *Journal of Physiology (London)* **342,** 181–215.

Fitzpatrick, D., Itoh, K., Conley, M., and Diamond, I. T. (1981). The projection of the lateral geniculate body to extrastriate cortex in the Owl monkey and Squirrel monkey. *Society for Neuroscience Abstracts* **7,** 830.

Fitzpatrick, D., Itoh, K., and Diamond, J. T. (1983). The laminar organization of the lateral geniculate body and the striate cortex in the Squirrel monkey (*Saimiri sciureus*). *Journal of Neuroscience* **3,** 673–702.

Fitzpatrick, D., Penny, G. R., and Schmechel, D. E. (1984). Glutamic acid decarboxylase—immunocytoreactive neurons and terminals in the lateral geniculate nucleus of the cat. *Journal of Neuroscience* **4,** 1809–1829.

Freeman, R. D., Sclar, G., and Ohzawa, I. (1983). An electrophysiological comparison of convergent and divergent strabismus in the cat: Visual evoked potentials. *Journal of Neurophysiology* **49,** 227–237.

Fregnac, Y., and Imbert, M. (1978). Early development of visual cortical cells in normal and dark-reared kittens: Relationship between orientation selectivity and ocular dominance. *Journal of Physiology (London)* **278,** 27–44.

Friedlander, M. J., Lin, C.-S., and Sherman, S. M. (1979). Structure of physiologically identified X- and Y-cells in the cat's lateral geniculate nucleus. *Science* **204,** 1114–1117.

Friedlander, M. J., Lin, C.-S., Stanford, L. R., and Sherman, S. M. (1981). Morphology of functionally identified neurons in the lateral geniculate nucleus of the cat. *Journal of Neurophysiology* **46,** 80–129.

Friedlander, M. J., Stanford, L. R., and Sherman, S. M. (1982). Effects of monocular deprivation on the structure/function relationship of individual neurons in the cat's lateral geniculate nucleus. *Journal of Neuroscience* **2**, 321–330.

Fukada, Y., and Saito, H. (1972). Phasic and tonic cells in the cat's lateral geniculate nucleus. *Tohoku Journal of Experimental Medicine* **106**, 209–210.

Fukada, Y., and Stone, J. (1974). Retinal distribution and central projections of Y-, X-, and W-cells of the cat's retina. *Journal of Neurophysiology* **37**, 749–772.

Fukada, Y., Sumitomo, I., Sugitani, M., and Iwama, K. (1979). Receptive-field properties of cells in the dorsal part of the albino rat's lateral geniculate nucleus. *Japanese Journal of Physiology* **29**, 283–307.

Ganz, L., and Fitch, M. (1968). The effect of visual deprivation on perceptual behavior. *Experimental Neurology* **22**, 683–690.

Garey, L. J., and Blakemore, C. (1977). Monocular deprivation: Morphological effects on different classes of neurons in the lateral geniculate nucleus. *Experimental Brain Research* **28**, 259–278.

Garey, L. J., and Powell, T. P. S. (1967). The projection of the lateral geniculate nucleus upon the cortex in the cat. *Proceedings of the Royal Society of London, Series B* **169**, 107–126.

Garey, L. J., Jones, E. G., and Powell, T. P. S. (1968). Interrelationships of striate and extrastriate cortex with the primary relay sites of the visual pathway. *Journal of Neurology, Neurosurgery and Psychiatry* **31**, 135–157.

Geisert, E. E. (1980). Cortical projections of the lateral geniculate nucleus in the cat. *Journal of Comparative Neurology* **190**, 793–812.

Gilbert, C. D. (1977). Laminar differences in receptive field properties of cells in cat primary visual cortex. *Journal of Physiology (London)* **268**, 391–421.

Gilbert, C. D. (1983). Microcircuitry of the visual cortex. *Annual Review of Neuroscience* **6**, 217–247.

Gilbert, C. D., and Wiesel, T. N. (1979). Morphology and intracortical projections of functionally characterized neurones in the cat visual cortex. *Nature (London)* **280**, 120–125.

Gilbert, C. D., and Wiesel, T. N. (1983). Clustered intrinsic connections in cat visual cortex. *Journal of Neuroscience* **3**, 1116–1133.

Ginsburg, A. (1978). Visual information processing based upon spatial filters constrained by biological data. Ph.D. thesis, University of Cambridge.

Ginsburg, A. P., Carl, J. W., Kabrisky, M., Hall, C. F., and Gill, P. A. (1976). Psychological aspects of a model for the classification of visual images. *In* "Advances in Cybernetics and Systems" (J. Rose, ed.), pp. 1289–1306. Gordon & Breach, London.

Graham, J. (1977). An autoradiographic study of the efferent connections of the superior colliculus in the cat. *Journal of Comparative Neurology* **173**, 629–654.

Graybiel, A. M. (1972). Some fiber pathways related to the posterior thalamic region in the cat. *Brain, Behavior and Evolution* **6**, 363–393.

Graybiel, A. M., and Berson, D. M. (1980). Autoradiographic evidence for a projection from the pretectal nucleus of the optic tract to the dorsal lateral geniculate complex in the cat. *Brain Research* **195**, 1–12.

Guedes, R., Watanabe, S., and Creutzfeldt, O. D. (1983). Functional role of association fibers for a visual association area: The posterior suprasylvian sulcus of the cat. *Experimental Brain Research* **49**, 13–27.

Guillery, R. W. (1966). A study of Golgi preparations from the dorsal lateral geniculate nucleus of the adult cat. *Journal of Comparative Neurology* **128**, 21–50.

Guillery, R. W. (1967). Patterns of fiber degeneration in the dorsal lateral geniculate nucleus of the cat following lesions in the visual cortex. *Journal of Comparative Neurology* **130**, 197–222.

Guillery, R. W. (1969). A quantitative study of synaptic interconnections in the dorsal lateral geniculate nucleus of the cat. *Zeitschrift der Zellforschung* **96**, 39–48.

Guillery, R. W., and Stelzner, D. J. (1970). The differential effects of unilateral lid closure upon the monocular and binocular segments of the dorsal lateral geniculate nucleus in the cat. *Journal of Comparative Neurology* **139**, 413–422.

Guillery, R. W., Geisert, E. E., Polley, E. H., and Mason, C. A. (1980). An analysis of the retinal afferents to the cat's medial interlaminar nucleus and to its rostral thalamic extension, the "geniculate wing." *Journal of Comparative Neurology* **194**, 117–142.

Hamos, J., Raczkowski, D., Van Horn, S., and Sherman, S. M. (1983). Ultrastructural substrates for retinogeniculate circuitry of an X retinogeniculate axon. *Society for Neuroscience Abstracts* **9**, 814.

Harting, J. K., Diamond, I. T., and Hall, W. C. (1973). Anterograde degeneration study of the cortical projections of the lateral geniculate and pulvinar nuclei in the tree shrew (*Tupaia glis*). *Journal of Comparative Neurology* **150**, 393–440.

Harvey, A. R. (1980). The afferent connexions and laminar distribution of cells in area 18 of the cat. *Journal of Physiology (London)* **302**, 483–505.

Hendrickson, A. E., Wilson, J. R., and Ogren, M. P. (1978). The neuroanatomical organization of pathways between the dorsal lateral geniculate nucleus and visual cortex in old world and new world primates. *Journal of Comparative Neurology* **182**, 123–136.

Henry, G. H. (1977). Receptive field classes of cells in the striate cortex of the cat. *Brain Research* **133**, 1–28.

Hess, R. F., and Garner, L. F. (1977). The effect of corneal edema on visual function. *Investigative Ophthalmology and Visual Science* **16**, 5–13.

Hess, R. F., and Howell, E. R. (1977). The threshold contrast sensitivity function in strabismic amblyopia: Evidence for a two type classification. *Vision Research* **17**, 1049–1055.

Hess, R., and Woo, G. (1978). Vision through cataracts. *Investigative Ophthalmology and Visual Science* **17**, 428–435.

Hickey, T. L. (1980). Development of the dorsal lateral geniculate nucleus in normal and visually deprived cats. *Journal of Comparative Neurology* **189**, 467–481.

Hickey, T. L., and Guillery, R. W. (1974). An autoradiographic study of retinogeniculate pathways in the cat and the fox. *Journal of Comparative Neurology* **156**, 239–254.

Hochstein, S., and Shapley, R. M. (1976a). Quantitative analysis of retinal ganglion cell classifications. *Journal of Physiology (London)* **262**, 237–264.

Hochstein, S., and Shapley, R. M. (1976b). Linear and non-linear subunits in Y cat retinal ganglion cells. *Journal of Physiology (London)* **262**, 265–284.

Hoffmann, K.-P. (1973). Conduction velocity in pathways from retina to superior colliculus in the cat: A correlation with receptive-field properties. *Journal of Neurophysiology* **36**, 409–424.

Hoffmann, K.-P., and Schoppmann, A. (1975). Retinal input to direction selective cells in the nucleus tractus opticus of the cat. *Brain Research* **99**, 359–366.

Hoffmann, K.-P., and Sherman, S. M. (1974). Effects of early monocular deprivation on visual input to cat superior colliculus. *Journal of Neurophysiology* **37**, 1267–1286.

Hoffmann, K.-P., and Sherman, S. M. (1975). Effects of early binocular deprivation on visual input to cat superior colliculus. *Journal of Neurophysiology* **38**, 1049–1059.

Hoffmann, K.-P., and Stone, J. (1971). Conduction velocity of afferents to cat visual cortex: A correlation with cortical receptive-field properties. *Brain Research* **32**, 460–466.

Hoffmann, K.-P., and Stone, J. (1973). Central terminations of W-, X-, and Y-type ganglion cell axons from cat retina. *Brain Research* **49**, 500–501.

Hoffmann, K.-P., Stone, J., and Sherman, S. M. (1972). Relay of receptive field properties in dorsal lateral geniculate nucleus of the cat. *Journal of Neurophysiology* **35**, 518–531.

Hollander, H. (1970). The projection from the visual cortex to the lateral geniculate body (LGB). An experimental study with silver impregnation methods in the cat. *Experimental Brain Research* **10**, 219–235.

Hollander, H. (1972). Autoradiographic evidence for a projection from the striate cortex to the dorsal part of the lateral geniculate nucleus in the cat. *Brain Research* **41**, 464–466.

Hollander, H., and Vanegas, H. (1977). The projection from the lateral geniculate nucleus onto the visual cortex in the cat. A quantitative study with horseradish peroxidase. *Journal of Comparative Neurology* **173**, 519–536.

Hubel, D. H., and Wiesel, T. N. (1961). Integrative action in the cat's lateral geniculate body. *Journal of Physiology (London)* **155**, 385–398.

Hubel, D. H., and Wiesel, T. N. (1962). Receptive fields, binocular interaction and functional architecture in the cat's visual cortex. *Journal of Physiology (London)* **160**, 106–154.

Hubel, D. H., and Wiesel, T. N. (1965). Receptive fields and functional architecture in two nonstriate visual areas (18 and 19) of the cat. *Journal of Neurophysiology* **28**, 229–289.

Hubel, D. H., and Wiesel, T. N. (1969). Visual area of the lateral suprasylvian gyrus (Clare-Bishop area) of the cat. *Journal of Physiology (London)* **202**, 251–260.

Hubel, D. H., and Wiesel, T. N. (1972). Laminar and columnar distribution of geniculo-cortical fibers in the macaque monkey. *Journal of Comparative Neurology* **146**, 421–450.

Hubel, D. H., and Wiesel, T. N. (1977). Functional architecture of macaque monkey visual cortex (Ferrier lecture). *Proceedings of the Royal Society of London, Series B* **198**, 1–59.

Hughes, A. (1981). Population magnitudes and distribution of the major classes of cat retinal ganglion cell as estimated from HRP filling and a systematic survey of the soma diameter spectra for classical neurones. *Journal of Comparative Neurology* **197**, 303–339.

Hughes, A., and Wassle, H. (1976). The cat optic nerve fibre total count and diameter spectrum. *Journal of Comparative Neurology* **169**, 171–184.

Humphrey, A. L., Sur, M., Uhlrich, D. J., and Sherman, S. M. (1984a). Projection patterns of individual X- and Y-cell axons from the lateral geniculate nucleus to cortical area 17 in the cat. *Journal of Comparative Neurology,* in press.

Humphrey, A. L., Sur, M., Uhlrich, D. J., and Sherman, S. M. (1984b). Termination patterns of individual X- and Y-cell axons in the visual cortex of the cat: Projections to area 18, to the 17–18 border region, and to both areas 17 and 18. *Journal of Comparative Neurology,* in press.

Ide, L. S. (1982). The fine structure of the perigeniculate nucleus in the cat. *Journal of Comparative Neurology* **210**, 317–334.

Ikeda, H., and Wright, M. J. (1972). Receptive field organisation of "sustained" and "transient" retinal ganglion cells which subserve different functional roles. *Journal of Physiology (London)* **227**, 769–800.

Illing, R.-B., and Wassle, H. (1981). The retinal projection to the thalamus in the cat: A quantitative investigation and a comparison with the retinotectal pathway. *Journal of Comparative Neurology* **202**, 265–285.

Itoh, K., Mizuno, N., Sugimoto, T., Nomura, S., Nakamura, Y., and Konishi, A. (1979). A cerebello-pulvino-cortical and a retino-pulvino-cortical pathway in the cat as revealed by the use of the anterograde and retrograde transport of horseradish peroxidase. *Journal of Comparative Neurology* **187**, 349–358.

Jones, K. R., and Berkley, M. A. (1983). Loss of temporal sensitivity in the dorsal lateral geniculate nucleus and area 18 of the cat following monocular deprivation. *Journal of Neurophysiology* **49,** 254–268.

Kaas, J. H. (1978). The organization of visual cortex in primates. *In* "Sensory Systems of Primates" (C. R. Noback, ed.), pp. 151–179. Plenum, New York.

Kaas, J. H. (1980). A comparative survey of visual cortex organization in mammals. *In* "Comparative Neurology of the Telencephalon" (S. O. E. Ebbesson, ed.), pp. 483–502. Plenum, New York.

Kabrisky, M., Tallman, O., Day, C. M., and Radoy, C. M. (1970). A theory of pattern perception based on human physiology. *Ergonomics* **13,** 129–142.

Kalil, R. E., and Chase, R. (1970). Corticofugal influence on activity of lateral geniculate neurons in the cat. *Journal of Neurophysiology* **33,** 459–474.

Kaplan, E., Marcus, S., and So, Y. T. (1979). Effects of dark adaptation on spatial and temporal properties of receptive fields in cat lateral geniculate nucleus. *Journal of Physiology (London)* **294,** 561–580.

Kaplan, E., and Shapley, R. M. (1982). X and Y cells in the lateral geniculate nucleus of macaque monkeys. *Journal of Physiology (London)* **330,** 125–143.

Kawamura, S., Sprague, J. M., and Niimi, K. (1974). Corticofugal projections from the visual cortices to the thalamus, pretectum, and superior colliculus. *Journal of Comparative Neurology* **158,** 339–362.

Kaye, M., Mitchell, D. E., and Cynader, M. (1981). Selective loss of binocular depth perception after ablation of cat visual cortex. *Nature (London)* **293,** 60–62.

Keating, E. G. (1980). Residual spatial vision in the monkey after removal of striate and preoccipital cortex. *Brain Research* **187,** 271–290.

Kelly, J. P., and Van Essen, D. C. (1974). Cell structure and function in the visual cortex of the cat. *Journal of Physiology (London)* **238,**, 515–547.

Killackey, H., Snyder, M., and Diamond, I. T. (1971). Function of striate and temporal cortex in the tree shrew. *Journal of Comparative Physiology and Psychology* **74,** 1–29.

Kolb, H. (1979). The inner plexiform layer in the retina of the cat: Electron microscopic observations. *Journal of Neurocytology* **8,** 295–329.

Kratz, K. E. (1982). Spatial and temporal sensitivity of lateral geniculate cells in dark-reared cats. *Brain Research* **251,** 55–63.

Kratz, K. E., Webb, S. V., and Sherman, S. M. (1978). Studies of the cat's medial interlaminar nucleus: A subdivision of the dorsal lateral geniculate nucleus of the cat. *Journal of Comparative Neurology* **181,** 601–614.

Kratz, K. E., Mangel, S. C., Lehmkuhle, S., and Sherman, S. M. (1979a). Retinal X- and Y-cells in monocularly lid-sutured cats: Normality of spatial and temporal properties. *Brain Research* **172,** 545–551.

Kratz, K. E., Sherman, S. M., and Kalil, R. (1979b). Lateral geniculate nucleus in dark-reared cats: Loss of Y cells without changes in cell size. *Science* **203,** 1353–1355.

Kuffler, S. (1953). Discharge patterns and functional organization of mammalian retina. *Journal of Neurophysiology* **16,** 37–68.

Kulikowski, J. J., and Tolhurst, D. J. (1973). Psychophysical evidence for sustained and transient detectors in human vision. *Journal of Physiology (London)* **232,** 149–162.

Laties, A. M., and Sprague, J. M. (1966). The projection of optic fibers to the visual centers in the cat. *Journal of Comparative Neurology* **127,** 35–70.

Lehmkuhle, S., Kratz, K. E., Mangel, S. C., and Sherman, S. M. (1980a). Spatial and temporal sensitivity of X- and Y-cells in the dorsal lateral geniculate nucleus of the cat. *Journal of Neurophysiology* **43,** 520–541.

Lehmkuhle, S., Kratz, K. E., Mangel, S. C., and Sherman, S. M. (1980b). Effects of early monocular lid suture on spatial and temporal sensitivity of neurons in dorsal lateral geniculate nucleus of the cat. *Journal of Neurophysiology* **43**, 542–556.

Lehmkuhle, S., Kratz, K. E., and Sherman, S. M. (1982). Spatial and temporal sensitivity of normal and amblyopic cats. *Journal of Neurophysiology* **48**, 372–387.

Lehmkuhle, S., Sherman, S. M., and Kratz, K. E. (1984). Spatial contrast sensitivity of dark reared cats with striate cortex lesions. *Journal of Neuroscience* **4**, 2419–2424.

Lennie, P. (1980a). Perceptual signs of parallel pathways. *Philosophical Transactions of the Royal Society of London, Series B* **290**, 23–37.

Lennie, P. (1980b). Parallel visual pathways. *Vision Research* **20**, 561–594.

Lennie, P., and Perry, V. H. (1981). Spatial contrast sensitivity of cells in the lateral geniculate nucleus of the rat. *Journal of Physiology (London)* **315**, 69–79.

LeVay, S., and Ferster, D. (1977). Relay cell classes in the lateral geniculate nucleus of the cat and the effects of visual deprivation. *Journal of Comparative Neurology* **172**, 563–584.

LeVay, S., and Ferster, D. (1979). Proportions of interneurons in the cat's lateral geniculate nucleus. *Brain Research* **164**, 304–308.

LeVay, S., and Gilbert, C. D. (1976). Laminar patterns of geniculocortical projections in the cat. *Brain Research* **113**, 1–19.

Leventhal, A. G. (1979). Evidence that the different classes of relay cells of the cat's lateral geniculate nucleus terminate in different layers of the striate cortex. *Experimental Brain Research* **37**, 349–372.

Leventhal, A. G. (1982). Morphology and distribution of retinal ganglion cells projecting to different layers of the dorsal lateral geniculate nucleus in normal and Siamese cats. *Journal of Neuroscience* **2**, 1024–1042.

Leventhal, A. G., and Hirsch, H. V. B. (1978). Receptive-field properties of neurons in different laminae of the visual cortex of the cat. *Journal of Neurophysiology* **41**, 948–962.

Leventhal, A. G., and Hirsch, H. V. B. (1980). Receptive-field properties of different classes of neurons in visual cortex of normal and dark-reared cats. *Journal of Neurophysiology* **43**, 1111–1132.

Leventhal, A. G., and Hirsch, H. V. B. (1983). Effects of visual deprivation upon the morphology of retinal ganglion cells projecting to the dorsal lateral geniculate nucleus of the cat. *Journal of Neuroscience* **3**, 332–344.

Leventhal, A. G., Keens, J., and Tork, L. (1980a). The afferent ganglion cells and cortical projections of the retinal recipient zone (RRZ) of the cat's "pulvinar complex." *Journal of Comparative Neurology* **194**, 535–554.

Leventhal, A. G., Rodieck, R. W., and Dreher, B. (1980b). Morphology and central projections of different types of retinal ganglion cells in cat and old-world monkey (*M. fascicularis*). *Society for Neuroscience Abstracts* **6**, 582.

Leventhal, A. G., Rodieck, R. W., and Dreher, B. (1981). Retinal ganglion cell classes in the old-world monkey: Morphology and central projections. *Science* **213**, 1139–1142.

Lin, C.-S., and Sherman, S. M. (1978). Effects of early monocular eyelid suture upon development of relay cell classes in the cat's lateral geniculate nucleus. *Journal of Comparative Neurology* **181**, 809–832.

Lin, C.-S., Kratz, K. E., and Sherman, S. M. (1977). Percentage of relay cells in the cat's lateral geniculate nucleus. *Brain Research* **131**, 167–173.

Lin, C.-S., Friedlander, M. J., and Sherman, S. M. (1979). Morphology of physiologically identified neurons in the visual cortex of the cat. *Brain Research* **172**, 344–348.

Lindstrom, S. (1982). Synaptic organization of inhibitory pathways to principal cells in the lateral geniculate nucleus of the cat. *Brain Research* **234,** 447–453.

Loop, M. S., and Sherman, S. M. (1977). Visual discriminations of cats with cortical and tectal lesions. *Journal of Comparative Neurology* **174,** 79–88.

Lorente de No, R. (1949). Cerebral cortex: Architecture, intracortical connections, motor projections. *In* "Physiology of the Nervous System" (J. F. Fulton, ed.), pp. 288–312. Oxford Univ. Press, London and New York.

Lund, J. S. (1973). Organization of neurons in the visual cortex, area 17, of the monkey (*Macaca mulatta*). *Journal of Comparative Neurology* **147,** 455–496.

Lund, J. S. (1981). Intrinsic organization of the primate visual cortex, area 17, as seen in Golgi preparations. *In* "The Organization of the Cerebral Cortex" (F. O. Schmitt, F. G. Worden, G. Adelman, and S. G. Dennis, eds.) pp. 105–124. MIT Press, Cambridge, Massachusetts.

Lund, J. S., Henry, G. H., MacQueen, C. L., and Harvey, A. R. (1979). Anatomical organization of the primary visual cortex (area 17) of the cat. A comparison with area 17 of the macaque monkey. *Journal of Comparative Neurology* **184,** 599–618.

Maffei, L., and Fiorentini, A. (1977). Spatial frequency rows in the striate visual cortex. *Vision Research* **17,** 257–264.

Malpeli, J. G. (1983). Activity of cells in area 17 of the cat in absence of input from layer A of the lateral geniculate nucleus. *Journal of Neurophsiology* **49,** 595–610.

Mangel, S. C., Wilson, J. R., and Sherman, S. M. (1983). Development of neuronal response properties in the cat dorsal lateral geniculate nucleus during monocular deprivation. *Journal of Neurophysiology* **50,** 240–264.

Martin, K. A. C., and Whitteridge, D. (1984). Form, function, and intracortical projections of spiny neurones in the striate visual cortex of the cat. *Journal of Physiology (London)* **353,** 463–504.

Mason, R. (1975). Cell properties in the medial interlaminar nucleus of the cat's lateral geniculate complex in relation to the transient/sustained classification. *Experimental Brain Research* **22,** 327–329.

Merzenich, M. M., and Kaas, J. H. (1980). Principles of organization of sensory-perceptual systems of mammals. *In* "Progress in Psychobiology and Physiological Psychology" (J. M. Sprague and A. N. Epstein, eds.), Vol. 9, pp. 1–41. Academic Press, New York.

Meyer, G., and Albus, K. (1981). Topography and cortical projections of morphologically identified neurons in the visual thalamus of the cat. *Journal of Comparative Neurology* **201,** 353–374.

Miller, M., Pasik, P., and Pasik, T. (1980). Extrageniculostriate vision in the monkey. VII. Contrast sensitivity functions. *Journal of Neurophysiology* **43,** 1510–1526.

Mitzdorf, U., and Singer, W. (1978). Prominent excitatory pathways in the cat visual cortex (A17 and A18): A current source density analysis of electrically evoked potentials. *Experimental Brain Research* **33,** 371–394.

Mitzdorf, U., and Singer, W. (1980). Monocular activation of visual cortex in normal and monocularly deprived cats: An analysis of evoked potentials. *Journal of Physiology (London)* **304,** 203–220.

Molotchnikoff, S., and Lachapelle, P. (1978). Lateral geniculate cell responses to electrical stimulation of the retina. *Brain Research* **152,** 81–95.

Movshon, J. A., and Van Sluyters, R. C. (1981). Visual neural development. *Annual Review of Psychology* **32,** 477–522.

Movshon, J. A., Thompson, I. D., and Tolhurst, D. J. (1978). Spatial summation in the receptive fields of simple cells in the cat's striate cortex. *Journal of Physiology (London)* **283,** 53–77.

Mower, G. D., and Christen, W. G. (1982). Effects of early monocular deprivation of the acuity of lateral geniculate neurons in the cat. *Developmental Brain Research* **3**, 475–480.

Mower, G. D., Burchfiel, J. L., and Duffy, F. H. (1981). The effects of dark-rearing on the development and plasticity of the lateral geniculate nucleus. *Developmental Brain Research* **1**, 418–424.

Mucke, L., Norita, M., Benedek, G., and Creutzfeldt, O. (1982). Physiologic and anatomic investigation of a visual cortical area situated in the ventral bank of the anterior ectosylvian sulcus of the cat. *Experimental Brain Research* **46**, 1–11.

Mullikin, W. H., Jones, J. P., and Palmer, L. A. (1981). Receptive fields and laminar distribution of X-like and Y-like simple cells. *Society for Neuroscience Abstracts* **7**, 356.

Murakami, D. M., and Wilson, P. D. (1980). Monocular deprivation affects cell morphology in laminae C and C1 in cat lateral geniculate nucleus. *Society for Neuroscience Abstracts* **6**, 789.

Niimi, K., Miki, M., and Kawamura, S. (1970). Ascending projections of the superior colliculus in the cat. *Okajimas Folia Anatomica Japonica* **45**, 269–287.

Niimi, K., Kawamura, S., and Ishimaru, S. (1971). Projections of the visual cortex to the lateral geniculate and posterior thalamic nuclei in the cat. *Journal of Comparative Neurology* **143**, 279–312.

Norton, T. T. (1982). Geniculate and extrageniculate visual systems in the tree shrew. *In* "Changing Concepts of the Nervous System" (A. R. Morrison and P. L. Strick, eds.), pp. 377–409. Academic Press, New York.

Norton, T. T., and Casagrande, V. A. (1982). Laminar organization of receptive-field properties in lateral geniculate nucleus of bush baby (*Galago crassicaudatus*). *Journal of Neurophysiology* **47**, 715–741.

O'Leary, J. L. (1941). Structure of area striata of the cat. *Journal of Comparative Neurology* **75**, 131–161.

Olson, C. R., and Graybiel, A. M. (1981). A visual area in the anterior ectosylvian sulcus of the cat. *Society for Neuroscience Abstracts* **7**, 831.

Orban, G. A., and Callens, M. (1977). Receptive field types of area 18 neurones in the cat. *Experimental Brain Research* **30**, 107–123.

Peichl, L., and Wassle, H. (1979). Size, scatter and coverage of ganglion cell receptive field centres in the cat retina. *Journal of Physiology (London)* **291**, 117–141.

Peichl, L., and Wassle, H. (1981). Morphological identification of on- and off-centre brisk transient (Y) cells in the cat retina. *Proceedings of the Royal Society of London, Series B* **212**, 139–156.

Peters, A., and Regidor, J. (1981). A reassessment of the forms of nonpyramidal neurons in Area 17 of cat visual cortex. *Journal of Comparative Neurology* **203**, 685–716.

Pettigrew, J. D. (1974). The effect of visual experience on the development of stimulus specificity by kitten cortical neurones. *Journal of Physiology (London)* **237**, 49–74.

Raczkowski, D., and Rosenquist, A. C. (1980). Connections of the parvocellular C laminae of the dorsal lateral geniculate nucleus with the visual cortex in the cat. *Brain Research* **199**, 447–451.

Raczkowski, D., and Rosenquist, A. C. (1983). Connections of the multiple visual cortical areas with the lateral posterior-pulvinar complex and adjacent thalamic nuclei. *Journal of Neuroscience* **3**, 1912–1942.

Rizzolatti, G., and Tradari, V. (1971). Pattern discrimination in monocularly reared cats. *Experimental Neurology* **33**, 181–194.

Robson, J. A., and Mason, C. A. (1979). The synaptic organization of terminals traced from individual labeled retino-geniculate axons in the cat. *Neuroscience* **4**, 99–111.

Rodieck, R. W. (1967). Receptive fields in the cat retina: A new type. *Science* **157**, 90–92.

Rodieck, R. W. (1973). "The Vertebrate Retina." Freeman, San Francisco, California.

Rodieck, R. W. (1979). Visual pathways. *Annual Review of Neuroscience* **2**, 193–225.

Rodieck, R. W., and Brening, R. K. (1983). Retinal ganglion cells: Properties, types, genera, pathways, and trans-species comparisons. *Brain, Behavior and Evolution* **23**, 121–164.

Rogawski, M. A., and Agajanian, G. K. (1980). Modulation of lateral geniculate neurone excitability by noradrenaline microiontophoresis or locus coeruleus stimulation. *Nature (London)* **283**, 731–734.

Rosenquist, A. C. (1984). Connections of visual cortical areas in the cat. *In* "Cerebral Cortex" (E. G. Jones and A. Peters, eds.), Vol. 3. Plenum, New York, in press.

Rosenquist, A. C., Edwards, S. B., and Palmer, L. A. (1974). An autoradiographic study of the projections of the dorsal lateral geniculate nucleus and the posterior nucleus in the cat. *Brain Research* **80**, 71–93.

Rosenquist, A. C., Raczkowski, D., and Symonds, L. (1982). The functional organization of the lateral posterior-pulvinar complex in the cat. *In* "Changing Concepts of the Nervous System" (A. R. Morrison and P. L. Strick, eds.), pp. 261–279. Academic Press, New York.

Rowe, M. H., and Dreher, B. (1982). W cell projection to the medial interlaminar nucleus of the cat: Implications for ganglion cell classification. *Journal of Comparative Neurology* **204**, 117–133.

Rowe, M. H., and Stone, J. (1976). Properties of ganglion cells in the visual streak of the cat's retina. *Journal of Comparative Neurology* **169**, 99–126.

Rowe, M. H. and Stone, J. (1977). Naming of neurones. *Brain, Behavior and Evolution* **14**, 185–216.

Saito, H.-A. (1983). Morphology of physiologically identified X-, Y-, and W-type retinal ganglion cells of the cat. *Journal of Comparative Neurology* **221**, 279–288.

Sanderson, K. J. (1971a). The projection of the visual field to the lateral geniculate and medial interlaminar nuclei in the cat. *Journal of Comparative Neurology* **143**, 101–118.

Sanderson, K. J. (1971b). Visual field projection columns and magnification factors in the lateral geniculate nucleus of the cat. *Experimental Brain Research* **13**, 159–177.

Sanderson, K. J., Bishop, P. O., and Darian-Smith, I. (1971). The properties of the binocular receptive fields of lateral geniculate neurons. *Experimental Brain Research* **13**, 178–207.

Schilder, P., Pasik, P., and Pasik, T. (1972). Extrageniculostriate vision in the monkey. III. Circle vs. triangle and "red vs. green" discrimination. *Experimental Brain Research* **14**, 436–448.

Schiller, P. H., and Malpeli, J. G. (1977). Properties and tectal projections of monkey retinal ganglion cells. *Journal of Neurophysiology* **40**, 428–445.

Schneider, G. E. (1969). Two visual systems. *Science* **163**, 895–902.

Schoppmann, A., and Stryker, M. P. (1981). Physiological evidence that the 2-deoxyglucose method reveals orientation columns in cat visual cortex. *Nature (London)* **293**, 574–576.

Sekuler, R., Pantle, A., and Levinson, E. (1978). Physiological basis of motion perception. *In* "Handbook of Sensory Physiology. Vol. VIII. Perception" (R. Held, H. W. Leibowitz, and H. L. Teuber, eds.), pp. 67–96. Springer-Verlag, Berlin and New York.

Shapley, R., and So, Y. T. (1980). Is there an effect of monocular deprivation on the proportions of X and Y cells in the cat lateral geniculate nucleus? *Experimental Brain Research* **39**, 41–48.

Shatz, C. J., and Stryker, M. P. (1978). Ocular dominance in layer IV of the cat's visual cortex and the effects of monocular deprivation. *Journal of Physiology (London)* **291**, 267–283.

Shatz, C. J., Lindstrom, S., and Wiesel, T. N. (1977). The distribution of afferents representing the right and left eyes in the cat's visual cortex. *Brain Research* **131**, 103–116.

Sherk, H. (1978). Area 18 cell responses in cat during reversible inactivation of area 17. *Journal of Neurophysiology* **41**, 204–215.

Sherman, S. M. (1973). Visual field deficits in monocularly and binocularly deprived cats. *Brain Research* **49**, 25–45.

Sherman, S. M. (1979). The functional significance of X- and Y-cells in normal and visually deprived cats. *Trends in Neuroscience* **2**, 192–195.

Sherman, S. M. (1982). Parallel pathways in the cat's geniculocortical system: W-, X-, and Y-cells. *In* "Changing Concepts of the Nervous System" (A. R. Morrison and P. L. Strick, eds.), pp. 337–359. Academic Press, New York.

Sherman S. M., and Spear, P. D. (1982). Organization of visual pathways in normal and visually deprived cats. *Physiological Reviews* **62**, 738–855.

Sherman, S. M., and Spear, P. D. (1983). Neural development of cats raised with deprivation of visual patterns. *In* "The Clinical Neurosciences" (R. N. Rosenberg, ed.), pp. 385–434; Section V: "Neurobiology" (W. D. Willis, ed.). Churchill-Livingstone, Edinburgh.

Sherman, S. M., and Sprague, J. M. (1979). Effects of visual cortex lesions upon visual fields of monocularly deprived cats. *Journal of Comparative Neurology* **188**, 291–312.

Sherman, S. M., and Stone, J. (1973). Physiological normality of the retina in visually deprived cats. *Brain Research* **60**, 224–230.

Sherman, S. M., Hoffmann, K.-P., and Stone, J. (1972). Loss of a specific cell type from the dorsal lateral geniculate nucleus in visually deprived cats. *Journal of Neurophysiology* **35**, 532–541.

Sherman, S. M., Guillery, R. W., Kaas, J. H., and Sanderson, K. J. (1974). Behavioral, electrophysiological and morphological studies of binocular competition in the development of the geniculo-cortical pathways of cats. *Journal of Comparative Neurology* **158**, 1–18.

Sherman, S. M., Norton, T. T., and Casagrande, V. A. (1975a). X- and Y-cells in the dorsal lateral geniculate nucleus of the tree shrew (*Tupaia glis*). *Brain Research* **93**, 152–157.

Sherman, S. M., Wilson, J. R., and Guillery, R. W. (1975b). Evidence that binocular competition affects the postnatal development of Y-cells in the cat's lateral geniculate nucleus. *Brain Research* **100**, 441–444.

Sherman, S. M., Wilson, J. R., Kaas, J. H., and Webb, S. V. (1976). X- and Y-cells in the dorsal lateral geniculate nucleus of the Owl monkey (*Aotes trivirgatus*). *Science* **192**, 415–417.

Sherman, S. M., Shumer, R. A., and Movshon, J. A. (1984). Functional cell classes in the macaque's LGN. *Society for Neuroscience Abstracts* **10**, 296.

Sholl, D. A. (1955). The organization of the visual cortex in the cat. *Journal of Anatomy* **89**, 33–46.

Singer, W. (1977). Control of thalamic transmission by corticofugal and ascending reticular pathways in the visual system. *Physiological Reviews* **57**, 386–420.

Smith, K. U. (1938). The relation between pattern vision and visual acuity and the optic projection centers of the nervous system. *Journal of General Psychology* **53**, 251–272.

Snyder, A., and Shapley, R. (1979). Deficits in the visual evoked potentials of cats as a result of visual deprivation. *Experimental Brain Research* **37**, 73–86.

Snyder, M., and Diamond, I. T. (1968). The organization and function of the visual cortex in the tree shrew. *Brain, Behavior and Evolution* **1**, 244–288.

So, F.-S. (1983). Both fast and slow relay cells in lateral geniculate nucleus of rabbit receive recurrent inhibition. *Brain Research* **271**, 331–338.

So, Y.-T., and Shapley, R. (1981). Spatial tuning of cells in and around lateral geniculate nucleus of the cat: X and Y relay cells and perigeniculate interneurons. *Journal of Neurophysiology* **45**, 107–120.

Spear, P. D., and Baumann, T. P. (1975). Receptive-field characteristics of single neurons in lateral suprasylvian visual area of the cat. *Journal of Neurophysiology* **38**, 1403–1420.

Spear, P. D., and Braun, J. J. (1969). Pattern discrimination following removal of visual neocortex in the cat. *Experimental Neurology* **25**, 331–348.

Spear, P. D., and Ganz, L. (1975). Effects of visual cortex lesions following recovery from monocular deprivation in the cat. *Experimental Brain Research* **23**, 181–201.

Spear, P. D., Smith, D. C., and Williams, L. L. (1977). Visual receptive-field properties of single neurons in cat's ventral lateral geniculate nucleus. *Journal of Neurophysiology* **40**, 390–409.

Sprague, J. M. (1966). Interaction of cortex and superior colliculus in mediation of visually guided behavior in the cat. *Science* **153**, 1544–1547.

Sprague, J. M., Berkley, M., Tunkl, J., and Berlucchi, G. (1976). Neural mechanisms mediating pattern and form discriminations in the cat. *Society for Neuroscience Abstracts* **2**, 1093.

Sprague, J. M., Levy, J., DiBerardino, A., and Berlucchi, G. (1977). Visual cortical areas mediating form discrimination in the cat. *Journal of Comparative Neurology* **172**, 441–488.

Sprague, J. M., Hughes, H. C., and Berlucchi, G. (1981). Neural mechanisms mediating pattern and form discriminations in the cat. *In* "Brain Mechanisms and Perceptual Awareness and Purposeful Behavior" (O. Pompeiano and C. Ajmone Marsan, eds.), pp. 107–132. Raven, New York.

Stanford, L. R., and Sherman, S. M. (1984). Structure/function relationships of retinal ganglion cells in the cat. *Brain Research* **297**, 381–386.

Stanford, L. R., Friedlander, M. J., and Sherman, S. M. (1981). Morphology of physiologically identified W-cells in the C laminae of the cat's lateral geniculate nucleus. *Journal of Neuroscience* **1**, 578–584.

Stanford, L. R., Friedlander, M. J., and Sherman, S. M. (1983). Morphological and physiological properties of geniculate W-cells: A comparison with X- and Y-cells. *Journal of Neurophysiology* **50**, 502–608.

Stevens, J. K., and Gerstein, G. L. (1976). Spatiotemporal organization of cat lateral geniculate receptive fields. *Journal of Neurophysiology* **39**, 213–238.

Stone, J. (1978). The number and distribution of ganglion cells in the cat's retina. *Journal of Comparative Neurology* **180**, 753–772.

Stone, J., and Campion, J. E. (1978). Estimate of the number of myelinated axons in the cat's optic nerve. *Journal of Comparative Neurology* **180**, 799–806.

Stone, J., and Clarke, R. (1980). Correlation between soma size and dendritic morphology in cat retinal ganglion cells: Evidence of further variation in the γ-cell class. *Journal of Comparative Neurology* **192**, 211–217.

Stone, J., and Dreher, B. (1973). Projection of X- and Y-cells of the cat's lateral geniculate nucleus to areas 17 and 18 of visual cortex. *Journal of Neurophysiology* **36**, 551–567.

Stone, J., and Fabian, M. (1966). Specialized receptive fields of the cat's retina. *Science* **152**, 1277–1279.

Stone, J., and Fukuda, Y. (1974). Properties of cat retinal ganglion cells: A comparison of W-cells with X- and Y-cells. *Journal of Neurophysiology* **37**, 722–748.

Stone, J., and Hoffmann, K.-P. (1972). Very slow-conducting ganglion cells in the cat's retina: A major, new functional type? *Brain Research* **43**, 610–616.

Stone, J., Dreher, B. and Leventhal, A. (1979). Hierarchical and parallel mechanisms in the organization of visual cortex. *Brain Research Reviews* **1**, 345–394.

Sur, M., and Sherman, S. M. (1982a). Linear and nonlinear W-cells in the C-laminae of the cat's lateral geniculate nucleus. *Journal of Neurophysiology* **47**, 869–884.

Sur, M., and Sherman, S. M. (1982b). Retinogeniculate terminations in cats: Morphological differences between X and Y cell axons. *Science* **218**, 389–391.

Sur, M., and Sherman, S. M. (1984). The position sensitivity of retinal X- and Y-cells in cats. *Experimental Brain Research* **56**, 497–501.

Sur, M., Humphrey, A. L., and Sherman, S. M. (1982). Monocular deprivation affects X- and Y-cell retinogeniculate terminations in cats. *Nature (London)* **300**, 183–185.

Suzuki, H., and Takahashi, M. (1973). Distribution of binocular inhibitory interaction in the lateral geniculate nucleus of the cat. *Tohoku Journal of Experimental Medicine* **11**, 393–403.

Symonds, L. L., Rosenquist, A. C., Edwards, S. B., and Palmer, L. A. (1981). Projections of the pulvinar-lateral posterior complex to visual cortical areas in the cat. *Neuroscience* **6**, 1995–2020.

Tanaka, K. (1983a). Distinct X- and Y-streams in the cat visual cortex revealed by bicuculine application. *Brain Research* **265**, 143–147.

Tanaka, K. (1983b). Cross-correlation analysis of geniculostriate neuronal relationships in cats. *Journal of Neurophysiology* **49**, 1303–1318.

Thibos, L. N., and Levick, W. R. (1983). Spatial frequency characteristics of brisk and sluggish ganglion cells of the cat's retina. *Experimental Brain Research* **51**, 16–22.

Tigges, J., Tigges, M., and Perachio, A. A. (1977). Complementary laminar terminations of afferents to area 17 originating in area 18 and in the lateral geniculate nucleus in Squirrel monkey. *Journal of Comparative Neurology* **176**, 87–100.

Tolhurst, D. J., and Thompson, I. D. (1982). Organization of neurones preferring similar spatial frequencies in cat striate cortex. *Experimental Brain Research* **48**, 217–227.

Tong, L., Kalil, R. E., and Spear, P. D. (1982). Thalamic projections to visual areas of the middle suprasylvian sulcus in the cat. *Journal of Comparative Neurology* **212**, 103–117.

Tootell, R. B., Silverman, M. S., and DeValois, R. L. (1981). Spatial frequency columns in primary visual cortex. *Science* **214**, 813–815.

Torrealba, F., Partlow, G. D., and Guillery, R. W. (1981). Organization of the projection from the superior colliculus to the dorsal lateral geniculate nucleus of the cat. *Neuroscience* **6**, 1341-1360.

Troy, J. B. (1983). Spatial contrast sensitivities of X and Y type neurones in the cat's dorsal lateral geniculate nucleus. *Journal of Physiology (London)* **334**, 399–417.

Tretter, F., Cynader, M., and Singer, W. (1975). Cat parastriate cortex: A primary or secondary visual area? *Journal of Neurophysiology* **38**, 1099–1113.

Tsumoto, T., Creutzfeldt, O. D., and Legendy, C. R. (1978). Functional organization of the corticofugal system from visual cortex to lateral geniculate nucleus in the cat. *Experimental Brain Research* **32**, 345–364.

Tusa, R. J. (1982). Visual cortex: Multiple areas and multiple functions. *In* "Changing Concepts of the Nervous System" (A. R. Morrison and P. L. Strick, eds.), pp. 235–259. Academic Press, New York.

Tusa, R. J., Palmer, L. A., and Rosenquist, A. C. (1981). Multiple cortical visual areas in cat. *In* "Cortical Sensory Organization Vol. 2. Multiple Visual Areas" (C. N. Woolsey, ed.), pp. 1–31. Humana Press, Clifton, New Jersey.

Updyke, B. V. (1975). The patterns of projection of cortical areas 17, 18, and 19 onto the laminae of the dorsal lateral geniculate nucleus in the cat. *Journal of Comparative Neurology* **163**, 377–396.

Updyke, B. V. (1977). Topographic organization of the projections from cortical areas 17, 18, and 19 onto the thalamus, pretectum and superior colliculus in the cat. *Journal of Comparative Neurology* **173**, 81–122.

Updyke, B. V. (1981). Projections from visual areas of the middle suprasylvian sulcus onto the lateral posterior complex and adjacent thalamic nuclei in the cat. *Journal of Comparative Neurology* **201**, 477–506.

Van Essen, D. C. (1979). Visual areas of the mammalian cerebral cortex. *Annual Review of Neuroscience* **2**, 227–263.

von Grunau, M., and Frost, B. J. (1983). Double-opponent-process mechanism underlying RF-structure of directionally specific cells of cat lateral suprasylvian visual area. *Experimental Brain Research* **49**, 84–92.

Ware, C. B., Diamond, I. T., and Casagrande, V. A. (1972). Effects of ablating the striate cortex on a successive pattern discrimination: Further study of the visual system in the tree shrew (*Tupaia glis*). *Brain, Behavior and Evolution* **5**, 18–29.

Wassle, H. (1982). Morphological types and central projections of ganglion cells in the cat retina. *In* "Progress in Retinal Research" (N. Osborne and G. Chader, eds.), pp. 125–152. Pergamon, Oxford.

Wassle, H., and Illing, R.-B. (1980). The retinal projection to the superior colliculus in the cat: A quantitative study with HRP. *Journal of Comparative Neurology* **190**, 333–356.

Wassle, H., Levick, W. R., and Cleland, B. G. (1975). The distribution of the alpha type of ganglion cells in the cat's retina. *Journal of Comparative Neurology* **159**, 419–438.

Wassle, H., Boycott, B. B., and Illing, R.-B. (1981a). Morphology and mosaic of on- and off-beta cells in the cat retina and some functional considerations. *Proceedings of the Royal Society of London, Series B* **212**, 177–195.

Wassle, H., Peichl, L., and Boycott, B. B. (1981b). Morphology and topography of on- and off-alpha cells in the cat retina. *Proceedings of the Royal Society of London, Series B* **212**, 157–175.

Watkins, D. W., Wilson, J. R., and Sherman, S. M. (1978). Receptive-field properties of neurons in binocular and monocular segments of striate cortex in cats raised with binocular lid suture. *Journal of Neurophysiology* **41**, 322–337.

Weber, J. T., Huerta, M. F., Kaas, J. H., and Harting, J. K. (1983). The projections of the lateral geniculate nucleus of the Squirrel monkey: Studies of the interlaminar zones and the S layers. *Journal of Comparative Neurology* **213**, 135–145.

Weiskrantz, L. (1972). Behavioural analysis of the monkey's visual nervous system. *Proceedings of the Royal Society of London, Series B* **182**, 427–455.

Wiesel, T. N., and Hubel, D. H. (1963). Single-cell responses in striate cortex of kittens deprived of vision in one eye. *Journal of Neurophysiology* **26**, 1003–1017.

Wiesel, T. N., and Hubel, D. H. (1965). Comparison of the effects of unilateral and bilateral eye closure on cortical unit responses in kittens. *Journal of Neurophysiology* **28**, 1029–1040.

Williams, R. W., and Chalupa, L. M. (1983). An analysis of axon caliber within the optic nerve of the cat: Evidence of size groupings and regional organization. *Journal of Neuroscience* **3**, 1554–1564.

Wilson, J. R., and Sherman, S. M. (1977). Differential effects of early monocular deprivation on binocular and monocular segments of cat striate cortex. *Journal of Neurophysiology* **40**, 892–903.

Wilson, J. R., Tessin, D. E., and Sherman, S. M. (1982). Development of the electrophysiological properties of Y-cells in the kitten's medial interlaminar nucleus. *Journal of Neuroscience* **2**, 562–571.

Wilson, P. D., Rowe, M. H., and Stone, J. (1976). Properties of relay cells in the cat's lateral geniculate nucleus: A comparison of W-cells with X- and Y-cells. *Journal of Neurophysiology* **39**, 1193–1209.

Winans, S. S. (1967). Visual form discrimination after removal of the visual cortex in cats. *Science* **158**, 944–946.

Wong-Riley, M. T. T. (1976). Projections from the dorsal lateral geniculate nucleus to prestriate cortex in the squirrel monkey as demonstrated by retrograde transport of horseradish peroxidase. *Brain Research* **109**, 595–600.

Yukie, M., and Iwai, E. (1981). Direct projection from the dorsal lateral geniculate nucleus to the prestriate cortex in macaque monkeys. *Journal of Comparative Neurology* **201**, 81–97.

Author Index

Numbers in italics refer to the pages on which the complete references are listed.

Schulte, R. H., 27, *61*

Schutz, H. G., 143, *194*

Schwartz, G. J., 13, 14, 23, 25, *59*

Schwartz, J. H., 21, *57, 59*

Schwartzbaum, J. S., 84, 181, *191*

Sclar, G., 283, *301*

Sefton, A. J., 261, 263, *301*

Segal, S., 217, *232*

Sekuler, R., 240, 241, *309*

Semba, K., 68, 69, 71, 73, 76, 79, 81, 85, 87, 112, 113, 114, 117, 152, 168, *190, 196*

Sequin, J. J., 109, *191*

Sessle, B. J., 85, 88, 109, *188, 194*

Sevenster, P., 25, *59*

Seward, J. P., 177, *194*

Shair, H., 110, *189*

Shambes, G. M., 81, 82, 83, *194*

Shapley, R. M., 235, 237, 240, 241, 243, 244, 252, 261, 265, 280, 283, 293, *303, 305, 309, 310, 311*

Shatz, C. J., 274, 283, 284, *310*

Sherk, H., 275, *310*

Sherman, S. M., 235, 236, 237, 240, 241, 244, 245, 249, 251, 252, 253, 255, 256, 257, 261, 263, 264, 265, 266, 267, 268, 269, 270, 271, 273, 274, 277, 278, 280, 281, 282, 283, 284, 285, 286, 292, 293, 294, 296, *301, 302, 303, 304, 305, 306, 307, 310, 311, 312, 313, 314*

Sherrington, C. S., 7, *58*, 87, *194*

Shizgal, P., 5, *56*

Sholl, D. A., 272, 273, *310*

Shuford, E. H., Jr., 7, *61*

Shumer, R. A., 293, *310*

Shuto, S., 87, *190*

Siegel, A., 174, *187*

Siegel, J., 174, *188*

Silverman, M. S., 275, *312*

Simpson, P. C., 136, 146, *187, 194*

Singer, G., 104, *186*

Singer, W., 264, 270, 273, 275, 283, *307, 310, 312*

Smith, D. A., 174, *194*

Smith, D. C., 244, 257, *311*

Smith, G. P., 14, 41, *57,* 198, 200, 222, 224, *230, 231*

Smith, G. T., 226, *232*

Smith, K. U., 277, *310*

Smith, R. L., 80, 182, *194*

Snowdon, C. T., 127, 178, *194*

Snyder, A., 283, *310*

Snyder, M., 297, *300, 305, 311*

So, F.-S., 296, *311*

So, Y. T., 240, 241, 252, 261, 265, 280, 283, *305, 309, 311*

Spear, P. D., 235, 236, 240, 244, 257, 270, 273, 275, 277, 282, 283, 284, 285, 296, *298, 310, 311, 312*

Spence, K. W., 177, *194*

Sprague, J. M., 234, 260, 264, 265, 277, 278, 279, 280, 282, 284, *299, 305, 310, 311*

Spurrell, W. R., 199, *231*

Squibb, R. L., 137, *187, 191*

Stanford, L. R., 244, 255, 261, 263, 265, 266, 267, 268, 269, 283, *301, 302, 311*

Steffens, A. B., 8, *59*

Steiner, J. E., 7, *59*

Stellar, E., 10, 14, *59, 60,* 115, *194*

Stelzner, D. J., 284, *303*

Sterling, P. L., 266, *301*

Sterman, M. B., 88, *187*

Stevens, J. K., 235, 240, *311*

Stolerman, I. P., 20, *59*

Stone, J., 234, 235, 236, 237, 240, 251, 155, 256, 257, 261, 263, 265, 267, 268, 269, 270, 271, 273, 282, 283, 285, 288, 292, 297, 298, *303, 304, 309, 310, 311, 312, 314*

Storey, A. T., 85, 88, 109, *188*

Stricker, E. M., 89, 181, *195,* 198, 219, *230, 232*

Stryker, M. P., 274, 283, 284, *309, 310*

Stubbs, D. F., 201, 206, *231*

Sugimoto, T., 270, *304*

Sugitani, M., 296, *302*

Sumino, R., 87, *190*

Sumitomo, I., 296, *302*

Sur, M., 168, *192,* 240, 244, 245, 249, 252, 256, 257, 261, 263, 264, 269, 270, 271, 273, 274, 280, 283, 293, *304, 312*

Suter, S., 67, 177, *189*

Suzuki, H., 240, *312*

Sybirska, E., 265, *298*

Symonds, L. L., 236, 238, 270, *309, 312*

T

Takahashi, M., 240, *312*

Takatori, M., 88, *192*

Tallman, O., 287, 288, *305*

Subject Index